NATIONAL CURRICULUM

UNDERSTANDING MATHEMATICS

Second Edition

4

C. J. Cox & D. Bell

JOHN MURRAY

Acknowledgements

The authors have been delighted with the enthusiastic reception given to the Understanding Mathematics series and wish to thank their publishers, reviewers, and all who have written with encouraging comments and helpful suggestions, especially the Devon Users Group, John Collins (Devon Mathematics Inspector), Sue Jennings (Exeter University School of Education), and the pupils who have written (from as far away as Kuwait!) in response to our 'challenges'.

Thanks are also due to the editorial and production staff at John Murray. Their skills have much improved our original manuscripts.

Illustrations by Tony Langham and Technical Art Services.

The following have provided photographs or given permission for copyright photographs or items to be reproduced:

Shell U.K. Administrative Services (p. 25), David Purdie (p. 34), NPA (p. 44), John R. Bradshaw (p. 93), The Mathematical Association (p. 141), Barnaby's Picture Library (p. 149), GSF Picture Library (p. 173), Robin Cox (p. 178), John Shaw/NHPA (p. 192), British Telecommunications plc (Call Charge Information, pp. 239, 242).

First published 1986
by John Murray (Publishers) Ltd
50 Albemarle Street, London W1X 4BD

Reprinted 1987 (twice), 1989

Second edition 1992

Reprinted 1993, 1994

Typeset by Blackpool Typesetting Services Ltd,
Blackpool

Printed in Great Britain at the
University Press, Cambridge

A CIP catalogue entry for this book can be
obtained from the British Library

ISBN 0-7195-5030-0

Preface to the National Curriculum edition

Understanding Mathematics is a widely used complete course of five books for secondary pupils in the 11–16 age range. This is the first of the two-book 14–16 course which covers the National Curriculum programme up to Level 10. The 14–16 course of the parallel series, **Steps in Understanding Mathematics**, covers up to Level 7 with some extension to Level 8.

The development of each topic has been planned with reference to the National Curriculum, the research project *Concepts in Secondary Mathematics and Science* (CSMS), and the Assessment and Performance Unit's reports.

The common core/development/extension format has proved very successful, permitting the same book to be used by pupils of a wide range of abilities. The emphasis on constant revision within the exercises, together with the weekly revision papers and the glossary, has proved a very successful confidence-building approach. Schools have reported excellent examination results following use of the series.

The **Teachers' Resource Books** have teaching notes and demonstration examples; transparency masters; answers, including diagrams; aural tests; practical worksheet masters; assessment tests; computer teaching programs; attainment target tests; and photocopiable reference notes.

Two further publications accompany the main course: **Aural Tests in Mathematics** (Books 1–5, ISBNs: 0 7195-4588 9, –4589 7, –4590 0, –4591 9, –4592 7) provide essential practice and **Mathematics Coursework 1–3** (ISBN: 0 7195 4565 X) encourages pupils to explore mathematical ideas – to say 'What if . . .?'

Notes on the National Curriculum edition

Book 4 has undergone major restructuring.

- The order has been changed to align with National Curriculum Levels, starting at Level 5 (core) and 7 (development), and concluding with the new material required at Level 10.

- Some new material has been added where the original edition did not fully meet National Curriculum requirements.

- The content for pupils of intermediate ability has been significantly increased with more emphasis on the financial mathematics needed in society.

Full details of the changes made, and a comparison with the original edition of UM Book 4, are in the Teachers' Resource Book.

Contents

About this book

This is the first book in the widely used two-book **Understanding Mathematics** course for Key Stage 4 leading to GCSE mathematics at National Curriculum Levels 5 to 10.

Although best used after the first three books in the series, Understanding Mathematics Books 4 and 5 may be used as a separate course for the final two years leading to Key Stage 4 (16 +) as they include full revision notes and examples of all the work expected to have been covered by Key Stage 3 (14 +).

Many chapters begin with a 'You need to know' section, summarising the mathematics you should already know. This is followed by a 'Test yourself' exercise to ensure your knowledge is secure. Answers to these are provided at the back of the book.

New material is introduced in the tinted sections, with points to discuss with your class and your teacher.

The exercises are structured as follows:

- **Introductory questions** (common core) are for everyone.

- **Starred questions** (reinforcement) are optional for those who find the introductory questions very easy.

- **Further questions** (development) follow. These continue the topic to a higher level.

- **Boxed questions** (extension) challenge those who are keen and quick, and give ideas for investigations and practical work.

This structure helps you to learn at your own pace and builds up your confidence.

Answers to most of the development and extension questions are given at the back; the remainder are in the Teachers' Resource Book.

The **Papers** should be worked at about one per week, possibly as homework. They provide essential revision so that you do not forget topics.

A **Glossary** lists most of the mathematical words you will meet, so that you can look up any that you do not understand.

A **Contents** list at the front and an **Index** at the back will help you to find notes on topics when revising or working the Papers.

Computer programs, in this edition mainly photocopiable from the Teachers' Resource Books, will develop your logical skills. They are in BASIC and will work on most popular micros.

The authors will be delighted to hear from you, perhaps answering some of our challenges, giving your own computer programs, or just telling us what you like about the course or what you would like added or changed.

1 Transformations: review

● You need to know . . .

● Coordinates, and the lines $y = 0$, $x = 0$, $y = x$ and $y = -x$

Point A has coordinates (2, 0).

Point B has coordinates (0, 1).

Point C has coordinates (−1, −1).

Line DE is the x-axis. Its equation is $y = 0$.

Line FG is the y-axis. Its equation is $x = 0$.

The x-axis crosses the y-axis at the origin.

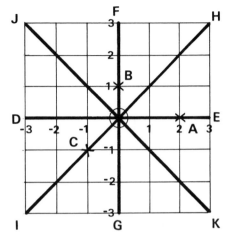

Fig. 1:1

Line HI has the equation $y = x$. Each point on $y = x$ has its x-coordinate the same as its y-coordinate, e.g. (3, 3); (−2, −2); (1.5, 1.5).

Line JK has the equation $y = -x$. Each point on $y = -x$ has its y-coordinate equal to its x-coordinate times −1, e.g. (3, −3); (0, 0); (−2, 2).

● The transformations of rotation, reflection, translation and enlargement

Rotation
To describe a rotation, state the centre of rotation and the angle turned (positive rotations are anticlockwise).

Example In Figure 1:2, triangle ABC has rotated through 270° about O.

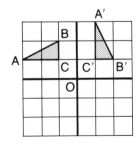

Fig. 1:2

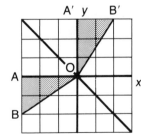

Fig. 1:3

Reflection
To describe a reflection, state the equation, or the name, of the mirror line.

Example In Figure 1:3, triangle ABO has been reflected in the line $y = -x$.

1

Translation

In Figure 1:4, X is translated to Y by the vector $\begin{pmatrix} 6 \\ 3 \end{pmatrix}$. This means a move of 6 units to the right and 3 units up.

Y is translated to X by the vector $\begin{pmatrix} -6 \\ -3 \end{pmatrix}$. What does this mean?

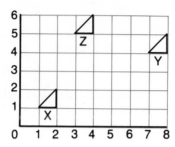

Fig. 1:4

Enlargement

To describe an enlargement, state the scale factor by which the figure has been enlarged and the centre of the enlargement.

Figures 1:5 to 1:8 illustrate four kinds of enlargement. In each diagram △ABC is mapped onto △A′B′C′.

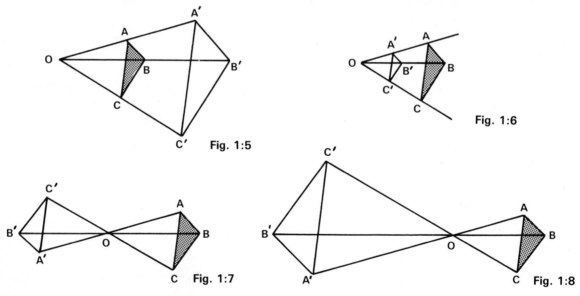

Fig. 1:5

Fig. 1:6

Fig. 1:7

Fig. 1:8

Figure 1:5 is an enlargement of scale factor 2 from centre O.

Figure 1:6 is an enlargement of scale factor $\frac{1}{2}$ from centre O. (Note that we refer to the transformation as an enlargement even when the image is smaller than the object.)

Figure 1:7 is an enlargement of scale factor -1 from centre O. (Note that in a negative enlargement the image is on the opposite side of the centre.)

Figure 1:8 is an enlargement of scale factor -2 from centre O.

Test yourself

1 State the coordinates of points A, B, C and D in Figure 1:9.

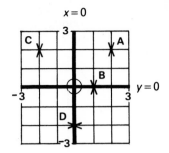

Fig. 1:9

2 In Figure 1:9, which point (A, B, C or D) lies on the line:
(a) $y = 0$ (b) $x = 0$ (c) $y = x$ (d) $y = -x$?

3 Copy and complete the following coordinates so that the points will all lie on the line $y = x$.
(4,); (, $2\frac{1}{2}$); (, 0); (−3,); (, −1)

4 Repeat question 3, but this time make the points lie on the line $y = -x$.

*5 Copy Figure 1:10, then draw the reflection of the pentagon in the y-axis and in the x-axis.

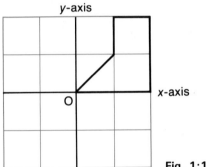

Fig. 1:10

*6 In Figure 1:4, what vector translates:
(a) X to Z   (b) Z to X   (c) Z to Y   (d) Y to Z?

*7 Copy Figure 1:11, then enlarge △DEF by scale factor 2 from centre O.

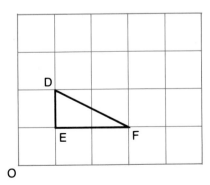

Fig. 1:11

8 Using tracing paper, or otherwise, find the coordinates of the centre of the rotation that maps the black triangle onto the red triangle in each diagram in Figure 1:12. Also state the angle of each rotation.

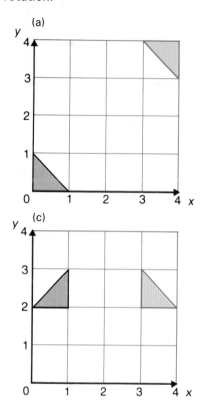
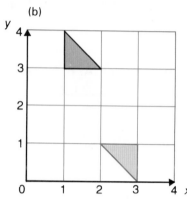
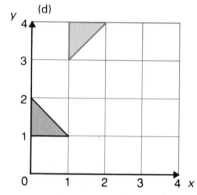

Fig. 1:12

9 In Figure 1:13, state the vector that translates shape A to shape B.

Fig. 1:13

10 Copy Figure 1:14. Enlarge shape P:
(a) by scale factor 0.75 from centre (10, 3)
(b) by scale factor −0.5 from centre (3, −1).

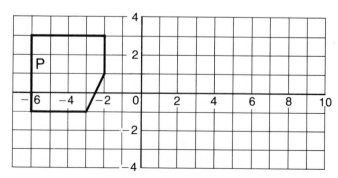

Fig. 1:14

11 Which letters have been rotated to make the shapes in Figure 1:15?

Fig. 1:15

12 In Figure 1:16, the hatched (///) square is transformed into
the shaded square. Describe the transformation if it is:
(a) a rotation   (b) a reflection   (c) an enlargement
(d) a double reflection (give two possible answers).

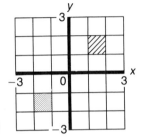

Fig. 1:16

13 Draw *x*- and *y*-axes from −4 to 4 each. Plot the triangle whose vertices are at (−2, 1), (−2, 3)
and (−1, 3). Draw the image of this triangle after:
(a) a rotation of −90° about (0, 0)   (b) a reflection in *y* = *x*
(c) an enlargement of scale factor 2 from (0, 3).

14 (a) Copy Figure 1:17. A is the image of T
after it has been rotated through a half-
turn about the origin. Draw and label A.
(b) B is the image of T after it has been
rotated through a half-turn about the
point (3, 0). Draw and label B.
(c) C is the image of triangle T after it has
been reflected in the *y*-axis. Draw and
label C.
(d) Describe fully the transformation which
maps (i) A onto B, and (ii) A onto C.

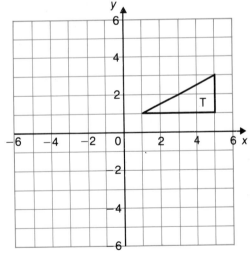

Fig. 1:17

15 Transformations provide lots of opportunities for coursework. You could look into how
rotation is used in machinery; how transformations are used in design, such as wallpaper,
cloth patterns, and tile tessellations; how computers can be programmed to operate
robots; etc.

● You need to know . . .

● Basic algebraic notation

When using letters to stand for numbers, you do not need to write multiplication signs.

Example $3 \times a \times b$ is usually written as $3ab$.

Note that $3 \times 4 \times 5$ cannot be written as 345, and that a computer needs 3 * 4 * 5 and 3 * a * b.

When using letters to stand for numbers, the division sign is usually replaced by writing the expression as a fraction.

Example $3 \div a$ is usually written as $\dfrac{3}{a}$.

Note that $3 \div 4$ can also be written as $\frac{3}{4}$ or 3/4, and that a computer needs 3/4 for both $3 \div 4$ and $\frac{3}{4}$.

● Directed numbers

Negative (−ve) numbers   Positive (+ve) numbers

$$-3 \quad -2.5 \quad -2 \quad -1.5 \quad -1 \quad -0.5 \quad 0 \quad 0.5 \quad 1 \quad 1.5 \quad 2 \quad 2.5 \quad 3$$

Positive (plus) numbers need no signs; negative (minus) numbers need − signs.

Like signs multiply to make a plus:
$$- \; -3 \to +3 \qquad -3 \times -2 \to +6$$
Unlike signs multiply to make a minus
$$- \; +3 \to -3 \qquad + \; -3 \to -3 \qquad -3 \times +2 \to -6 \qquad +3 \times -2 \to -6$$

Examples If $a = -2$, $b = -3$ and $c = 4$, then:

$$a + b = -2 + -3 \;\to\; -2 - 3 = -5$$

$$bc = -3 \times 4 = -12$$

$$ab = -2 \times -3 = 6$$

$$\frac{c}{a} = 4 \div -2 = -2$$

$$\frac{a}{b} = -2 \div -3 = \tfrac{2}{3}$$

−2 −3 can be thought of as 'down 2 then down another 3'. The two minuses do not make a plus here, as they are not multiplied.

The same rules apply for division as for Multiplication.

● Brackets

Any term written directly before a bracket multiplies each term in the bracket.

Examples $2(4 + a) \rightarrow 8 + 2a$ Working: $2 \times 4 = 8$; $2 \times a = 2a$

Read '→' as 'becomes'.

$-2(4 + a) \rightarrow -8 - 2a$ Working: $-2 \times 4 = -8$; $-2 \times a = -2a$

$-2(4 - a) \rightarrow -8 + 2a$ Working: $-2 \times 4 = -8$; $-2 \times -a = +2a$

$-(4 + a) \rightarrow -4 - a$ Working: $-(4 + a) \Rightarrow -1(4 + a)$; $-1 \times 4 = -4$; $-1 \times a = -a$

The sign ⇒ means 'implies' or 'means'.

$a + 2(b - c) \rightarrow a + 2b - 2c$

$a - 2(b - c) \rightarrow a - 2b + 2c$

A computer needs the * (multiply) sign between the term and the bracket, e.g. $-2*(4 - a)$.

● Inspection method for equation solving

Equations with only one letter-term are nearly always solved (to find the value of the letter) most easily by the 'inspection' approach, not by using 'rules'.

Examples   If $b - 2 = 8$ then b must be $\underline{10}$ (as $10 - 2 = 8$).

If $8 + c = 6$ then c must be $\underline{-2}$ (as $8 + -2 = 6$).

If $7 - 2x = 8$ then $2x$ must be -1 (as $7 - -1 \rightarrow 7 + 1 = 8$) so x must be $\underline{-\frac{1}{2}}$
(as $2 \times -\frac{1}{2} = -1$).

If $3e = 2$ then e must be $\frac{2}{3}$ (because 3 thirds make 1 whole, so 3 times two-thirds makes 2 wholes).

If $\dfrac{24}{1 - n} = 8$ then $1 - n$ must be 3 (as $24 \div 3 = 8$)

so n must be $\underline{-2}$ (as $1 - -2 \rightarrow 1 + 2 = 3$).

If $4(2a - 7) = 12$ then $2a - 7$ must be 3 (as $4 \times 3 = 12$)
so $2a$ must be 10 (as $10 - 7 = 3$)
so a must be $\underline{5}$ (as $2 \times 5 = 10$).

The above solutions can be written as follows:

$b - 2 = 8 \Rightarrow \underline{b = 10}$

$8 + c = 6 \Rightarrow \underline{c = -2}$

$7 - 2x = 8 \Rightarrow 2x = -1 \Rightarrow \underline{x = -\frac{1}{2}}$

$3e = 2 \Rightarrow \underline{e = \frac{2}{3}}$

$\dfrac{24}{1 - n} = 8 \Rightarrow 1 - n = 3 \Rightarrow \underline{n = -2}$

$4(2a - 7) = 12 \Rightarrow 2a - 7 = 3 \Rightarrow 2a = 10 \Rightarrow \underline{a = 5}$

2

● Solution of simultaneous equations

When there are two unknown letters to be found, you need two equations. For instance, $x + y = 8$ is true for an infinite number of pairs of values for x and y. But if you also know that $x = y + 2$ then the only possible solution is $x = 5$ and $y = 3$.

Three methods are possible:

Method 1   **Draw intersecting graphs.**

Method 2   **Substitute for one letter its value in the other equation.** This is best used when one of the equations is in the form $x = \ldots$ or $y = \ldots$ For example, $y = x - 6$ and $3y - 2x = 8$.

Method 3   **Add or subtract the equations to eliminate one of the letter-terms,** having multiplied as necessary to make one letter-term the same absolute value in both. ('Absolute' means 'ignoring the sign'; ABS in BASIC.)

Method 1

Example   Solve simultaneously

$$y = 2x - 1 \text{ and } y - x = 1.$$

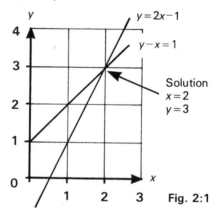

Fig. 2:1

Method 2

Example   Solve $x = 2$ and $2x + 2y = 11$ simultaneously.

We can think of this as finding where the line $x = 2$ crosses the line $2x + 2y = 11$. Substitute the value $x = 2$ into $2x + 2y = 11$, giving $4 + 2y = 11$. Then $4 + 2y = 11 \rightarrow 2y = 7 \rightarrow y = 3\frac{1}{2}$.

Answer: $\underline{\underline{x = 2, y = 3\frac{1}{2}}}$. (The lines cross at $(2, 3\frac{1}{2})$.)

Example   Solve $y = x - 6$ and $x + y = 4$ simultaneously.

Substitute the value $y = x - 6$ into $x + y = 4$, giving $x + (x - 6) = 4$. Then $x + (x - 6) = 4 \rightarrow x + x - 6 = 4 \rightarrow 2x - 6 = 4 \rightarrow 2x = 10 \rightarrow x = 5$. We know that $y = x - 6$, so if $x = 5$ then y must be -1.

Answer: $\underline{x = 5, y = -1}$.

Example   Solve $x = 2y - 1$ and $y + 2x = 2$ by substitution.

Substitute x, giving $y + 2(2y - 1) = 2$. $y + 2(2y - 1) = 2 \rightarrow y + 4y - 2 = 2 \rightarrow 5y - 2 = 2 \rightarrow 5y = 4 \rightarrow y = \frac{4}{5}$. Now as we know that $x = 2y - 1$, then $x = \frac{8}{5} - 1 = \frac{3}{5}$.

Answer: $\underline{x = \frac{3}{5}, y = \frac{4}{5}}$.

Method 3

Find the values of x and y that satisfy both $x + 3y = 9$ and $x - 2y = -1$.

Example
$$x + 3y = 9$$
$$x - 2y = -1 \quad \text{SUBTRACT}$$
$$5y = 10$$
$$y = 2$$

Substitute $y = 2$
into $x + 3y = 9$,
giving $x + 6 = 9$,
so $\underline{x = 3.}$

Check both equations are true
for $x = 3$, $y = 2$:
$3 + 6 = 9$; $3 - 4 = -1$.

Note: By subtracting, the x terms have been eliminated. If the two given equations are true, then the result of the subtraction is true.

Compare: $2 + 3 = 5$
$$1 + 2 = 3 \quad \text{SUBTRACT}$$
$$1 + 1 = 2$$

When subtracting,
$+3y - -2y \rightarrow +3y + 2y = 5y$
and $9 - -1 \rightarrow 9 + 1 = 10$.

Example Solve $3x + 5y = 21$ and $7x - 2y = 8$ simultaneously.

$$3x + 5y = 21 \xrightarrow{\times 2} 6x + 10y = 42$$

$$7x - 2y = 8 \xrightarrow{\times 5} 35x - 10y = 40 \quad \text{ADD}$$
$$41x \qquad = 82$$
$$x = 2$$

Substitute $x = 2$ into $3x + 5y = 21 \rightarrow 6 + 5y = 21 \rightarrow 5y = 15 \rightarrow \underline{y = 3.}$

Check this for yourself.

Test yourself

1 In this question, $m = -1$, $n = -2$ and $p = 3$. Evaluate (find the numerical value of):
(a) $3m$ (b) $p - n$ (c) $m - n$ (d) $m + p$ (e) $m + n$ (f) mp
(g) mn (h) $\dfrac{p}{m}$ (i) $\dfrac{m}{n}$.

2 Multiply out (as in the examples on page 7):
(a) $3(x + 4)$ (b) $2(a - 5)$ (c) $4(3 + 2a)$ (d) $2(2a - 5)$ (e) $-(3 + a)$
(f) $-(h - 1)$ (g) $-3(2x + 1)$ (h) $-2(x - 4)$ (i) $-3(3 + 4a)$.

3 Solve (find the value of the letter):
(a) $4z = -12$ (b) $12d = 3$ (c) $3r - 5 = 4$ (d) $6y - 6 = 0$ (e) $e + 6 = 4$
(f) $x + 3 = -4$ (g) $2t + 4 = -8$ (h) $4u + 1 = 6$ (i) $3 + 2m = -2$
(j) $17 - 3d = 1$ (k) $13 = 7 - 2b$ (l) $3 = 1 - 3v$.

*4 Multiply out:
(a) $3(2 + 3a)$ (b) $3(3a - 4)$ (c) $-(x + 1)$ (d) $-2(x + 4)$ (e) $-4(2 - a)$
(f) $-2(2a - 3)$ (g) $2(3a - 8)$.

*5 Solve:

(a) $4k - 9 = 7$ (b) $8 - 3w = 2$ (c) $24 + 3x = 3$ (d) $5t + 13 = 3$
(e) $4 - 2n = 8$ (f) $5 - 3q = -4$ (g) $4x - 18 = 16$ (h) $2 - 3r = 5$
(i) $3y + 12 = 5$ (j) $-11 = 6x + 7$ (k) $14 = -3a + 2$ (l) $-3 = -4f + 5.$

6 Solve:

(a) $\dfrac{x}{4} = 3$ (b) $\dfrac{d}{8} = -2$ (c) $\dfrac{15}{u} = 3$ (d) $\dfrac{16}{e} = -4$ (e) $\dfrac{18}{2t} = 9.$

7 Solve:

(a) $\dfrac{x}{4} + 6 = 14$ (b) $\dfrac{3s}{5} + 4 = 10$ (c) $16 - \dfrac{f}{3} = 12$ (d) $6 - \dfrac{2w}{3} = 4$

(e) $\dfrac{20}{n} - 4 = 6$ (f) $12 - \dfrac{25}{2x} = 7.$

8 Solve simultaneously by substitution:

(a) $x = y + 3$ and $x + 2y = 21$
(b) $y = 3x - 4$ and $x + y = 4$
(c) $y = 3x - 1$ and $x - 2y = -13.$

9 Solve simultaneously by elimination:

(a) $2x - 3y = 5$ and $x + 3y = -2$
(b) $3x - 2y = 10$ and $x - 2y = 2$
(c) $a + b = 15$ and $2a - 4b = -3$
(d) $3s - 2t = 5$ and $2s - 5t = 10.$

10 **Examples** $\quad -2(4a - 5) + 3 \rightarrow -8a + 10 + 3 \rightarrow -8a + 13$
$\qquad\qquad\qquad 3(a - 6) + 2(3 - a) \rightarrow 3a - 18 + 6 - 2a \rightarrow a - 12$

Simplify:

(a) $2(a + 3) + 3(2 - a)$ (b) $3(2 + 5a) - 4(2a - 3)$
(c) $5(a - 3) - 4(a + 5)$ (d) $2(a + 4) + 3(6 - 2a)$
(e) $-8(2 - 5a) - 4a - 9$ (f) $-5 - (3a - 7) + 2(1 - 8a) + a.$

11 Solve:

(a) $\dfrac{3x}{5} = -4$ (b) $\dfrac{12}{3w} = 8$ (c) $\dfrac{46}{7g} = 2$ (d) $3 = \dfrac{2}{3x} - 18.$

12 Solve simultaneously:

(a) $2a - \dfrac{b}{3} = 4$ and $3a + \dfrac{b}{2} = 12$ (b) $\dfrac{a}{10} + b = 2$ and $\dfrac{a}{2} - 2b = 3$
(c) $6a = 2b + 9$ and $3a + 4b = 12$
(d) $3a + 7b = 1$ and $5b + 2a + 1 = 0.$

Equations with two letter-terms

For discussion

In solving equations like $3n - 2 = 5 + 2n$, we cannot use the inspection approach until one of the two letter-terms has been removed. We remove one letter-term by adding to or subtracting from both sides of the equation a term which reduces it to zero, as in the following examples.

Examples   (a) $3n - 2 = 5 + 2n \xrightarrow{-2n \text{ on both sides}} 3n - 2 - 2n = 5 + 2n - 2n \rightarrow n - 2 = 5$

(b) $5 - 2w = 2 + 3w \xrightarrow{+2w \text{ on both sides}} 5 - 2w + 2w = 2 + 3w + 2w$
$\rightarrow 5 = 2 + 5w$

(c) $4 - 3x = 5 - 2x \xrightarrow{+3x \text{ on both sides}} 4 - 3x + 3x = 5 - 2x + 3x \rightarrow 4 = 5 + x$

(d) $4 - 3z = 5 + 2z \xrightarrow{+3z \text{ on both sides}} 4 - 3z + 3z = 5 + 2z + 3z \rightarrow 4 = 5 + 5z$

It does not really matter which letter-term you reduce to zero, but the remainder of the solution is usually easier if you leave a positive letter-term, as we did in the above examples. This can be remembered by the following rule, if you like rules!

Remove the term with the smaller coefficient.

The 'coefficient' is the number in front of it. Note that in example (c), -3 is smaller than -2. Because we perform the same operation on each side of the equation, it remains true or 'in balance'. We can see this in number statements:

$3 + 2 = 5 \xrightarrow{-2 \text{ on both sides}} 3 + 2 - 2 = 5 - 2 \rightarrow 3 = 5 - 2$

$3 - 2 = 1 \xrightarrow{+2 \text{ on both sides}} 3 - 2 + 2 = 1 + 2 \rightarrow 3 = 3$

Examples   Solve $6n + 7 = 4n + 13$.
$6n + 7 = 4n + 13 \xrightarrow{-4n} 2n + 7 = 13 \Rightarrow 2n = 6 \Rightarrow \underline{\underline{n = 3}}$

Solve $7 - 5x = 4x - 2$.
$7 - 5x = 4x - 2 \xrightarrow{+5x} 7 = 9x - 2 \Rightarrow 9x = 9 \Rightarrow \underline{\underline{x = 1}}$

1   Solve the following equations.
(a) $3y - 5 = 2y + 3$ (b) $6t - 4 = 5 + 3t$ (c) $4e + 8 = 11e + 15$
(d) $12 - 4c = 8 - 2c$ (e) $6x + 10 = 13 - 12x$ (f) $6 - 5n = 4n + 24$.

2   Find the solution of:
(a) $x + 8 = 3x + 4$ (b) $9 + 2k = 4k + 11$ (c) $3 - 2t = 4t + 15$
(d) $4f + 1 = 10 - 2f$ (e) $3g + 2 = g + 2$ (f) $1 - 3h = 2\frac{1}{2} - 2h$.

3   Example   Solve $3(x + 2) = 2(x - 1)$.
$3(x + 2) = 2(x - 1) \rightarrow 3x + 6 = 2x - 2 \xrightarrow{-2x} x + 6 = -2 \Rightarrow \underline{\underline{x = -8}}$

Solve:
(a) $2(x - 3) = x + 4$ (b) $2(x + 2) = x + 5$ (c) $3(3w - 4) = 4(w + 2)$.

4   Solve:
(a) $2(4a - 6) = 5(2a - 2)$ (b) $5(2 + 2k) = 2(3 + 3k)$ (c) $4(4r - 6) = 8(r + 3)$.

5 Solve:

(a) $4(3 + 2h) = 6(5 + h)$ (b) $3(2x - 4) = 5(-2x + 4)$.

6 If necessary, 'collect terms' on each side of the equation before beginning to solve it.

Example Solve $3(a - 2) - 1 = 4(a + 4) + 2a - 2$.

First multiply out the brackets and collect like terms:
$$3(a - 2) - 1 = 4(a + 4) + 2a - 2 \rightarrow 3a - 6 - 1 = 4a + 16 + 2a - 2$$
$$\rightarrow 3a - 7 = 6a + 14.$$

Now solve the equation:
$$3a - 7 = 6a + 14 \xrightarrow{-3a} -7 = 3a + 14 \Rightarrow 3a = -21 \Rightarrow \underline{\underline{a = -7}}$$

Solve:

(a) $1 + 3(n - 1) = 2n + 4$ (b) $7(s - 3) = 4(s + 2) - 2$
(c) $3e - 4(3e - 2) = 3(2 - 3e) + 2 - 2e$.

7 Solve:

(a) $4(r - 3) - 3(2 - r) = 2r + 7$ (b) $7(2p - 5) + 8(3p - 4) - 4(7p + 2) = 0$
(c) $9(6x + 7) - 4(2x + 5) = 40 - (x - 3)$
(d) $5y - 3(y - 2) = 8 - 2(2 - 5y) + 2(y - 5)$.

---

8 (a) Josie is 5 and her dad is 25. Using axes labelled 'Josie's age' (j-axis, from 0 to 50) and 'Dad's age' (d-axis, from 20 to 70), draw a straight line to represent the connection between their two ages.

(b) Draw the line $d + 2j$. Explain the significance of the intersection of this line with the line in part (a).

(c) Is dad ever three times Josie's age?

(d) Write and solve an equation to find when dad is $1\frac{1}{2}$ times Josie's age.

9 An aeroplane averaging 300 knots (300 nautical miles per hour) reaches its destination 10 minutes early, whilst if it averages 240 knots it is 6 minutes late. What is the planned time for the journey?

10 Isaac forgets to write the units, and makes the area of a square equal to its perimeter. What sizes could the square be?

11 An isosceles triangle has sides $x - 2$ cm, $3x - 7$ cm and $\frac{2}{3}x$ cm. What are the possible values of x? Draw each possible triangle.

12 A card box with no lid has to have a square base x cm by x cm, with upright sides y cm. What values of x and y will use the smallest area of card and give the box a volume of 4000 cm³?

● You need to know . . .

● How to change a fraction to a percentage

Multiply by 100 (to find what fraction of 100 it is).

Example $\dfrac{11}{15} \to \dfrac{11}{{}_3\cancel{15}} \times \cancel{100}^{20}\% \to \dfrac{220\%}{3} \to 73\tfrac{1}{3}\%$

● How to find a percentage of an amount

Example   Find 35% of £45.

35% is another way of writing $\dfrac{35}{100}$.

Hence 35% of £45 $\to \dfrac{35}{100} \times £45 \to \dfrac{{}^7\cancel{35}}{{}_{4\,20}\cancel{100}} \times £\cancel{45}^9 \to £15.75$

● How to find one amount as a percentage of another

Write it as a fraction, then use the method of the first note above.

Example   Find 32 as a percentage of 128.

Write this as $\dfrac{32}{128}$, then $\dfrac{32}{128} \to \dfrac{32}{128} \times 100\% \to \dfrac{{}^{1}{}_{8}\cancel{32}}{{}_{4}{}_{32}\cancel{128}} \times 100\% \to 25\%$

Remember   **One amount as a percentage of another amount is the first over the second times 100%.**

● Percentage changes

A change can be an increase, a decrease, a profit, a loss, etc.

Remember   **Change % = change over original times 100**

Example   Find the percentage loss if a book bought for £20 is re-sold for £18.

The change in the cost is £2.
The original cost was £20.

Hence the percentage loss is $\dfrac{2}{20} \times 100\% = 10\%$

● To increase or decrease by a percentage

It is possible just to find the increase, then add it on, but a better method to use is:

To increase by r%, multiply by $\dfrac{100 + r}{100}$.

To decrease by r%, multiply by $\dfrac{100 - r}{100}$.

Examples   To increase by 12%, multiply by 1.12.
               To decrease by 12%, multiply by 0.88.

● Using a calculator percentage key

Unfortunately different calculators do not always use the same method, but one of the following methods will probably work.

To find 8% of £60, key: 60 $\boxed{\times}$ 8 $\boxed{\%}$ or 60 $\boxed{\times}$ 8 $\boxed{\%}$ $\boxed{=}$.

To increase £60 by 8%, key: 60 $\boxed{+}$ 8 $\boxed{\%}$ or 60 $\boxed{+}$ 8 $\boxed{\%}$ $\boxed{=}$ or 60 $\boxed{\times}$ 8 $\boxed{\%}$ $\boxed{+}$.

To decrease £60 by 8%, key: 60 $\boxed{-}$ 8 $\boxed{\%}$ or 60 $\boxed{-}$ 8 $\boxed{\%}$ $\boxed{=}$ or 60 $\boxed{\times}$ 8 $\boxed{\%}$ $\boxed{-}$.

Test yourself

1 (a) Express as a decimal fraction:
 (i) 20% (ii) 35% (iii) $12\frac{1}{2}$%.

 (b) Express the above percentages as common fractions in their lowest terms.

2 Express as a percentage:
 (a) $\frac{1}{4}$ (b) $\frac{4}{5}$ (c) $\frac{5}{8}$ (d) $\frac{1}{3}$ (e) 0.42 (f) 0.02 (g) 0.625

3 Find:
 (a) 40% of £2 (b) 10% of £75 (c) 30% of 150 g (d) 140% of 15 m
 (e) 52% of £2.50 (f) $2\frac{1}{2}$% of £120.

4 Find:
 (a) £6 as a percentage of £24 (b) 9 as a percentage of 45
 (c) 28 cm as a percentage of 35 cm (d) 57p as a percentage of 19p
 (e) 3.5 kg as a percentage of 2.8 kg.

5 (a) Increase 50 by 20%. (b) Decrease 20 by 10%.
 (c) Increase 50 kg by 25%. (d) Decrease 96 m by 15%.

6 Find the profit or loss, saying which it is, if:
 (a) an article costing £15 is then sold for £18
 (b) an article costing £20 is then sold for £18.

7 A pupil is given 48 marks out of 60. What percentage is this?

8 Gunpowder is made of 75% nitre, 10% sulphur and 15% charcoal. How many grams of each are needed to make 500 g of gunpowder?

9 A man buys a carpet for £400 and sells it for £500. Find the percentage profit.

10 Lois gives 30% of her wages to her mother. How much does she give if she earns £70?

11 Hardcheese school has 725 pupils, of whom 29 are absent on April 1st. What percentage is present?

12 My car's petrol tank holds 45 litres when full. How many litres are in the tank when it is 30% full?

13 Electromart allows 5% discount for cash. Find the reduced price of a television marked at £324.

---

14 Find $8\frac{1}{3}$% of 84 g.

15 What is $37\frac{1}{2}$% of 30 kg?

16 Joseph buys a cycle for £153 and sells it a year later for £136. Find the percentage loss.

17 A wholesaler charges £2.25 for a can of paint which the retailer sells as a special offer for £2.52. What is the retailer's percentage profit?

18 Potatoes are bought at £4.80 for 56 kg and sold at 16p per kg. Find the percentage profit:
(a) reckoned on the cost price   (b) reckoned on the selling price.

19 Harvey invests £5000, and after one year is pleased to find that it has appreciated by 6%. In the next three years it appreciates by 10%, 4% and 10%.

Find:
(a) the value of his investment at the end of each year.
(b) the percentage profit on his original investment at the end of four years, correct to two significant figures.

Percentage changes (inverse calculations)

Sometimes you know the amount resulting from a percentage change and have to find the amount before the change took place. This would occur in a shop where the price given includes 17.5% VAT and the customer wants to know what the price was before VAT.

A shopkeeper once told me that the VAT included in the price of a £100 television was £17.50, because 17.5% of £100 was £17.50. He was wrong, because the VAT was 17.5% of the 'before-VAT' price. This is what he should have done:

To increase by 17.5%, multiply by 1.175,
so 1.175 × before-VAT price = £100
→ before-VAT price = £100 ÷ 1.175 = £85.12.
The VAT was therefore £14.88.

Percentage profit or loss in mathematics questions is, by tradition, assumed to be reckoned on the cost price, unless stated otherwise.

3

Example   Selling price £28, profit 12%; find the cost price.

The temptation is to work out 12% of £28, then take this away from the £28, but this is not correct, for the 12% profit is reckoned on the cost price. The correct method is:

To increase by 12%, multiply by $\dfrac{112}{100}$ or 1.12.

Then 1.12 × cost price = £28 → cost price = £28 ÷ 1.12 = £25.

Example   Selling price £21, loss 40%; find the cost price.

To reduce by 40%, multiply by $\dfrac{100-40}{100} \rightarrow \dfrac{60}{100}$ or 0.60.

Then 0.60 × cost price = £21 → cost price = £21 ÷ 0.60 = £35.

1   Find the cost price for the following.

	(a)	(b)	(c)	(d)	(e)
Selling price	£45	£21	£15	£8	£5.20
Profit/loss	10% loss	40% profit	50% profit	20% loss	4% profit

2   (a) Increase 15 by 25%.

(b) After an increase of 25% a number becomes 35. Find the number.

(c) Decrease 60 by 55%.

(d) What number becomes 18 when it is decreased by 20%?

(e) Find the cost price of an article sold for £15 at a profit of 25%.

(f) With VAT of 17.5% a vase costs £47. What did it cost before VAT?

3   A dealer buys a book for £4 and sells it at a profit of 36%. Find the selling price.

4   Ahmed spends 24% of his money and has 38p left. How much had he at first?

5   Leah buys a bicycle for £15 and sells it for £18. Her sister, Rachel, buys a bicycle for £27 and sells it for £36. Who makes the greater percentage profit and by how much?

6   A cruise cost £720 after a 20% reduction. What was the original cost?

7   Hashi owns a dress shop. He reckons his profit as a percentage of his cost price. If he makes 75% profit on a dress selling for £105, what did the dress cost him?

8   Roger sells a car for £686 and reckons that he has lost 30% of what it cost him. What was the original cost?

9   Sue is given a $12\frac{1}{2}$% rise in her annual salary of £3880. What is her new monthly salary?

10   Lizzie is given a 7% pay rise, bringing her pay up to £481.50. What was her pay before the rise?

11 A manufacturer is asked to produce an operating lever. He is allowed a tolerance of $\pm 2\%$ on the specified length, giving 153 mm as the longest acceptable lever. What is the specified length?

12 A car-battery manufacturer makes up the electrolyte to contain 30% acid and 70% water by volume. How many litres of electrolyte can she make from 25 litres of acid?

13 Find the original value of a car if after losing $8\frac{1}{3}\%$ of its value it is worth £528.

14 Shelley sells a record for £2.40, thereby losing 4% on what she paid for it. At what price should she have sold to *gain* 6%?

15 A manufacturer sells an article to a wholesaler, who then adds 25% to the price before selling it to a shopkeeper. The shopkeeper adds 35% to his cost price and sells the article to a customer for £5.40.

   (a) What did the manufacturer charge the wholesaler?

   (b) If the manufacturer is making 60% profit and the cost of making the article is made up of raw materials, labour, and overheads in the ratio 1 : 4 : 3 respectively, what is the cost of the raw material?

16 Collect examples of the uses of percentages in everyday life. Write a report on your findings.

● You need to know . . .

● The three statistical averages

Mean
The total score distributed equally to each item. The mean of 2, 7 and 9 is the total (18) divided by 3, giving 6.

Mode
The item that occurs most frequently. There may be several modes, or no mode.

Median
The middle score of an odd number of items. For an even number of items it is usually taken as the mean of the two middle scores, although it could be anywhere between them.

● Frequency tables

These are used to simplify the arithmetic with a large amount of data. (Processing such large amounts take a long time, so examples in books usually apply the method to a small amount of data!)

Example Find the mean of £16, £16, £17, £17, £17, £18, £18, £18, £18, £19, £19, £19, £20.

Score (x)	Frequency (f)	Total (f × x)
£16	2	£32
£17	3	£51
£18	4	£72
£19	3	£57
£20	1	£20
TOTALS	13	£232

$$\text{Mean} = \frac{£232}{13} \simeq £18$$

Mode = £18   (highest frequency)
Median = £18   (score of the 7th item, which is clearly in the £18 frequency:
2 + 3 = 5; 2 + 3 + 4 = 9)

Test yourself

1 Find   (a) the mean   (b) the mode(s)   (c) the median:
   (i) 7, 2, 4, 3, 4   (ii) 37, 32, 34, 33, 34 (look at (a))   (iii) 10, 16, 24, 32, 15, 11
   (iv) 109, 116, 124, 132, 116, 109, 113   (v) 7, −4, 12, −9, −4, 0, −2
   (vi) 1, 7, 8, 4, 8, 8

2   Find the mean of:

   (a) 13 years, 15 years, 12 years   (b) 8 min, 12 min, 11 min

   (c) 12 years 6 months, 8 years 9 months, 14 years 7 months, 16 years 2 months.

*3   The midday Celsius temperatures during a week in August were: 24, 25, 28, 26, 22, 20 and 23°C. What was the mean for the week?

*4   The wages of 8 people in a firm are:
£108, £112, £96, £83, £130, £112, £118, and £121.

   (a) What is
      (i) the mean wage   (ii) the median wage?

   (b) If the managing director, earning £335, is included, what would be:
      (i) the new mean   (ii) the new median?

*5   Joanna's monthly earnings for a year were:
£540, £568, £539, £572, £572, £568, £570, £581, £578, £579, £572, and £565.
What was her mean monthly earning?

*6   The ages of a family of five are:
40 years 5 months, 37 years 3 months, 16 years 9 months,
14 years 6 months, and 11 years 11 months.
What is the mean age of the family?

*7   In a race the time recorded by members of a team of six were:
13 min 42 s,   13 min 50 s,   13 min 57 s,   14 min 3 s,   14 min 29 s,   14 min 59 s.

   What was:

   (a) the total time taken by the team

   (b) the mean time?

*8   The price of a Betex washing machine in six different shops was:
£258, £236, £288, £274, £252, and £264.

   (a) What was the mean price?

   (b) How much cheaper than the mean was the cheapest?

   (c) How much more expensive than the mean was the most expensive?

9   During a January the midday temperatures in °C were:
3, 7, 3, 11, 10, 3, 0, 0, −3, −8, −7, −5, −8, −8, −3, 2, 5, 6, 9, 7, 5, 5, 5, 5, 8, 6, 5, 1, 10, 9, 10.

   What was:
   (a) the mean temperature   (b) the modal temperature   (c) the median temperature?

10   The mean age of four girls is 14 years 7 months. If three of the girls have ages of 14 years 11 months, 14 years 4 months, and 16 years 6 months, what is the age of the fourth girl?

11 The marks scored in a mental arithmetic test by a class of 30 pupils were:

Marks	0	1	2	3	4	5	6	7	8	9	10
No. of pupils	0	3	0	1	2	4	5	6	5	3	1

What was:
(a) the modal mark   (b) the median mark   (c) the mean mark?

12 The members of a school club took part in a sponsored walk and the following record was made of their sponsors.

Number of sponsors	6	9	11	12	15	16	17	19
Number of walkers	2	3	14	8	16	2	3	2

Find:
(a) the median number of sponsors   (b) the modal number of sponsors
(c) the mean number of sponsors.

13 A cinema manager has to sell an average of 240 tickets a day to 'break-even'. On the first six days of a week she sold 234, 180, 202, 233, 320, and 330 tickets.

(a) How many tickets had she to sell during the seventh day to avoid making a loss?
(b) If she sold 372 tickets on the seventh day and the tickets cost on average £2 each, how much profit did she make in the week?

14 During a twelve-month period Adrian used a rain gauge which enabled him to record the following monthly rainfalls (in mm):
84, 111, 49, 70, 28, 56, 98, 26, 104, 27, 30, 31.

(a) What was the mean rainfall per month?
(b) If the rainfall for the next five months was 116, 109, 41, 115, and 60 mm, what would the average have to be for the remaining seven months so that the twelve-month mean rainfall was the same as the previous year?

15 In a class examination 16 boys averaged 68% and 14 girls averaged 71%. What was the average mark for the 30 pupils?

16 The average age of six men is 24 years 5 months, and that of five of them is 23 years 11 months. How old is the sixth man?

18 In a factory, parts were tested in batches of 1000, one batch per day. During February the number of rejects were:

Week one   8, 6, 4, 7, 4, 5, 2
Week two   11, 0, 2, 3, 0, 3, 2
Week three   10, 3, 6, 5, 4, 2, 3
Week four   14, 6, 3, 2, 4, 0, 5

(a) What was the mean reject rate per batch:
   (i) each week   (ii) for the month?

(b) The firm expected a reject rate of not more than 0.5%. In which week did the reject rate surpass this allowance and by what percentage?

19 Design a computer program to give the mean, median and mode for sets of data. You might also illustrate the data with a diagram.

Modal class; mean from grouped data

For discussion

▷ Example
Form 4B's exam marks:
51, 72, 37, 72, 39, 79, 38, 32, 68, 57, 34, 58, 62, 49, 47, 78, 61, 57, 63, 69, 48, 58, 42, 68, 52, 46, 63, 52, 57, 48.

Class	Tally	Frequency (f)	Middle (x)	Totals (fx)
30–39				
40–49				
50–59				
60–69				
70–79				

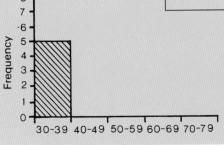

Fig. 4:1 Bar-chart for 4B's exam

The class which has the highest frequency is called the **modal class**. As with the mode, there can be more than one modal class. In the example above the modal class is 50–59.

To calculate the mean from grouped data, you assume that each frequency scores the mid-value (middle) of the range. This mid-value is the mean of the upper and lower limits of the range, e.g. the middle of 0–9 is $\dfrac{0 + 9}{2} = 4.5$, and the middle of 31–35 is $\dfrac{31 + 35}{2} = 33$.

What is the middle of:
(a) 50–59   (b) 62–70   (c) 10–14?

Example

Class	Frequency (f)	Middle (x)	Totals (fx)
30–39	23	34.5	793.5
40–49	55	44.5	2447.5
50–60	32	55	1760
	110		5001

Mean $\simeq \dfrac{5001}{110} \simeq 45$

1 The following data shows the absentees at a school each day during an 80-day term.

16, 29, 41, 6, 24, 31, 19, 46, 30, 27, 22, 35, 34, 36, 11, 25, 38, 45, 26, 39, 36, 52, 12, 51, 24, 35, 47, 53, 26, 4, 37, 32, 44, 31, 15, 43, 20, 31, 29, 39, 22, 38, 42, 32, 21, 38, 37, 34, 18, 33, 36, 34, 16, 42, 30, 28, 30, 37, 32, 20, 37, 27, 56, 43, 17, 57, 46, 33, 54, 47, 17, 39, 41, 48, 28, 35, 13, 31, 33, 21.

(a) Using class intervals of 0–9, 10–19, . . . , 50–59, make a frequency distribution table for this data.

(b) Represent the data by a bar chart.

(c) Indicate the modal class on your bar chart.

2 Calculate the mean of the data in the table.

Class	Frequency (f)	Middle (x)	Totals (fx)
0–9	5		
10–19	6		
20–29	8		
30–39	10		
40–49	7		
50–60	4		

3 (a) Find the mean for the following tables of data.

(i)

Class	0–4	5–9	10–14	15–19	20–25
Frequency	3	5	6	4	2

(ii)

Class	1–5	6–10	11–15	16–20	21–25
Frequency	2	4	6	5	3

(iii)

Class	10–19	20–29	30–39	40–49	50–59	60–69	70–79	80–89
Frequency	2	10	15	25	22	18	5	3

(iv)

Class	5–9	10–14	15–19
Frequency	30	32	28

(b) Draw a pie chart to represent the data in table (i).

4 By grouping the following marks in ranges 0–9, 10–19, 20–29, 30–39, and 40–50, calculate an approximation to the mean mark of the 100 pupils represented.

40, 43, 35, 33, 43, 45, 30, 40, 38, 46, 33, 40, 43, 34, 34, 40, 47, 41, 34, 23, 41, 35, 31, 44, 28, 42, 45, 43, 31, 37, 37, 37, 29, 46, 36, 19, 43, 37, 32, 31, 34, 42, 24, 34, 33, 41, 47, 36, 26, 43, 29, 22, 36, 26, 32, 29, 18, 36, 40, 33, 30, 24, 32, 29, 22, 26, 28, 36, 30, 25, 31, 18, 37, 26, 35, 35, 32, 24, 32, 36, 20, 39, 35, 35, 31, 16, 35, 44, 38, 36, 18, 23, 16, 36, 21, 23, 32, 32, 17, 30.

---

5 An approximate modal value can be found by considering the ratio of the scores above and below the modal class, although the result is of very dubious value. It can best be done from a bar chart. See Figure 4:2.

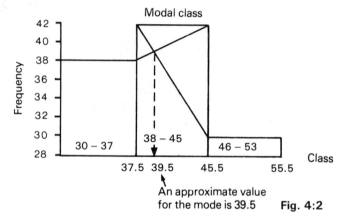

An approximate value for the mode is 39.5   **Fig. 4:2**

(a) Use the bar chart drawn in the 'For discussion' section to estimate the mode for the data.

(b) Draw bar charts for the tables in question 3, and estimate the modes from them.

6 For the data in question 1 find:
(a) an estimate for the mean   (b) the true mode
(c) the true mean   (d) the median.

Using your calculator

Piston speeds

You're cruising on the motorway at 70 m.p.h. At the same time, parts of your engine are covering greater distances than the car. Each minute your pistons race up and down nearly 3500 times. The four pistons travel a total of about $1\frac{3}{4}$ times the distance covered by the average car. Yet only millionth fractions of a centimetre separate the pistons from the cylinder.

Use the above information and your calculator to answer the following questions.

1   What product do you think this could be advertising?

2   How many times do the pistons move up and down in a second?

3   In the same gear as described in the advertisement, how many times will the pistons move up and down per minute at:
(a)   35 m.p.h.   (b)   60 m.p.h.   (c)   100 m.p.h.?

4   If the car travels 60 miles, how many miles will the pistons have travelled altogether, up and down?

5   At 70 m.p.h., how many times do the pistons move up and down per mile?

6   Using your answer to question 5, and the fact that the four pistons' total travel amounts to about $1\frac{3}{4}$ times the distance covered, what is the length of stroke of a piston in cm? (That is, the distance it moves one way up the cylinder. Take 5 miles = 8 km.)

5 Ratios

● You need to know . . .

● The meaning of a ratio

A ratio states the connection between two quantities, e.g. the ratio of cheese to eggs for a cheese omelette could be 20 g cheese to every one egg.

Ratios are often expressed with a colon (:), e.g. 2 : 3 (say '2 to 3'). In this case, both numbers must be in the same units, so we could not write the omelette example in this way, but we could say that the ratio of the weights of flour to margarine for plain scones is 4 : 1. That is, you use 4 times as much flour as margarine, e.g. 400 g flour and 100 g margarine.

● Simplifying ratios

Ratios may be simplified by dividing by a common factor, as we do with fractions.

Example 2 litres water to 12 cl Jeyes Fluid

$\xrightarrow{\text{becomes}}$ 200 : 12 (both units are now cl)

$\xrightarrow{\hspace{2cm}}$ 50 : 3 (dividing both 200 and 12 by 4).

● Expressing a ratio in the form $n : 1$ and $1 : n$

Ratios are easier to use if one of the quantities is 1, e.g. a ratio $1 : 2\frac{1}{4}$ clearly shows that the second amount is $2\frac{1}{4}$ times the first; this is not so obvious when the same ratio is written as 4 : 9.

Example Express 17 : 6 in the ratio (a) $n : 1$ (b) $1 : n$.

  (a) 17 : 6 $\xrightarrow{\div \text{ both by 6}}$ $2\frac{5}{6} : 1$

  (b) 17 : 6 $\xrightarrow{\div \text{ both by 17}}$ $1 : \frac{6}{17}$

● Given one amount, how to find the other

Example A 200 g jar of coffee granules makes about 120 cups of coffee.
The ratio of coffee to cups is 200 to 120 → 5 to 3.
Therefore a 250 g jar should make about $250 \times \frac{3}{5}$ cups = 150 cups.
For 50 cups we need about $50 \times \frac{5}{3} \simeq 85$ g of coffee.

Note how the ratio 5 : 3 became $\frac{3}{5}$ or $\frac{5}{3}$, depending on whether the required answer is to be bigger or smaller than the given amount.

● Given the total, how to find each (divide in a ratio)

Example Concrete for a path should consist of 1 part cement, 2 parts sand, and 3 parts coarse aggregate. If 3 m³ of dry mix is required, what volume of each material should be purchased?

Cement : sand : aggregate = 1 : 2 : 3
Total = 1 + 2 + 3 = 6 parts
3 m³ in 6 parts → $\frac{1}{2}$ m³ per part
so use $1 \times \frac{1}{2} = \frac{1}{2}$ m³ cement
$2 \times \frac{1}{2} = 1$ m³ sand
$3 \times \frac{1}{2} = 1\frac{1}{2}$ m³ aggregate.

● Changing in a ratio

Example   Increase 16 in the ratio $11:6$.
An increase, so multiply by $\frac{11}{6}$.
$\overset{8}{\cancel{16}} \times 11 = \frac{88}{3} = 29\frac{1}{3}$
$\quad\ \ \cancel{6}_3 \quad\ \ 3$

Example   Decrease 35 in the ratio $6:11$.
A decrease, so multiply by $\frac{6}{11}$.
$35 \times \frac{6}{11} = \frac{210}{11} = 19\frac{1}{11}$

Example   6 men can paint a school in 46 days. How long should 8 men take?
The number of men has increased in the ratio $8:6$.
The time taken should *decrease* in the ratio $6:8$.
$\overset{23}{\cancel{46}} \times \cancel{6}^3 = \frac{69}{2} = 34\frac{1}{2}$ days
$\quad\ \ \cancel{8}\cancel{4}_2 \quad 2$

● Using a conversion graph

When two quantities are in a constant ratio, a straight-line conversion graph may be used to convert one to the other. Figure 5:1 shows conversion from gallons to litres.

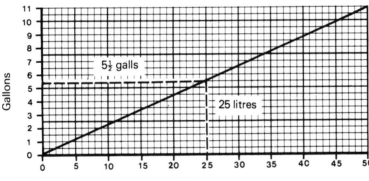

Fig. 5:1

● Proportion and the unitary method

When something changes in a ratio, we say it has changed **proportionally**, either in **direct** proportion or in **inverse** proportion. These are explained in the following examples.

The **unitary method** works out ratio changes by first finding a fact about one of the changing items.

Example   Find the cost of 9 pens, given that 7 cost £1.40.

This is an example of direct proportion. To check for direct proportion, double one amount and see if the other amount also doubles. In this example twice the number of pens would cost twice as much money.

To use the unitary method, we find the cost of 1 pen, then use that to find the cost of 9.

1 pen costs £1.40 ÷ 7 = 20p
so 9 pens cost 9 × 20p = £1.80.

Example Find the cost each if 36 people share a coach, given that 50 people would have to pay £3 each.

This is an example of inverse proportion. To check for inverse proportion, double one amount and see if the other amount halves. In this example twice the number of people would halve each person's share of the fare (until the bus was full).

1 person would have to pay 50 × £3 = £150
so 36 people would have to pay £150 ÷ 36 ≃ £4.17 each.

Test yourself

1 Write the following ratios (i) in the form $x:y$ as simply as possible, (ii) in the form $1:n$, (iii) in the form $n:1$
(a) 21:30   (b) 5 kg to 200 g   (c) 2 cm² to 3 mm²   (d) 5 m to 3 km

2 Increase £18 in the ratio 6:5.

3 Decrease 400 g in the ratio 4:5.

4 Share £360 in the ratio 5:7.

5
> *Recipe for Nettle Soup*
>
> 400 g nettle tops   30 g butter
> 1 large onion $\frac{3}{4}$ litre stock
> 15 cl cream
> Spinach, salt, pepper, lemon juice, to taste
> Cook for 30 min
> Serves 5

Alter the recipe for a dinner party of 8 guests.

*6 Simplify the following ratios:

(a) £5 to 50p (first make them both pence)
(b) 1 km to 200 m (first make them both metres)
(c) 15 mm to 5 cm (first make them both mm)
(d) 250 g to 2 kg (first make them both g)
(e) 1 cm represents 1 km (first make them both cm).

*7 Gemma has to make up 250 ml of calamine lotion (BP). The recipe for 100 ml of lotion is:

15 g calamine   0.5 ml liquified phenol
5 g zinc oxide   5 ml glycerin
3 g bentonite   94 ml water
500 mg sodium citrate

How much of each ingredient should Gemma use?

*8 Beth and Anna invest £5000 and £2500 respectively to start up a florist shop. They agree to share the profits in the same ratio as their investment.

(a) Write the ratio of their investment as simply as possible.

(b) In the first year their profit is £12 600. How much should Beth receive?

(c) The next year they both invest £3000 in an extension to their shop. In what ratio should they share the next year's profits?

9 In the UK, a car's fuel consumption is usually given in miles per gallon (m.p.g.). In Europe it is given in litres per 100 kilometres (litres/100 km).

50 m.p.g. $\approx$ 5.6 litres/100 km

(a) Copy and complete the following table, then draw a conversion graph between m.p.g. and litres/100 km to read from 0 to 50 m.p.g.

m.p.g.	10	20	30	40	50
litres/100 km	28.4				5.6

(b) From your graph, what is the European equivalent for the following average readings as given in *Which?* magazine?

Citroen 2CV   42 m.p.g.
Honda Civic 1340 auto 34 m.p.g.
Rover SD1 3530 auto   20 m.p.g.
Citroen Visa diesel   52 m.p.g.

10 Say whether the following are examples of direct proportion or inverse proportion, then calculate the answers.

(a) 5 identical packages cost £12.75 to post. What would 12 of the same packages cost to post?

(b) 6 men can paint a school in 15 days. How long should 10 men take?

(c) 10 m^2 of carpet cost £120. What will 16 m^2 of the same carpet cost?

(d) When the exchange rate is $1 to 60p, what should you get for $12?

(e) A car travels 100 km in $2\frac{1}{4}$ hours. How long would it have taken at twice the speed?

(f) Anouka's salary is £4500 in 5 months. What is her annual salary?

11 12 people take 6 days to pick the cider apples in an orchard. Working at the same rate, how long should it take:
(a) 6 people   (b) 3 people   (c) 48 people?

12 Eighty Lobos cost £250. How much should 260 Lobos cost?

13 (a) The map in Figure 5:2 has symbols to show various features. Draw and label the symbol used for: a church, a pub (public house), a post office, a windmill, a railway cutting, a marsh, pylon lines.

(b) Positions on an Ordnance Survey map are given by coordinates called six-figure grid references. In Figure 5:2, the six-figure grid reference for point X is 407305. Figure 5:3 explains this.

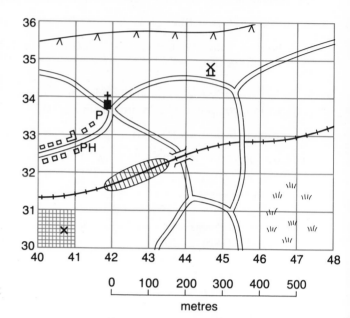

Fig. 5:2

Give the six-figure map reference in Figure 5:2 for:

(i) the church (ii) the inn
(iii) the post office
(iv) the windmill
(v) the middle of the railway cutting.

(c) What is the scale of the map?

(d) Estimate the shortest distance in metres from the pub to the windmill along the road.

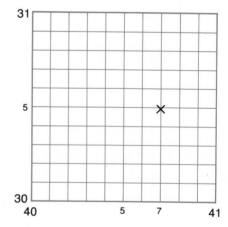

Fig. 5:3

14 The carat rating of any metal containing gold is found by dividing its weight into 24 equal parts. A 20-carat ring would be 20 parts pure gold and 4 parts other metal.

(a) Write the ratio of gold to other metal in a 16-carat ring.

(b) The ring has no stone and weighs 4.5 g. What weight of gold is in it?

15 A theatre offers one free ticket for every twelve purchased in a block-booking. The seats cost £5 each. How much should a party of 40 pay each if they are to share the cost equally?

16 The Wunderland Army, Air Force and Navy are given their share in the annual defence budget in the ratio 3:5:2 respectively.

(a) How much should each service receive if the 1992 budget is 3 million Wunderland dollars?

(b) If the army received 195 000 dollars in 1990, how much was the whole budget?

17 A headmaster allows his head of mathematics £3500 a year to supply books and materials to the 1250 pupils in the school. At the same rate, how much should he allow the German department, which teaches only 450 pupils?

18 Dot's teacher has recorded many short educational programmes to use in lessons. Recently the video recorder was stolen, and the replacement one has a counter which runs at a different rate, so all the start-point readings are wrong. The teacher says she will have to spend hours watching all the tapes and writing down the new readings, but Dot says a conversion graph would be much quicker.

The table shows the counter readings on the two recorders.

Time (min)	5	10	15	20	25	30	35	40	45	50	55	60
Old counter	0500	1000	1500	2000	2500	3000	3500	4000	4500	5000	5500	6000
New counter	0700	1280	1860	2300	2700	3060	3380	3660	3900	4100	4260	4380

(a) Draw a line graph with time on the horizontal axis and counter readings on the vertical axis. Illustrate the two counter readings with two different colour lines.

(b) From your graph estimate the two counter readings at 18 minutes and at 48 minutes.

(c) Draw a conversion graph, with the old counter horizontal and the new counter vertical.

(d) Use your graph to convert the following data to the new counter.
   0000 Decimals   3640 Volumes
   0600 Sequences   4630 Graphs
   2150 Percentages   5745 Circles

19 The circulation department on the *Daily Globe* polls 1300 readers to find their age groups. The result is:

Age group	15 to 30	31 to 45	46 to 60	61 +
Readers	500	320	90	70

(a) How many readers did not bother to reply?

(b) What percentage of the readers who replied come in each group?

(c) The daily circulation of the *Daily Globe* is about 1 600 000. How many readers would you expect to be in each age range?

(d) Advise the advertising manager of the *Globe* on the kind of advertising she should carry.

20 Sally spent £1.33 on two kinds of sweets, 3p red ones and 5p green ones. She shared them with some friends until each had the same number of red and the same number of green sweets as Sally. How many red and how many green sweets did Sally buy, and how many friends did she share them with?

21 Judy is born when Alison is 2 years old. What is the ratio of their ages when Judy is 1? When is Alison twice as old as Judy? When are their ages in the ratio 2:3? When is Judy three-quarters of Alison's age? Judy says, 'I am catching you up!' Is she? Write about your discoveries.

22 Investigate the ratio of weight supportable to length of span for the model bridge illustrated in Figure 5:4.

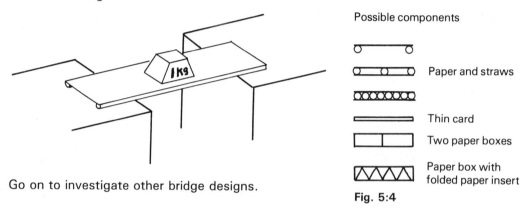

Possible components

Paper and straws

Thin card

Two paper boxes

Paper box with folded paper insert

Go on to investigate other bridge designs.

Fig. 5:4

For discussion

1. How is probability involved in the following?

   (a) Tom, aged 18, pays twice the car insurance of Hassan, aged 40.

   (b) Eileen, living in a city centre, pays treble the contents insurance of Anne, who lives in a village.

   (c) Astrid, a smoker, pays a 25% higher life insurance premium than Toni, a non-smoker.

   (d) Football-pool companies make a lot of profit.

2. How could Tom, Eileen and Astrid reduce their costs?

●   You need to know . . .

- An **event** is something which could happen.
- A **trial** is the trying out of an event.
- An **outcome** is the result of a trial.

● The probability line

The probability of any one outcome from the trial of an event is a fraction between 0 (impossible) and 1 (certain).

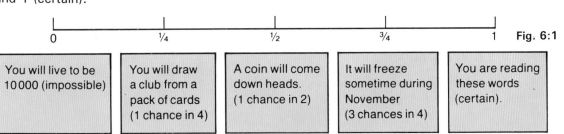

Fig. 6:1

| You will live to be 10 000 (impossible) | You will draw a club from a pack of cards (1 chance in 4) | A coin will come down heads. (1 chance in 2) | It will freeze sometime during November (3 chances in 4) | You are reading these words (certain). |

● The probability fraction

A successful trial is one that gives you the outcome you want. The probability fraction of a successful trial is:

$$\frac{\text{the number of successful outcomes possible}}{\text{the total number of possible outcomes}}$$

For this to be true, all the outcomes must be equally likely. For instance, although a loaded die can still fall in six ways, the chance of a 4 is not $\frac{1}{6}$.

For any one trial of an event, the probability of success plus the probability of failure is 1, as it is certain to be one or the other.

Examples

There are four suits of 13 playing cards in a full pack.

The probability of drawing a heart is $\frac{1}{4}$.
The probability of not drawing a heart is $1 - \frac{1}{4} = \frac{3}{4}$.

We can write this:

P(heart) = $\frac{1}{4}$ and   P(not heart) = $\frac{3}{4}$

Similarly
P(ace) = $\frac{1}{13}$
P(not ace) = $1 - \frac{1}{13} = \frac{12}{13}$.
P(ace of spades) = $\frac{1}{52}$
P(not ace of spades) = $1 - \frac{1}{52} = \frac{51}{52}$.

● Mutually exclusive outcomes to events

An event usually has several possible outcomes. However, only one outcome can result from any one trial, so the different outcomes are 'mutually exclusive'.

Example   The throw of a die can have six outcomes, but only one of the six happens each throw.

To find the probability that one or the other of two outcomes will happen you add their probabilities.

If you add the probabilities of all possible outcomes of an event the total will be 1.

Example   The probability that a die comes up 3 is $\frac{1}{6}$.
The probability that a die comes up 4 is $\frac{1}{6}$.

So the probability of a 3 or a 4 is $\frac{1}{6} + \frac{1}{6} = \frac{2}{6}$.

You can also find this answer by listing all possible outcomes.

The die can come up 1, 2, 3, 4, 5, 6.
Two of the 6 ways are 3 and 4.
P(3 or 4) is $\frac{2}{6}$ (or $\frac{1}{3}$).

Note   The probability that a die comes up 1 or 2 or 3 or 4 or 5 or 6 is certain, or:
$\frac{1}{6} + \frac{1}{6} + \frac{1}{6} + \frac{1}{6} + \frac{1}{6} + \frac{1}{6} = 1$.

● Independent outcomes to events

Outcomes are independent when one outcome happening does not exclude the others from happening.

When a set of outcomes are independent, the probability of the required overall outcome is found by multiplying the probabilities of the successful outcomes.

Example   What is the probability of throwing three heads with a fair coin?

The required overall outcome is HHH.

The probability of an H each trial is $\frac{1}{2}$.

So P(HHH) = $\frac{1}{2} \times \frac{1}{2} \times \frac{1}{2} = \frac{1}{8}$.

This can be illustrated by considering all possible outcomes:
HHH HHT HTH HTT THH THT TTH TTT

● Non-independent outcomes to events

Outcomes are non-independent when any one outcome happening does not prevent the others from happening, but does change the probability of the others happening.

As with independent events, the final probability is found by multiplying the individual probabilities.

Example   What is the probability of drawing three green balls from a bag of 10 red and 10 green balls?

P(green first pick) = $\frac{1}{2}$

but taking a green out changes the probability of a green for the next pick to $\frac{9}{19}$

and P(green third pick) = $\frac{8}{18}$.

So P(GGG) is $\frac{1}{2} \times \frac{9}{19} \times \frac{8}{18} = \frac{2}{19}$.

For discussion

❯ What is the probability of:

(a) picking an ace or a king from a shuffled pack of cards

(b) picking an ace or a king or a queen from a shuffled pack

(c) scoring a 1 or a 6 with a die

(d) scoring a 2 or a 4 or a 6 with a die

(e) picking a red or a blue from three red, two blue and five green counters

(f) picking a red or a blue or a green from the counters in part (e)

(g) picking a red and a blue from the counters in part (e)

(h) picking an ace and then a heart from a shuffled pack

(i) picking an ace and a heart from a shuffled pack?

6

1 A tetrahedral die has four faces, marked 1, 2, 3 and 4. What is the probability of the number on the base triangle, after the die is shaken and thrown, being:
   (a) 1   (b) 1, 1 (two throws)   (c) 1, 1, 1 (three throws)?

2 Calculate the following probabilities.

   (a) Picking from a pack:
       (i) the four of spaces   (ii) the five of hearts
       (iii) the four of spades *or* the five of hearts.

   (b) Scoring with a die:
       (i) a 3   (ii) a 6   (iii) a 3 *or* a 6.

   (c) Being born on:
       (i) a Saturday   (ii) a Sunday   (iii) a Saturday *or* a Sunday.

   (d) Picking from a bag of 8 black, 2 white and 2 red:
       (i) a black   (ii) a white   (iii) a black *or* a white.

3 Calculate the probability of:
   (a) 1 head only in 2 tosses of a coin
   (b) 2 boys only in a family of 3 (boy/girl equally likely)
   (c) a jack and a queen resulting from two picks, each from a full pack
   (d) 1 head only in 3 tosses of a coin
   (e) a red card and an ace resulting from two picks, each from a full pack.

4 A bag contains 6 black, 4 white and 2 grey counters. State the probability of picking (if each picked counter is replaced):
   (a) a black   (b) a white   (c) a black then a white   (d) a black then a black
   (e) a white then a white   (f) a black then a grey.

5 A card is picked from a full shuffled pack, then returned before further cards are picked. Give, in as simple a form as possible, the probability of picking:
   (a) a heart   (b) a heart twice in a row   (c) a club three times in a row
   (d) any king   (e) any king twice in a row   (f) the king of spades twice in a row
   (g) a picture card (K, Q, or J)   (h) an ace then a spade   (i) a club then a heart
   (j) the king of clubs then a red card   (k) any king, then the same king the second pick.

6 Repeat question 4, parts (c) to (f), if the first counter picked is not replaced (although each part starts with a full bag).

7 Repeat question 5 parts (b) to (f) only, if the picked cards are not replaced (although each part starts with a full pack).

8 The probability of a dry day in Uptown is $\frac{1}{3}$. What is the chance of:
   (a) a wet day   (b) two dry days in a row   (c) two wet days in a row
   (d) one dry day, the next day wet   (e) one day wet, the next day dry
   (f) one day dry out of any two days?

9 A coin is biased so that it is more likely to show 'heads'; the probability of heads is $\frac{3}{5}$. What is the probability of:
(a) tails   (b) two heads in a row   (c) a head then a tail
(d) a tail then a head   (e) a head and a tail in either order?

*10 Calculate the probability of:
(a) picking either the ace of spades or the ace of clubs from a full pack
(b) scoring 5 or 6 on one throw of a die
(c) a stranger's birthday being on a Monday *or* a Friday this year
(d) one head and one tail in two tosses of a coin
(e) one head in four tosses of a coin
(f) three heads in four tosses of a coin
(g) an ace and a king in two picks (each from a full pack)
(h) a red ace and a black card in two picks (each from a full pack)

11 Write out all the possible exclusive outcomes that give a successful overall outcome for each of the following.

Example   A score of 6 from two dice.
           Answer: 5, 1;   4, 2;   3, 3;   2, 4;   1, 5.

(a) A score of 4 from two dice
(b) A score of 5 from two dice
(c) At least one head in two tosses of a coin
(d) At least one head in 3 tosses of a coin.

12 Calculate the probability for each part of question 11.

13 A box contains pens of three colours: 3 red, 4 black, and 5 green. All the ways of picking three pens from the box, without replacement, can be shown on a tree diagram; see Figure 6:2 which also shows the probability of each event. Copy and complete it (fill in the '3rd pick' column first, which will have 27 rows).

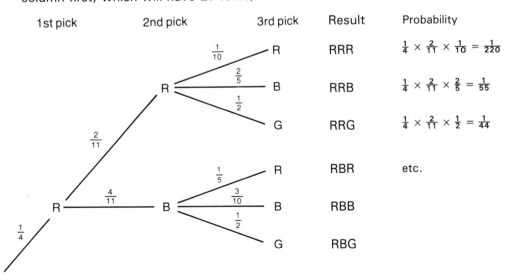

etc. to give 27 results altogether   Fig. 6:2

37

14 The probability that Miss Poisonfinger's pot-plants will die in a month is $\frac{5}{6}$. What is the probability of:
   (a) one of two pot-plants dying in a month
   (b) only one of three pot-plants living for more than a month?

15 A bag contains 4 pink, 3 black and 5 orange balls. By considering all the various ways each could occur, calculate the probability, with replacement of each picked ball, of:
   (a) a pink and a black (2 picks)   (b) a pink, a black and an orange (3 picks)
   (c) two pinks (2 picks)   (d) one pink and one black (3 picks)
   (e) two pinks (3 picks)   (f) no blacks (2 picks).

16 Calculate the probabilities of the following if each part is *without* replacement.

   (a) An ace then a black card in two picks. (Hint: Consider red ace/black card; black ace/black card.)

   (b) A red card then a king in two picks. (Hint: Consider (i) the red card is a king; (ii) the red card is not a king.)

   (c) A king then a hearts card in two picks. (Hint: Consider (i) the king is the king of hearts; (ii) the king is not the king of hearts.)

   (d) An ace and a black card in two picks. (Hint: See part (a).)

   (e) A red card and a king in two picks. (Hint: See part (b).)

   (f) A king and a hearts card in two picks. (Hint: See part (c).)

---

17 A fruit machine has three rotating wheels, each of which has 9 cherries, 6 lemons and 3 bells. State the probability of:
   (a) the middle wheel coming up with: (i) a bell   (ii) a lemon
   (b) all 3 wheels coming up with: (i) cherries   (ii) the same picture
   (c) all 3 wheels not coming up with the same picture (use the answer to part (b)).

18 Record in a table all the ways that three dice could give a score of 7, then state the probability that this will happen.

19 Design a suitable pay-out for the outcomes (c) to (f) in question 6 if the stake is 10p a go ('Pick 2 counters'). Test out your chosen answers experimentally to make sure that you are going to make a profit, then perhaps you could use the idea at a school fair.

20 Test some of your probability answers by writing computer programs to simulate the events.

$C = \pi d$ is the formula for the circumference of a circle; C is the **subject**.

When the formula is **transposed**, the subject is changed. The circumference formula can be transposed to make d the subject, giving $d = \dfrac{C}{\pi}$.

If the new subject-letter appears only once in the formula, the flow method may be used. If the new subject-letter appears more than once, you have to use the 'balance' or 'change sides' algebraic method, at least until you have only one occurrence of the subject-letter.

● Flow method

The inverse rules

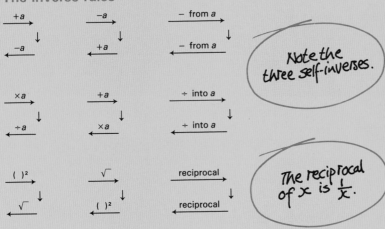

$$+a \rightarrow \qquad -a \rightarrow \qquad - \text{ from } a \rightarrow$$
$$\downarrow \qquad\qquad \downarrow \qquad\qquad \downarrow$$
$$\leftarrow -a \qquad \leftarrow +a \qquad \leftarrow - \text{ from } a$$

Note the three self-inverses.

$$\times a \rightarrow \qquad +a \rightarrow \qquad \div \text{ into } a \rightarrow$$
$$\downarrow \qquad\qquad \downarrow \qquad\qquad \downarrow$$
$$\leftarrow \div a \qquad \leftarrow \times a \qquad \leftarrow \div \text{ into } a$$

$$(\ )^2 \rightarrow \qquad \sqrt{\ } \rightarrow \qquad \text{reciprocal} \rightarrow$$
$$\downarrow \qquad\qquad \downarrow \qquad\qquad \downarrow$$
$$\leftarrow \sqrt{\ } \qquad \leftarrow (\ )^2 \qquad \leftarrow \text{reciprocal}$$

The reciprocal of x is $\frac{1}{x}$.

Examples

(a) $u = s - t$; new subject s

$$s \xrightarrow{\ -t\ } s - t$$
$$\downarrow$$
$$u + t \xleftarrow{\ +t\ } u$$

giving $s = u + t$

(b) $u = s - t$; new subject t

$$t \xrightarrow{\text{ taken from } s} s - t$$
$$\downarrow$$
$$s - u \xleftarrow{\text{ taken from } s} u$$

giving $t = s - u$

(c) $p = sr$; new subject s

$$s \xrightarrow{\ \times r\ } sr$$
$$\downarrow$$
$$\dfrac{p}{r} \xleftarrow{\ \div r\ } p$$

giving $s = \dfrac{p}{r}$

(d) $u = sr - t$; new subject s

$$s \xrightarrow{\ \times r\ } sr \xrightarrow{\ -t\ } sr - t$$
$$\downarrow$$
$$\dfrac{u + t}{r} \xleftarrow{\ \div r\ } u + t \xleftarrow{\ +t\ } u$$

giving $s = \dfrac{u + t}{r}$

● The balance method (advanced levels only)

If the subject-letter appears twice, change sides until you can make it a single common factor.

Gradually move the other letter-terms to the other side of the equals sign.

Examples

(a) $s = p - 3rp$; new subject p

$\quad s = p(1 - 3r)$ [factorise]

$\quad \dfrac{s}{1 - 3r} = p$ [divide both sides by $1 - 3r$]

$\quad$ Answer: $p = \dfrac{s}{1 - 3r}$

(b) $\dfrac{a}{3 - b} = \dfrac{2a}{t} + 5$; new subject a

$\quad at = 2a(3 - b) + 5t(3 - b)$ [multiply each term by $t(3 - b)$]
$\quad at - 2a(3 - b) = 5t(3 - b)$ [subtract $2a(3 - b)$ from both sides]
$\quad a(t - 6 + 2b) = 5t(3 - b)$ [factorise]
$\quad a = \dfrac{5t(3 - b)}{t + 2b - 6}$ [divide both sides by $t + 2b - 6$]

$\quad$ Answer: $a = \dfrac{5t(3 - b)}{t + 2(b - 3)}$

1 Make t the subject of each of the following formulae.

  (a) $a = t - g$ (b) $s = h - t$ (c) $f = 2t - y$

  (d) $r = 4w - 3t$ (e) $w = ag + et$ (f) $k = \dfrac{a + 3t}{4}$.

*2 Make b the subject of each of the following formulae.

  (a) $a = b + 3h$ (b) $k = 3 - 2b$ (c) $m = 3bc - 2$ (d) $a = \dfrac{b}{4} + c$

  (e) $w = \dfrac{7}{b}$ (f) $n = \dfrac{a}{b} + c$.

3 Make e the subject of each of the following formulae.

  (a) $f = \dfrac{3 - g}{e}$ (b) $x = 2e^2 - 4f$ (c) $h = 7 - \dfrac{6e^2}{a}$ (d) $a = \dfrac{1}{e} + h$

  (e) $v = c - \dfrac{2u}{e}$ (f) $t = \dfrac{h}{\sqrt{e}} - c$.

4 Make c the subject of each of the following formulae.

(a) $f = g - \frac{1}{2}(c + a)$ (b) $h = a^2 + c^2$ (c) $t = 2\pi\sqrt{c}$ (d) $d = ab(R - 2c)$

(e) $s = cr(a - t)$ (f) $f = \dfrac{3d - t}{c + b}$.

5 Make r the subject of each of the following formulae.

(a) $2g(r - p) + r = 3a$ (b) $r(2 + bc) = ar - st$ (c) $\dfrac{1}{r} - \dfrac{1}{t} = \dfrac{1}{a}$

(d) $\dfrac{2}{s} - \dfrac{b}{r} = 3a$ (e) $s = 3w\sqrt{\dfrac{2}{r}}$.

6 Make t the subject of each of the following formulae.

(a) $s = 3t - 2a^2t$ (b) $t - 3 = 2(a - t)$ (c) $\dfrac{t}{a} = \dfrac{b}{t}$ (d) $\dfrac{1}{t} = \dfrac{1}{a} + \dfrac{a}{t}$

(e) $e = 3a\sqrt{\dfrac{p}{t}}$ (f) $\dfrac{1}{\sqrt{t}} = g - 4s^2$.

8 Trigonometry: Pythagoras' theorem; tangents

● You need to know . . .

● Pythagoras' theorem

In all right-angled triangles, the square on the hypotenuse is equal to the sum of the squares on the other two sides.

In Figure 8:1, $h^2 = a^2 + b^2$

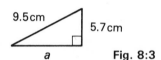

Fig. 8:1

The $\boxed{x^2}$ key is useful for finding the squares.

Examples   In Figure 8:2
$$h^2 = 5.6^2 + 8.2^2$$
$$h^2 = \underline{98.60}$$
$$h = \sqrt{98.60} \simeq 9.9 \text{ cm}$$
Key: 5.6 $\boxed{x^2}$ $\boxed{+}$ 8.2 $\boxed{x^2}$ $\boxed{=}$ $\boxed{\surd}$

Fig. 8:2

In Figure 8:3
$$9.5^2 = 5.7^2 + a^2$$
$$a^2 = 9.5^2 - 5.7^2$$
$$a^2 = \underline{57.76}$$
$$a = \sqrt{57.76} \simeq 7.6 \text{ cm}$$
Key: 9.5 $\boxed{x^2}$ $\boxed{-}$ 5.7 $\boxed{x^2}$ $\boxed{=}$ $\boxed{\surd}$

Fig. 8:3

Test yourself

1   Calculate the unknown side in each triangle in Figure 8:4. Give your answers correct to 1 decimal place.

(a)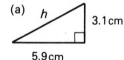

(b)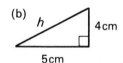

(c)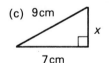

(d)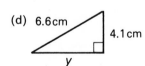

(e)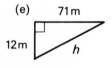

Fig. 8:4

(f)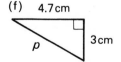

(g)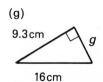

(h)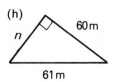

2   Investigate the extension of Pythagoras' theorem to acute- and obtuse-angled triangles.

A   Tangent function: finding a side

For discussion

▷ What is the same and what is different about the three triangles drawn full size in Figures 8:5, 8:6 and 8:7?

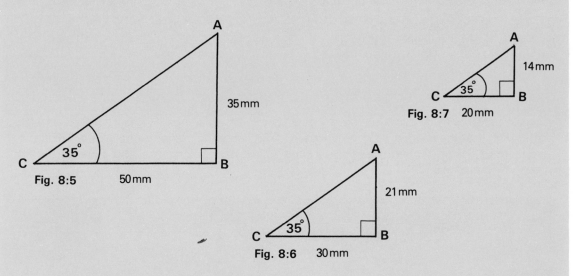

Fig. 8:5   50mm

Fig. 8:6   30mm

Fig. 8:7   20mm

▷ For each triangle calculate AB ÷ BC.

▷ Using a scientific calculator, enter 35 [TAN].

Learn this . . .

In the right-angled triangle drawn in Figure 8:8,

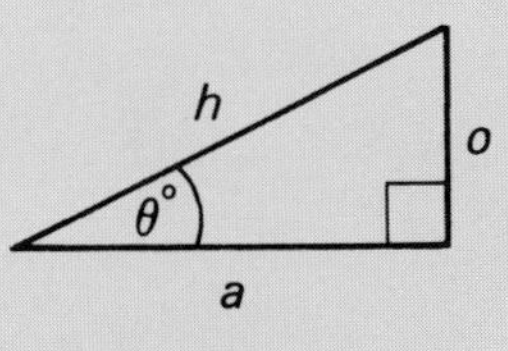

o is the side opposite the angle *θ*,

a is the side adjacent (next to) the angle *θ*,

h is the hypotenuse.

(Note that both *a* and *h* are adjacent to *θ*, so more strictly we should refer to *a* as 'adjacent, not the hypotenuse'.)

o ÷ *a* is called the **tangent** of the angle *θ*

$$\frac{o}{a} = \tan \theta$$

Changing the subject to *o* gives

$$o = a \times \tan \theta$$

You must learn both of these formulae. It may help you to note that in both of them the order of writing the letters is *o a t*.

43

Using the TAN key

A scientific calculator will have a TAN key, which calculates the value of $o \div a$ for any given angle.

Look at Figure 8:9. Remembering that $\dfrac{o}{a} = \tan \theta$, what should the value of tan 45° be? Test your answer with your calculator. (Make sure that you key the 45 before the TAN.)

Fig. 8:9

Using tangent to find the side of a right-angled triangle

A scientist wants to measure the height of a new volcanic island. He knows from a satellite photograph that the nearest point of land is 1.25 km from the centre of the island. Taking his theodolite to this point he measures the angle between the horizontal and a line to the top of the volcano as 19°.

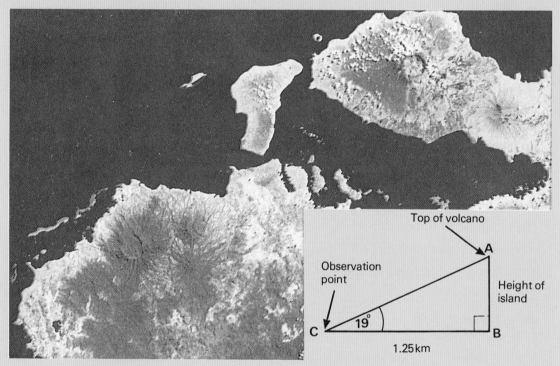

Fig. 8:10

From a simplified sketch, the scientist knows that BC is 1250 m and θ is 19°. Using $o = a \times \tan \theta$, he knows that AB = BC × tan θ = 1250 × tan 19°.

Keying on his calculator 1250 × 19 TAN = he finds that the volcanic island is about 430 metres high.

Then it starts to erupt again!!

1 **Example** Calculate HT in Figure 8:11.

HT = 7.6 × tan 57°
Key: 7.6 ⊠ 57 TAN =
Answer: HT ≃ 11.7 cm to 3 s.f.

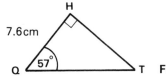
7.6cm
57°
Q   T   **Fig. 8:11**

Calculate, correct to 3 s.f., the side marked *x* in each triangle in Figure 8:12.

(a)
41°
5m
x

(b)
30°
7m
x

(c)
34.5°
4m
x

(d)
x
10m
26.7°

(e)
x
8m
53.8°   **Fig. 8:12**

*2 In △ABC, AB is opposite ∠C and AC is adjacent to ∠C, so AB = AC × tan C.
Similarly, AC is opposite ∠B and AB is adjacent to ∠B, so AC = AB × tan B.
Note: BC is the hypotenuse. We do not use the hypotenuse with tangents.

A   B
C

D
E   F

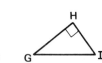
H
G   I

K
J   L

M   N
O

P
R   Q

Fig. 8:13

Copy and complete the following for the other triangles in Figure 8:13.
(a) DE = EF × tan . . .   (b) EF = . . . × tan D   (c) HG = . . . × tan I
(d) HI = HG × tan . . .   (e) KJ = JL × . . .   (f) JL = . . . × tan . . .
(g) MN = . . . × . . .   (h) NO = . . . × . . .   (i) PQ = ...   (j) RQ = ...

*3 **Example** In Figure 8:14
a = b × tan α and b = a × tan θ   **Fig. 8:14**

b
a
α
θ
h

Write similar formulae for sides *c*, *d*, *e*, *f*, *g*, *k*, *l* and *m* in Figure 8:15.

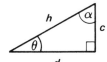
h
α
θ
c
d

α
h
θ
e
f

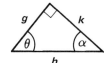
g
k
θ
α
h

h
α
θ
l
m

Fig. 8:15

4 For the three triangles in Figure 8:16 use tangents to calculate *x* correct to 3 s.f., then Pythagoras' theorem to find *h* correct to 3 s.f.

(a)
h
x
56.2°
27cm

(b)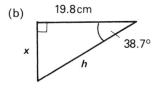
19.8cm
x
38.7°
h

(c)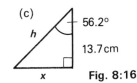
56.2°
h
13.7cm
x
Fig. 8:16

5 A ladder reaches 6.5 metres up a wall when leaning at an angle of 80° with the ground. How far away from the wall is the foot of the ladder?

6 Two ships set sail at the same time. One sails 8 nautical miles (n.m.) due north then drops anchor. The other takes a bearing of 035° until it is due east of the first.

   (a) How far are the ships then apart?
   (b) What distance has the second ship sailed?

7 Develop a computer program that will calculate a side of a triangle given an angle and another side. Remember that computers use radians, not degrees, and that π radians = 180°.

B Tangent function: finding an angle

The fact that $\dfrac{o}{a} = \tan\theta$ can be used to calculate θ given the two sides of the triangle that include (surround) the right angle.

Key: 45 [TAN]. The tangent of 45° is 1.

Now we need to be able to reverse the process, so that keying in 1 will give us the 45° again. Different calculators use different methods; the most common are:
1 [ARC][TAN];   1 [INV][TAN];   1 [ARCTAN];   1 [TAN⁻¹]

We shall use [ARCTAN] in this book. You must key in as your own calculator requires.

Example Calculate the size of angle θ in Figure 8:17.

   5.6 cm is opposite the angle θ, so $o = 5.6$
   4.8 cm is adjacent to the angle θ, so $a = 4.8$
   $\dfrac{o}{a} = \tan\theta \rightarrow \dfrac{5.6}{4.8} = \tan\theta$
   Key: 5.6 [÷] 4.8 [=] [ARCTAN]
   Answer: θ is 49.4° to the nearest tenth of a degree.

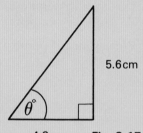

5.6cm

4.8cm   **Fig. 8:17**

1 Calculate the angle θ, correct to the nearest 0.1°, in each of the triangles in Figure 8:18. (Be careful that you use the correct two sides. We have marked the hypotenuse as well in some!)

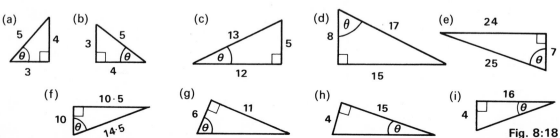

*2 **Example** If $\tan \theta = \frac{4}{7}$ then we could sketch any of the triangles in Figure 8:19.

 or or etc.

Fig. 8:19

Sketch three triangles with their right angles in different positions for each of the following.
(a) $\tan \theta = \frac{8}{11}$ (b) $\tan \theta = \frac{12}{7}$ (c) $\tan \theta = \frac{25}{6}$

3 For each of the following sketch △ABC with ∠B a right angle. Then mark on your sketch the given lengths and calculate the required angle, correct to the nearest 0.1°.
(a) AB = 2.4 cm; BC = 1.6 cm; calculate ∠C.
(b) AB = 3.9 cm; BC = 2.6 cm; calculate ∠C.
(c) AB = 2.8 cm; BC = 6.3 cm; calculate ∠A.

4 Sketch each of the following triangles PQR, with ∠R = 90°, then calculate both ∠P and ∠Q, correct to the nearest 0.1°.
(a) PR = 7.6 m; RQ = 5 m   (b) PR = 18 m; RQ = 15 m
(c) PR = 57 m; RQ = 27 m   (d) PR = 3.2 m; RQ = 8.8 m

---

5 Although it is not possible to have an angle bigger than 90° in a right-angled triangle, the tangent ratio continues to have values up to 360° (and beyond, although it then starts to repeat the cycle). Most calculators will give you the value of the tangent up to 360°.

Draw up a table of the tangents of every angle from 0° to 360° at 5° intervals, giving each correct to 2 s.f. (Note: tan 90° and tan 270° are infinitely large.)

On 1 mm graph paper draw a graph of 'Angle in degrees' (horizontal) against 'Tangent of angle' (vertical). Figure 8:20 shows you how to draw the curve at 90° and 270°. Line AB is called an 'asymptote'. The curve gets closer and closer to this line but never touches it.

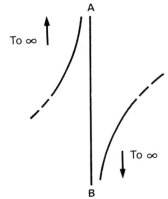

Fig. 8:20

6 By sketching suitable right-angled triangles, explain why tan 0° = 0, tan 45° = 1, and tan 90° = ∞ (infinity).

● You need to know . . .

● How a calculator carries out calculations

All calculators have two kinds of keys:

Digits and the decimal point: 0 1 2 3 4 5 6 7 8 9 .

Function keys, e.g. $\boxed{+}$ $\boxed{-}$ $\boxed{\times}$ $\boxed{\div}$ $\boxed{x^2}$ $\boxed{\sqrt{}}$ $\boxed{\frac{1}{x}}$ $\boxed{+/-}$ $\boxed{\text{TAN}}$

Most calculators also have an $\boxed{=}$ key and memory, or store, keys, e.g. $\boxed{\text{MS}}$ $\boxed{\text{STO}}$ $\boxed{\text{MR}}$ $\boxed{\text{M+}}$

It is important to remember that all function keys operate on the number showing in the display at the moment that they are pressed (but see the note on 'BODMAS' below). This is why $\frac{12}{2 \times 3}$ will come to the wrong answer if you key in 12 $\boxed{\div}$ 2 $\boxed{\times}$ 3 $\boxed{=}$. The correct answer is 2, because $12 \div 6 = 2$.

Key   12 $\boxed{\div}$ 2 $\boxed{\times}$ 3 $\boxed{=}$
Display   12   12   2   6   3   18
To get the right answer key in 12 $\boxed{\div}$ 2 $\boxed{\div}$ 3 $\boxed{=}$

Notice that the calculator does not appear to do anything when the first function key is pressed, but in fact it puts the display into a hidden memory called the 'y register'. When the next function key is pressed the calculator carries out the first operation, combining the number in the y register with the number on display (x). It then displays the answer (new x) and also stores the answer in the y register. ('BODMAS' calculators do not always follow this system; this is explained later.) This is what happens when you work out $\frac{12}{2 \times 3}$:

Key   12 $\boxed{\div}$ 2 $\boxed{\div}$ 3 $\boxed{=}$
Display (x)   12   12   2   6   3   →   2
Hidden (y)   —   12   12   6   6   2

Most scientific calculators follow the BODMAS (Brackets; Of; Divide; Multiply; Add; Subtract) rule, in as much as they save up additions and subtractions until any multiplications and divisions have been carried out. Mathematicians consider that the correct answer to $4 + 3 \times 2$ is $4 + 6 = 10$, not $7 \times 2 = 14$.

Key in: 4 $\boxed{+}$ 3 $\boxed{\times}$. If your display is still 3, then your calculator is following the BODMAS rule; if it shows 7 it is not going to give the correct answer.

A BODMAS calculator stores up the pending operations in a 'stack', for which it has extra hidden memories. The example $4 + 3 \times 2$ only needs one extra memory (z):

Key   4 $\boxed{+}$ 3 $\boxed{\times}$ 2 $\boxed{=}$
Display (x)   4   4   3   3   2   →   6   → 10
Stack (y)   —   +4   +4   3   3   6
Stack (z)   —   —   —   +4   +4   +4

Some calculators can switch the x and y registers using a key marked $\boxed{x \leftrightarrow y}$.

A similar effect is obtained by using bracket keys:
e.g. (4 + 3) × 2 = 4

Key	$($	4	$+$	3	$)$	$\times$	2		$=$
Display (x)	–	4	4	3	3	3	2		→14
Stack (y)	–	–	+4	+3	7	7	7		
Stack (z)	–	–	–	+4	–	–	–	

● Constant functions (k)

Most calculators will remember the last operation and keep repeating it. Some do this always, others need two presses of the function key or the use of a k key. Try the following. One of them, at least, will probably work out 2 × 2 × 2 = 8.

2 $\times$ $=$ $=$ 2 $\times$ $\times$ $=$ $=$.   2 $\times$ k $=$ $=$

Now try:
4 $\div$ 2 $=$ 6 $=$ 4 $\div$ 2 k $=$ 6 $=$ 4 $\div$ $\div$ 2 $=$ 6 $=$

● Memory keys

There are two kinds of memory; one is called a 'store', the other is called an 'accumulator'.
Store keys are usually marked MS, or STO, or $x \to M$, or Min.
Accumulator keys are usually marked $M+$ or $M+=$ or $M-$ or $M-=$ or ACC.

The memory content is recalled by a key usually marked RM or MR or REC.

Examples

Key	6	MS	8	MR	9	MS	MR
Display	6	6	8	6	9	9	9
Store	0	6	6	6	6	9	9

Key	6	M+	8	M+	9	MR	
Display	6	6	8	8	9	14	
Store	0	6	6	14	14	14	

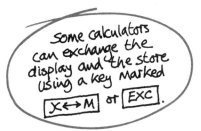

some calculators can exchange the display and the store using a key marked $X \leftrightarrow M$ or EXC.

You have to be careful to note whether or not the memory is empty when using the $M+$ key. Usually the display shows M to remind you that there is something in the memory. There is no problem with the MS store key, because the memory is automatically emptied as soon as this key is pressed. There are various ways of cancelling memories, usually a CM key or by storing zero, e.g. 0 Min.

● Modes

Many calculators have different modes of working. The $MODE$ key followed by a number is used to change the modes. It is vital to learn which mode number returns your calculator to its normal mode in case you accidentally get into one of the other modes.

The most common modes are:

● SD and COMP which switch between statistics and computation (arithmetic). The statistics functions are usually extra ones written on the calculator case. We will look into the use of some of them in Book 5.

● DEG and RAD and GRA which switch between the different angle measures (see page 127).

- FIX (N) and NORM which switch between a fixed decimal point with N figures after it, and the normal floating point.

- SCI and NORM which switch between scientific notation (see page 72) and normal denary columns display.

Note   To get back to normal working, use COMP, NORM, and DEG.

Test yourself

1   Calculate:
(a) 3.65×0.801 (b) $5.01 \div 6.27$ (c) $0.0954 - 0.312$.

2   Calculate:

(a) $\dfrac{51\,580\,000}{4163 \times 9129}$ (b) $\dfrac{306.2}{1.681 \times 5}$ (c) $\dfrac{71.6 \times 305}{42.3 \times 8.6}$ (d) $\dfrac{1002 \times 363}{928 \times 15.6}$

(e) $\dfrac{3121 - 14.56}{431.6 \times 1.06}$ (f) $\dfrac{22.41 + 380.1}{5.1 \times 16}$.

---

3   Calculate correct to 3 significant figures:

(a) $\dfrac{1.8 - 1.09}{7.6 \times 0.8154}$ (b) $\dfrac{18.15 \times 0.512}{6.631 \times 1.899}$ (c) $(14.26 \times 3.85) - (7.65 \div 91.3)$

(d) $(16 - 9.99) \div (1.284 \div 16.5)$ (e) $\sqrt{1.82} \times 16.5$ (f) $\sqrt{0.182} \times 16.5$

(g) $(0.652)^2 \times (1.763)^2$ (h) $\dfrac{(1.25)^2 + 1}{\sqrt{0.016}}$ (i) $\sqrt{\dfrac{4.215 \times 0.1668}{(3.59)^2 + (4.12)^2}}$.

4   Invent some number games that use a calculator.

Powers; roots; reciprocals; irrational numbers

Powers

Powers like 2^3 can be worked out using the constant facility explained on page 49, but scientific calculators usually have a $\boxed{y^x}$ key†, which is quicker if you have a large index, like 2^9.

Key	2	$\boxed{y^x}$	9	$\boxed{=}$
Display (x)	2	2	9	512
Store (y)	—	2	2	—

†Labelled $\boxed{x^y}$ on Casio calculators.

Roots

Use the $\sqrt{\ }$ key for square roots (and the $\sqrt[3]{\ }$ key for cube roots if you have one). For further roots you need either a $\boxed{y^{\frac{1}{x}}}$ key (sometimes marked $\boxed{\sqrt[x]{y}}$) or a $\boxed{y^x}$ and $\boxed{\frac{1}{x}}$ key (but see question 4 in the exercise for a 'trial and improvement' method that only uses basic functions). Remember that $8^{\frac{1}{2}}$ is an alternative way of writing $\sqrt{8}$, $8^{\frac{1}{3}} \equiv \sqrt[3]{8}$, and $8^{\frac{1}{4}} \equiv \sqrt[4]{8}$, so $y^{\frac{1}{x}} \equiv \sqrt[x]{y}$.

Example Find $\sqrt[4]{2}$.

Key: 2 $\boxed{y^{\frac{1}{x}}}$ 4 $\boxed{=}$ **or** 2 $\boxed{y^x}$ 4 $\boxed{\frac{1}{x}}$ $\boxed{=}$ **or** 2 $\boxed{\text{INV}}$ $\boxed{y^x}$ 4 $\boxed{=}$

Reciprocals

The $\boxed{\frac{1}{x}}$ (or $\boxed{1/x}$) key is the **reciprocal** key. The reciprocal of x is the fraction $\frac{1}{x}$, usually changed to a decimal. The reciprocal of 4 is 0.25.

Reciprocals of fractions sometimes cause trouble to students, e.g. the reciprocal of $\frac{3}{4}$ is $\frac{1}{\frac{3}{4}}$. Think of this as $1 \div \frac{3}{4} \to 1 \times \frac{4}{3} = 1.\dot{3}$. Your calculator would need the key sequence

3 $\boxed{\div}$ 4 $\boxed{=}$ $\boxed{\frac{1}{x}}$.

Remember that a function key operates on the number in the display. Function keys like $\boxed{x^2}$, $\boxed{\sqrt{\ }}$, $\boxed{\text{TAN}}$, etc. operate as soon as they are pressed. Others, like $\boxed{\times}$, $\boxed{+}$, $\boxed{y^x}$, etc., wait until another function key or $\boxed{=}$ is pressed before operating; this is because they combine the x and y registers.

To find the reciprocal of $\frac{3}{4}$ it would be wrong to key in 3 $\boxed{\div}$ 4 $\boxed{\frac{1}{x}}$ $\boxed{=}$. Why?

Reciprocals are 'self-inverses'. Try 4 $\boxed{\frac{1}{x}}\boxed{\frac{1}{x}}\boxed{\frac{1}{x}}\boxed{\frac{1}{x}}$.

In the following questions give all answers correct to 3 significant figures.

1 Calculate:
  (a) $(26.7)^3$ (b) $(13.2)^4$ (c) $(1.06)^2$.

2 Calculate:
  (a) $\sqrt[3]{20}$ (b) $\sqrt[4]{150}$ (c) $\sqrt[3]{182}$ (d) $\sqrt[3]{9.6}$ (e) $\sqrt[3]{17.6}$ (f) $\sqrt[4]{2000}$.

3 Calculate the reciprocal of:
  (a) 1.56   (b) 7.26   (c) $\frac{1}{3}$ (d) $1\frac{1}{2}$ (e) $1\frac{3}{4}$.

4 The following method is useful if you do not have a $\boxed{y^x}$ key, and also helps your understanding of decimals.

Example Find $\sqrt[3]{35.6}$.

As $3 \times 3 \times 3 = 27$ and $4 \times 4 \times 4 = 64$, $3 < \sqrt[3]{35.6} < 4$
Try 3.3 as the answer: $3.3 \times 3.3 \times 3.3 = 35.937$, so $\sqrt[3]{35.6} < 3.3$
Try 3.2: $3.2 \times 3.2 \times 3.2 = 32.768$, so $\sqrt[3]{35.6} > 3.2$
Try 3.25: $3.25^3 = 34.328\,125$, which is too small.
Try 3.27, etc. etc., say to $3.289\,652\,4$ which is sufficiently exact!

Repeat question 2 using this method.

5 **Using a calculator for non-decimal conversion**

Most calculators cannot cope simply with units like hours, minutes, seconds; degrees, minutes; etc. This is because these units are not based on the tens system. The main problem is that a calculator always gives a remainder as a decimal, so that 130 min divided by 60 gives 2.16666667 instead of 2 h 10 min. We can recover the 10 min by subtracting the 2, then multiplying the decimal part by the number we divided by (60). Try it.

The rule (or 'algorithm') to obtain a remainder to a division is: 'Subtract the integral part of the answer, then multiply by the divisor'. (There may be a small error, due to 'rounding errors', e.g. 2.999998 for remainder 3 is clearly the calculator's error.)

Example Convert 25 086 s to hours and minutes.

Key   25 086 $\boxed{\div}$ 60 $\boxed{=}$ $\boxed{-}$ 418 $\boxed{=}$ $\boxed{\times}$ 60 $\boxed{=}$
Display   25 086   60   418.1   418   0.1   60   6

Write down 418 min
(or save in memory)

This is the
6 s remainder.

(or recall memory)

Key   418 $\boxed{\div}$ 60 $\boxed{=}$
Display   418   60   6.9666667

This is the hours.
Write down 6 h.

Key $\boxed{-}$ 6 $\boxed{=}$ $\boxed{\times}$ 60 $\boxed{=}$
Display   0.9666667   60   58

These are the remaining minutes.

Answer: 25 086 s = 6 h 58 min 6 s.

Work the above example, making sure you really understand the reason for each step.

(a) Change to hours, minutes and seconds:
   (i) 31 012 s   (ii) 43 161 s   (iii) 100 301 s   (iv) 89 135 s   (v) 30 016 s
   (vi) 210 193 s.

(b) Change to degrees and minutes (1° = 60′) to the nearest minute:
   (i) 46.8°   (ii) 60.25°   (iii) 41.87°   (iv) 163.76°.

(c) Change to decimals of a degree, correct to 3 s.f.:
   (i) 32° 16′   (ii) 21° 5′   (iii) 80° 43′   (iv) 18° 54′.

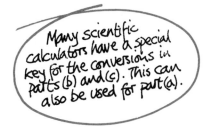

Many scientific calculators have a special key for the conversions in parts (b) and (c). This can also be used for part (a).

(d) Change to yards, feet and inches (1 yd = 3 ft, 1 ft = 12 in):
   (i) 6102 in   (ii) 8134 in   (iii) 10 000 in.

6   Rational and irrational numbers

A rational number can be written as a fraction $\dfrac{c}{d}$ where c and d are integers with no common factors. An irrational number cannot.

Examples of irrational numbers are the square roots of prime numbers, and π (remember that π is only approximately $\frac{22}{7}$ and $\frac{355}{113}$).

Example   Prove $\sqrt{2}$ is irrational.

> Suppose it isn't! Then let $\sqrt{2} = \dfrac{c}{d}$ where c and d are integers with no common factor.
> Then $c^2 = 2d^2$, so c^2 is a multiple of 2, therefore c is an even number.
> Say $c = 2r$, then $c^2 = 4r^2$, and as $c^2 = 2d^2$, $4r^2 = 2d^2$. Therefore $d^2 = 2r^2$, therefore d is an even number.
>
> But c and d cannot both be even numbers if they have no common factor, so we must have been wrong in thinking we could write $\sqrt{2}$ as $\dfrac{c}{d}$ so $\sqrt{2}$ is irrational.
>
> Can you prove that $\sqrt{3}$ is irrational?

7   Some basic calculators have only a $\boxed{\text{M}+}$ key and a combined memory recall and cancel key ($\boxed{\text{MRC}}$). Suppose you have 8 in the memory and 6 on the display. How can you replace the 8 by the 6 without using any number key except 0?

This weaving pattern is called 'honeysuckle'. It was made with a four heddle loom. The heddles lift certain of the warp threads, and the weft thread is passed through the gap to make the pattern.

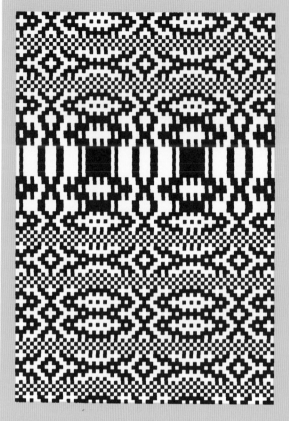

Fig. 10:1

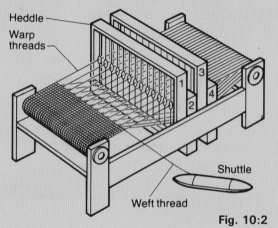

Heddle

Warp threads

Shuttle

Weft thread

Fig. 10:2

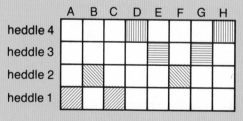

Fig. 10:3

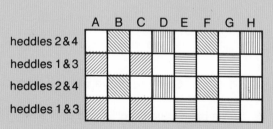

Fig. 10:4

'Rosengong' is a simple threading which is repeated every eight warp threads across the loom. It has the code 1 2 1 4 3 2 3 4 which tells which threads are lifted by each of the four heddles. Figure 10:3 shows the pattern in a code picture. When heddles 1 and 3 are lifted together, followed by heddles 2 and 4 together, the warp passes over and under alternate weft threads to give the basic 'tabby' weave (Figure 10:4).

Check that you understand the connection between the code picture in Figure 10:3 and the resulting pattern in Figure 10:4.

Now we look at the Rosengong pattern made when the heddles are lifted in the order: 1 & 4, 1 & 2, 1 & 2, 2 & 3, 1 & 2, 1 & 2, 1 & 4.

We have shown sixteen warp threads. Copy the pattern and complete it.

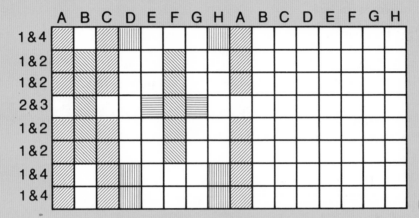

Fig. 10:5

Figure 10:6 shows the effect of using this pattern repeatedly, with some lines of tabby weave for strength.

The Teacher's Resource Book has more patterns for you to try.

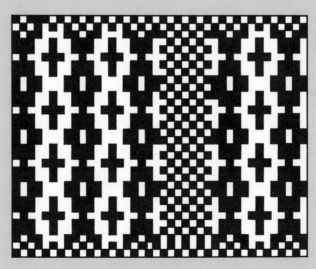

Fig. 10:6

1 Example

```
1    3    5    7    . . .
1st  2nd  3rd  4th  . . .
```

If you wanted to know the 200th term you could write out all 200 terms, but if you can find a rule it would be far easier.

By thinking hard you should spot that:
the 1st term is $1 \times 2 - 1 = 1$
the 2nd term is $2 \times 2 - 1 = 3$
the 3rd term is $3 \times 2 - 1 = 5$
the 4th term is $4 \times 2 - 1 = 7$
So the 200th term will be $200 \times 2 - 1 = 399$
and the nth term is $2n - 1$.

check these for yourself.

What are the first five terms of the sequence whose nth term is:
(a) $n + 1$ (b) $2n$ (c) $2n + 1$ (d) n^2 (e) $n - 1$?

*2 Copy these number patterns, continue them for four more terms, then explain the rule you used.

Example   1, 2, 3, 4, . . .
Answer: 1, 2, 3, 4, 5, 6, 7, 8, 9.
Our rule is 'Add 1'.

Example   1, 4, 16, 64, . . .
Our rule is 'Multiply by 4'.

(a) 1, 3, 5, 7, . . .   (b) 20, 17, 14, 11, . . .   (c) 2, 4, 8, 16, . . .
(d) 256, 128, 64, 32, . . .

*3 Write the next four terms in these sequences, then explain the rules you used.
(a) 3, 6, 9, 12, 15, . . .   (b) 4, 8, 16, 32, 64, . . .   (c) 6, 2, −2, −6, . . .
(d) $\frac{1}{2}, \frac{2}{3}, \frac{3}{4}, \frac{4}{5}, \ldots$

*4 Write the first six terms of a sequence starting with 1, 4, . . . using the rule:
(a) keep adding 3
(b) multiply the term before by 4
(c) the nth term is n^2
(d) multiply the term before by 3, then add 1.

5 Write the nth term for each sequence in question 2.

6 Write the nth term for each sequence in question 3.

7 Write the first ten terms of the sequence whose nth term is:
(a) $n^2 - n - 1$ (b) $\frac{1}{2}n(n + 1)$ (c) 2^n.

8 Copy these number patterns, continue them for four more terms, then write the nth term.
(a) $\frac{1}{2}, \frac{2}{4}, \frac{3}{6}, \frac{4}{8}, \ldots$ (b) 0, 2, 6, 12, 20, . . .
(c) 0, 3, 8, 15, 24, . . .   (d) 6, 3, $1\frac{1}{2}$, $\frac{3}{4}$, . . .

9 Figure 10:7 shows the start of a pattern. Each new pattern is made by increasing the number of rows across by 1 and the number of columns down by 2.

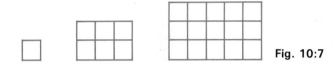

Fig. 10:7

(a) Copy Figure 10:7 then draw the next pattern in the sequence.

(b) Find the rule for the nth term of the sequence, and check it by calculating the 5th pattern, then drawing it.

10 Figure 10:8 shows a triangle pattern. Check the following facts:

Triangle number	1	2	3	4
Number of 'point-up' small triangles	1	3	6	10
Number of 'point-up' bigger triangles	0	1	4	10
Total 'point-up' triangles	1	4	10	20

Fig. 10:8

How many 'point-up' triangles will there be in triangle number 5? Show that the nth triangle has $\frac{1}{6}n(n+1)(n+2)$ triangles.

11 A pattern is made by joining the ends of equal rods to make enclosed shapes. Shapes must be different and point joins are not allowed. This is shown in Figure 10:9. Investigate possible patterns for various numbers of rods, and write about any rules you find.

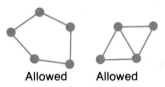

Allowed   Allowed

Not allowed   Fig. 10:9

12 Arithmetic progressions

These are sequences made by repeatedly adding the same number.

Example   1, 5, 9, 13, 17, . . .

In general: $a, a + r, a + 2r, a + 3r, a + 4r, . . .$

What is the nth term of the general arithmetic progression?

13 Geometric progressions

These sequences are made by repeatedly multiplying by the same number.

Example   1, 3, 9, 27, 81, 243, . . .

In general: $a, ar, ar^2, ar^3, ar^4, . . .$

What is the nth term of the general geometric progression?

14 Square numbers

This sequence (which is always the same) can be illustrated by a square of dots.

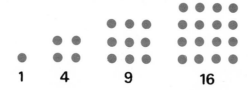

1   4   9   16

What is the nth term of the square number sequence?

15 Triangular numbers

This sequence (which is always the same) can be illustrated by right-angled triangles of dots.

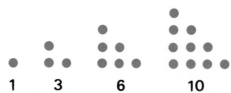

1   3   6   10

Check that the nth term of triangular numbers is $\frac{1}{2}n(n + 1)$, and hence state the 99th triangular number.

16 Summing sequences

We use the Greek symbol $\sum$ to mean 'the sum of'.

$\sum\limits_{s=4}^{8} s^2$ means the sum of the squares from 4^2 to 8^2.

(a) $\sum\limits_{1}^{n}$ (natural numbers) $= 1 + 2 + 3 + 4 + 5 + \ldots + n$

Most sum formulae are too difficult to prove in this book, but you should be able to follow this one:

$$\begin{array}{l} 1 + 2 + 3 + 4 + 5 \\ 5 + 4 + 3 + 2 + 1 \quad \text{ADD} \\ \hline 6 + 6 + 6 + 6 + 6 \quad = 5 \times 6 \;\rightarrow\; 1 + 2 + 3 + 4 + 5 = \tfrac{1}{2} \times 5 \times 6 \end{array}$$

Similarly, $1 + 2 + 3 + 4 + 5 + 6 + 7 = \tfrac{1}{2} \times 7 \times 8$

So $\sum\limits_{1}^{n}$ (natural numbers) $= \tfrac{1}{2}n(n + 1)$.

Write out the proof that $\sum\limits_{1}^{7}$ (natural numbers) $= \tfrac{1}{2} \times 7 \times 8$

(b) $\sum$ (arithmetic progression)

The general arithmetic progression is

$a, a + r, a + 2r, a + 3r, a + 4r, \ldots, a + (n - 1)r, \ldots$

This gives the following sequence of sums:

$a, 2a + r, 3a + 3r, 4a + 6r, 5a + 10r, \ldots$

So $\sum\limits_{1}^{n} (a + (n - 1)r) = na + [(n - 1)\text{th triangular number}] \times r$

$$= n(a + \tfrac{1}{2}r(n - 1))$$

Use this formula to calculate the sum of the first ten terms of the arithmetic progression that starts $12, 23, 34, \ldots$ Check your answer by writing out and adding all the terms.

(c) $\sum\limits_{1}^{n}$ (geometric progression) $= a + ar + ar^2 + ar^3 + \ldots + ar^{n-1}$

$$= \frac{a(r^n - 1)}{r - 1}$$

Show that this formula is correct for the geometric progressions:

(i) 2, 8, 32, 128   (ii) 3, 12, 48, 192, 768

(d) $\sum\limits_{1}^{n}$ (triangular numbers) $= 1 + 3 + 6 + 10 + 15 + \ldots + \tfrac{1}{2}n(n + 1)$

$$= \tfrac{1}{6}n(n + 1)(n + 2)$$

Find the sum of the first twelve triangular numbers.

(e) $\sum\limits_{1}^{n}$ (squares) $= 1 + 4 + 9 + 16 + \ldots + n^2$

$\qquad = \frac{1}{6}n(n + 1)(2n + 1)$

What is the sum of the first 20 squares?

(f) $\sum\limits_{1}^{n}$ (cubes) $= 1 + 8 + 27 + 64 + \ldots + n^3$

The following sequence of sums is obtained:
$1, 9, 36, 100, \ldots \rightarrow 1^2, 3^2, 6^2, 10^2, \ldots$

This is a sequence of triangular numbers squared, so

$\sum\limits_{1}^{n}$ (cubes) $= [\frac{1}{2}n(n + 1)]^2$

What is the sum of the first 20 cubes?

17 Find the rule for how many squares there are in:

(a) a strip of squares p squares long and 1 square wide

(b) a square of side q smaller squares.

18 Repeat question 17 to find rules for how many rectangles (including squares) there are in the two given shapes.

19 A rectangle is p squares long and q squares wide. Find a rule for how many of the following it contains:

(a) squares   (b) rectangles (including squares).

11   Geometry: review (proofs)

Straight-line and parallel-line angles

In Figure 11:1, angle *a* is **acute**,
angle *b* is **obtuse**,
angle *r* is **reflex**.

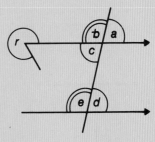

$a + b = 180°$ (adjacent angles on a straight line)
$a = c$ (vertically opposite angles)
$a = d$ (corresponding angles)
$c = d$ (alternate angles)
$c + e = 180°$ (allied angles)   [also known as interior angles]

Fig. 11:1

Hints: 'Adjacent' means 'next-door'.
'Corresponding' means 'in the same position'.
'Alternate' means 'on opposite sides' ('Z angles').
'Allied' means 'joined together'.

Angles that add up to 180° are said to be **supplementary**.

Construction methods

Figure 11:2 shows the compass construction for a 60° angle.
Figure 11:3 shows the way to bisect an angle.

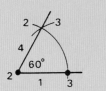

Fig. 11:2

Fig. 11:3

Centres of arcs (marked •) and corresponding arcs have the same number.

These two constructions can be combined to draw many other angles, e.g. 30° by bisecting 60°.

Figures 11:4(a) and 11:4(b) show two methods to construct a right angle. The first combines a 60° and a 30° angle; the second bisects a 180° angle.

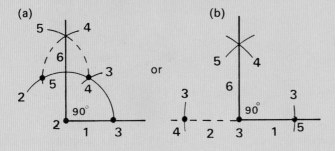

(a)   (b)   or   **Fig. 11:4**

Figures 11:5 to 11:11 show other constructions often required at a 16+ examination.

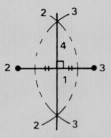

Fig. 11:5 Perpendicular bisector

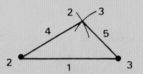

Fig. 11:6 △ given 3 sides

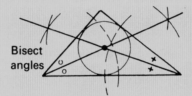

Fig. 11:7 Incircle of △

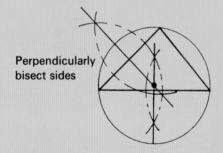

Fig. 11:8 Circumcircle of △

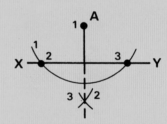

Fig. 11:9 Dropping a perpendicular

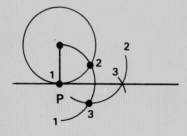

Fig. 11:10 Tangent to a circle

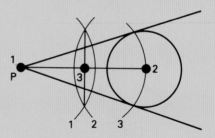

Fig. 11:11 Two tangents from a point

Names and properties of special quadrilaterals

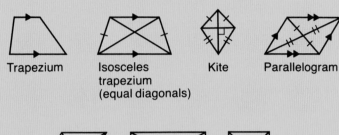

Trapezium   Isosceles   Kite   Parallelogram
              trapezium
              (equal diagonals)

Rhombus   Rectangle   Square
           (equal diagonals) (equal diagonals)   **Fig. 11:12**

Name	Sides	Angles	Diagonals
Trapezium	1 pair parallel	—	—
Isosceles trapezium	1 pair parallel, 1 pair non-parallel equal	2 equal pairs	equal
Kite	2 adjacent equal pairs	1 equal pair	one bisected, cross at 90°
Parallelogram	2 pairs equal and parallel	opposites equal	bisect each other
Rhombus	4 equal	opposites equal	bisect at 90°
Rectangle	as parallelogram	all 90°	equal
Square	as rhombus	all 90°	equal, cross at 90°

Properties can be observed from an accurate sketch.

Important facts:

- A parallelogram has no line of symmetry.
- The diagonals of a kite, a rhombus, and a square cross at right angles.
- The angle sum of all quadrilaterals is 360°.

Polygons

polygon: many-sided
pentagon: 5 sides   octagon: 8 sides
hexagon: 6 sides   nonagon: 9 sides
heptagon: 7 sides   decagon: 10 sides

The exterior angles of all polygons total 360° (Figure 11:13).

Fig. 11:13

The interior angles of an n-sided polygon total $(n-2) \times 180°$ (Figure 11:14).

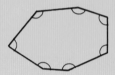

Fig. 11:14

1. (a) Construct a triangle with sides 10 cm, 8 cm and 6 cm.
   (b) Construct the incentre of your triangle.
   (c) Construct the triangle again.
   (d) Construct the circumcircle of your second triangle.

2. Name the three special quadrilaterals in which the diagonals cross at 90°.

3. Name the three special quadrilaterals in which the diagonals are equal.

4. In Figure 11:15, A and B are the positions of two cannons each side of Death Valley. A Light Brigade is at C, 5 km from both guns. An order to charge *at* the guns is mis-heard as charge *between* the guns. If the brigade keeps an equal distance from both guns, construct a map showing the route of their charge.

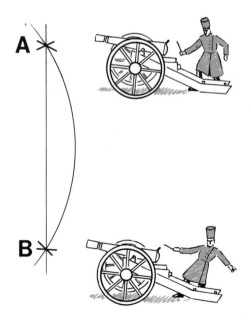

Fig. 11:15

5 (a) Lynne runs around the outside of a large rectangular scout hut, keeping always one metre from the nearest point on the hut wall. On a suitable diagram, show the locus of her run.

   (b) Maureen runs inside the same hut, also keeping one metre from the nearest point on the walls. On the same diagram show the locus of her run.

6 In Figure 11:16, PQ//RS//TU, and QT is a straight line.

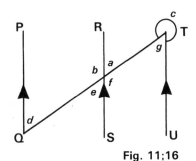

   (a) What kind of angle is:
       (i) a   (ii) b   (iii) c?

   // is a symbol for 'is parallel to'

   (b) Give the reason why:
       (i) a = e   (ii) a = g   (iii) a + b = 180°
       (iv) b + d = 180°   (v) a = d.

   (c) (i) If a = 75° find f.   (ii) If e = 80° find d.   (iii) If g = 62° find e.
       (iv) If f = 142° find g.   (v) If b = 113° find f.   (vi) If f = 125° find c.

7 In Figure 11:17 calculate x and hence the size of each angle.

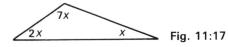

Fig. 11:17

8 In Figure 11:18 AB = AC. Calculate exterior angle BCE.

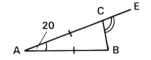

Fig. 11:18

9 Figure 11:19 shows part of a bronze-age brooch recently found by a Sussex teenager. Construct the figure. (The larger and smaller circles have their centres on the middle circle, angle ABC is 30° and the distance BO is 4 cm.)

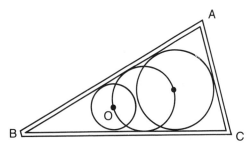

Fig. 11:19

10 Draw a diagram like Figure 11:20. By bisecting the two marked angles find the centre of a circle which touches, but does not cross, the lines XA, AC, and YC.

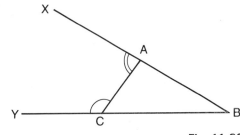

Fig. 11:20

11 Calculate the size of an interior angle in a regular nonagon.

12 How many sides has a polygon if its interior angle sum is 1620°?

13 Four of the exterior angles of an irregular pentagon are each 80°. Calculate:
(a) the fifth exterior angle   (b) the five interior angles.

14 In an octagon, how many diagonals can be drawn:
(a) from one vertex   (b) altogether?

*15 Copy the diagrams in Figure 11:21 and calculate the size of each lettered angle.

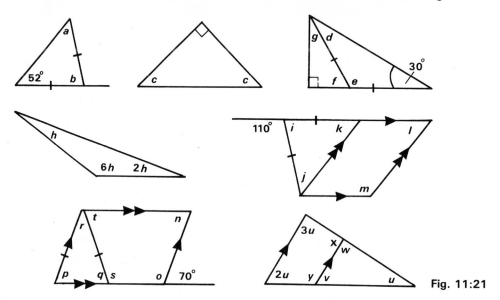

Fig. 11:21

*16 Make enlarged copies of the diagrams in Figure 11:22. Calculate the sizes of all angles less than 180° and write your answers on your diagrams.

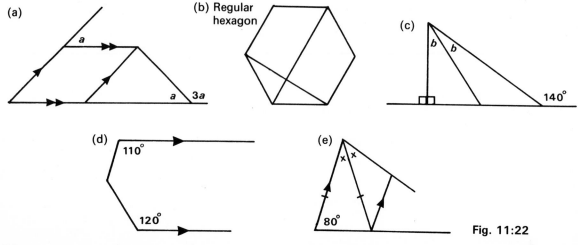

(a)

(b) Regular hexagon

(c)

(d)

(e)

Fig. 11:22

*17 State all the special quadrilaterals which fit the following descriptions.
    (a) All four sides are equal.
    (b) All angles are right-angles.
    (c) Opposite angles are equal.
    (d) The diagonals bisect each other.
    (e) Just two angles could be right-angles.

*18 A power-boat course is an equilateral triangle of side 1 km. *Eager Beaver* takes a route which is exactly 25 metres from all points on the course. Sketch a diagram (not to scale) to show *Eager Beaver's* track.

*19 In Figure 11:23, angle A is a right-angle, BC is 10 cm and AB is 5 cm. The three quadrilaterals are squares. Construct the diagram as accurately as possible.

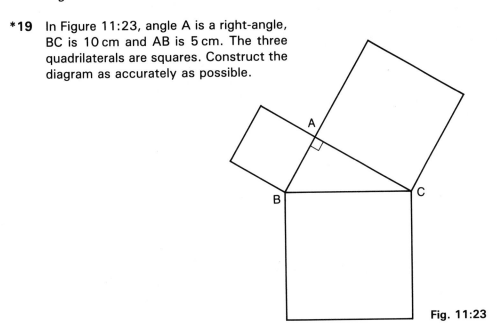

Fig. 11:23

20 A wheelbarrow is pulled backwards up some steps. Figure 11:24 shows the wheel at the start of the pull. Draw a diagram to show the locus of the centre of the wheel.

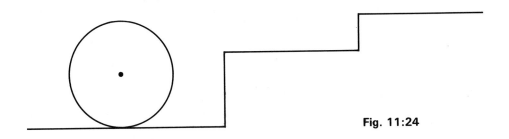

Fig. 11:24

21 In which regular polygon are the interior and exterior angles in the ratio 4:1?

22 A pilot takes the bearings of two beacons which are at each end of a 1 km long runway lying due north/south. One beacon bears 290 degrees; the other 200 degrees. Draw a plan of the runway and mark a possible position of the plane at the moment the bearings were taken.

23 Sketch a regular pentagon PQRST. Join QT and QS. Calculate and write on your sketch the sizes of the angles in triangles QRS, PQT and QTS.

24 Figure 11:25 represents a drawing board (AB), hinged at B to a ridged table (BC). The board is supported by a strut (AD) hinged at A. AB is 55 cm, BC is 70 cm and AD is 30 cm.

Show by construction that there are two possible positions of the strut when the board is inclined at 30°.

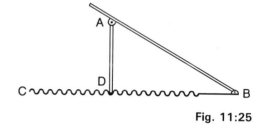

Fig. 11:25

25 (a) In Figure 11:26, M is the midpoint of AB, and MN//BC. Draw an enlarged copy of the figure, using any shape triangle. Check that AN = NC and that MN = $\frac{1}{2}$BC.

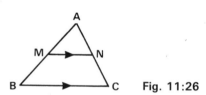

Fig. 11:26

(b) Repeat part (a) with another shape of triangle.

(c) The results of part (a) are true for any triangle. This is called 'the midpoint theorem'.

(d) Check by drawing that:
'The line joining the midpoints of two sides of a triangle is parallel to, and a half of the third side.'

26 In Figure 11:27, X is any point on AB and XY//BC.

It can be proved that $\frac{AX}{XB} = \frac{AY}{YC}$.

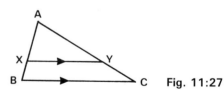

Fig. 11:27

(a) If AX = 5 cm, XB = 3 cm, and YC = 4 cm, calculate AY.

(b) If AB = 15 cm and AY:YC = 3:2, find AX and XB.

(c) Prove that triangles AXY and ABC are similar, then write the ratio-of-the-sides equation.

(d) If AX = 4 cm, XB = 3 cm, and XY = 8 cm, sketch △ABC then calculate BC using the equation in part (c).

27 In a trapezium ABCD, AB//DC and AB = AD. Prove that BD bisects ∠ADC.

28 S is a point on side PR of △PQR such that ∠RSQ = ∠PQR. If ∠P = 50° find ∠SQR.

29 In △ABC, ∠A = 50°. The bisectors of angles B and C meet at D. Calculate ∠BDC.

30 In Figure 11:28, prove that ∠ADC = 90°.

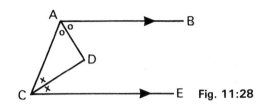

Fig. 11:28

31 In Figure 11:29, prove that BC = CD.

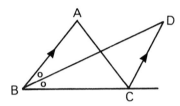

Fig. 11:29

32 In △DEF, M is the midpoint of EF and N is the midpoint of DM. Prove that:
(a) △DEM = △DMF (that is they are equal in area)   (b) △DEN = ½△DMF.

33 (a) Prove that the area of a kite is half the product of its diagonals.

(b) GHIJ is a kite with GH = GJ. A, B, C and D are the midpoints of GH, HI, IJ and JG respectively. Prove that:
(i) ABCD is a rectangle   (ii) area ABCD = ½ area GHIJ.

34 ABCD is a parallelogram, AB is produced to F such that AB = BF, AD is produced to E such that AD = DE. Prove that EF passes through C. (Hint: Join E and F to C, then prove that ECF is a straight line.)

35 Write a computer program that uses Pythagoras' theorem to state whether a triangle whose three sides are given is acute-, obtuse-, or right-angled.

● You need to know . . .

● Approximation methods

Many amounts used in life are approximations to (not exactly) the true amount. This may be because there is no exact amount (e.g. the length of a line), or to make the number easier to read or remember (e.g. a football crowd of 21 000).

Approximations may be expressed in many ways, e.g. 15.79 is 16 **to the nearest whole number**; 31 215 is 31 200 **to the nearest hundred**; 7.68 cm is 7.7 cm **to the nearest mm**; £10 ÷ 3 is £3.33 **to the nearest penny**.

You will often need to approximate calculator answers. How approximate you should make them usually depends on the information supplied, e.g. if a question is based on an average speed correct to the nearest km/h, and a distance correct to the nearest km, then it is silly to give a time for the journey correct to the nearest second, and even sillier to give an answer like 1.245367 hours.

Two special approximations are used in mathematics:

Decimal places (d.p.)
This states the number to a given number of figures after the decimal point. Clearly it is of no use when there are no figures after the point!

Examples 7.0145 → 7.015 to 3 d.p.
　　　　　7.0145 → 7.01 to 2 d.p.
　　　　　7.98　 → 8.0 to 1 d.p. (the 'key' 8 makes 9 → 10)

Significant figures (s.f.)
All figures are counted, except zeros between the decimal point and the first non-zero digit, and place-value zeros before the point.

Examples 126.87 → 130 to 2 s.f. (The zero is not a significant figure, but it is needed to show the empty units' column; otherwise 126.87 → 13, which is silly.)

　　　　　0.001 34 → 0.0013 to 2 s.f.
　　　　　0.0598　 → 0.060 to 2 s.f.

It is very important to check that your approximated answer *is* approximately the same size as the original number.

Test yourself

1 (a) By rounding each number to the nearest ten, find 'in your head' the approximate sum of: 16, 18, 23, 38, 40, 27, 8, 14 and 29.

　　(b) Find the accurate answer to (a).

2 As I go round the supermarket with my shopping list I roughly add up the costs to the nearest 50p so that I can check that I have enough cash to pay the bill. Compare my approximation with the correct bill if the goods cost: 35p, 82p, £1.14, £2.31, 15p, 15p, 61p, 73p, 67p, 82p, 50p, 97p, 75p.

3 Make up some questions like 1 and 2 above, comparing the approximate answers with the true ones. Or, even better, obtain some 'real' data, e.g. marks on a series of tests and some supermarket check-out till slips.

4 Write the following numbers correct to 2 d.p.
(a) 17.138   (b) 0.777   (c) 1.012 82   (d) 10.1059   (e) 19.1051
(f) 206.796

5 Write the numbers in question 4 correct to 2 s.f.

6 If you need more practice it is easy to work in pairs, making up questions and testing each other.

7 What is rather strange about 9.99 when corrected to 2 s.f.?

---

8 **Approximating with a computer**

The INT function is used in BASIC when approximating. INT takes the integral part of a number and ignores the decimal part, so that INT(2.48) = 2 and INT(0.81) = 0.

If we want 3.4125 correct to 2 d.p. we first multiply by 100 to move the 2 decimal place figures in front of the point (3.4125 × 100 = 341.25). Then we use the INT function to 'lose' the rest of the number (INT(341.25) = 341). Finally divide by 100 to restore the figures' true place value.

Here it is in BASIC:

```
1Ø LET A = 3.4125
2Ø LET B = 3.4125*1ØØ
3Ø LET C = INT(B)
4Ø LET D = C/1ØØ
5Ø PRINT A; "˄correct to 2 d.p. is ˄"; D
```

By combining lines 2Ø to 5Ø we can shorten the program to:

```
1Ø LET A = 3.4125
2Ø PRINT A; "˄correct to 2 d.p. is˄"; (INT(3.4125*1ØØ))/1ØØ
```

The above program would not be correct if A = 3.4156, as it would fail to take account of the 'key' figure 5. We allow for this by increasing the key figure, whatever it is, by 5. This will automatically round-up the preceding figure if the key figure is 5 or more:

$$
\begin{array}{cc}
3.4156 \quad \text{and} & 3.4125 \\
+0.005 & +0.005 \\
\hline
3.4206 & 3.4175 \\
\end{array}
$$

There is a further problem when a 9 is involved, as the computer would drop any zeros after the point so that 4.7961 would be printed as 4.8 to 2 d.p., not 4.80, and 4.998 would be printed as 5, not 5.00.

In the following program lines 5Ø and 6Ø correct this fault. Work out how they do it.

```
 5 REM "2DP"
1Ø PRINT "Please type your number"
2Ø INPUT A
3Ø LET B = (INT((A + Ø.ØØ5) * 1ØØ))/1ØØ
4Ø PRINT A; " correct to 2 d.p. is "; B;
5Ø IF B − INT(B) = Ø THEN PRINT ".Ø";
6Ø IF B * 1Ø − INT(B * 1Ø) = Ø THEN PRINT "Ø"
```

When you fully understand the above program, try this one:

```
 5 REM "ANYDP"
1Ø PRINT "Please type your number"
2Ø INPUT A
3Ø PRINT "To how many places of decimals?"
4Ø INPUT B
5Ø IF LEN(STR$(A)) − LEN(STR$(INT(A))) < B + 2 THEN GOTO 1Ø
6Ø LET C = INT(1Ø↑B)   (Use * * on some computers)
7Ø LET D = (INT((A + 5/(C * 1Ø)) * C))/C          Note
8Ø PRINT A; " to "; B; " d.p. is "; D;            BBC computers
9Ø IF D − INT(D) = Ø THEN PRINT ".Ø";             switch to standard
1ØØ IF B = 1 THEN GOTO 15Ø                         form when A < 0.1
11Ø FOR F = 2 to B
12Ø LET D = D * 1Ø
13Ø IF D − INT(D) < Ø.ØØØ1 THEN PRINT "Ø";   (0.0001 instead of 0 allows for
14Ø NEXT F                                    inaccurate computer arithmetic)
15Ø PRINT
16Ø GOTO 1Ø
```

9 Significant figure approximation can be done in a similar way, but as you have to allow for the original length of the number, for leading zeros, and for necessary place value zeros before the point, it is *much* more difficult. Do you like a challenge?

A Standard form: numbers above 1

1.2346 08

This shows the way most scientific calculators display the answer to 123 456 × 1000. Because the answer (123 456 000) is too long for the display, it has been switched to **standard form**. The calculator we used cuts off all figures after the first five, so the number has also been rounded to 5 s.f. Yours may show more, or fewer, figures.

The 08 at the right is called the **exponent**. It tells you that 1.2346 is 8 columns too small. Moving the figures up the 8 columns gives the answer as 123 460 000, which is the most accurate this calculator can achieve. You may find it easier to think of the 08 as meaning that there are 8 figures between the first figure and the decimal point.

When we handwrite standard form, we use the form $A \times 10^n$, where A is between 1 and 10 and n is an integer.

$$123\,456\,000 \rightarrow 1.234\,56 \times 10^8 \quad \text{(i.e. } 1.234\,55 \times 100\,000\,000\text{)}$$
$$318 \rightarrow 3.18 \times 10^2 \quad \text{(i.e. } 3.18 \times 100\text{)}$$

A calculator would not normally use standard form for numbers like 318, but using the $\boxed{\text{EXP}}$ or $\boxed{\text{EE}}$ key you can type in 318 as 3.18 $\boxed{\text{EXP}}$ 2 to give the display 3.18 02. When you type $\boxed{=}$ the calculator will probably switch it back to 318. If it does not, try typing $\boxed{\times}$ 1 $\boxed{=}$ or $\boxed{\text{INV}}$ $\boxed{\text{EXP}}$ instead.

Computers also use standard form for very large numbers (how large depends on your computer), but they show the exponent by an E, without leaving a gap, so 1.234 06 becomes 1.234E6.

1 Each of the following shows a number in standard form. Copy them, replacing the * by the correct number.
(a) $426 \rightarrow * \times 10^2$ (b) $* \rightarrow 2.75 \times 10^2$ (c) $3128 \rightarrow 3.128 \times *$
(d) $4000 \rightarrow 4 \times *$

2 Write in standard form:
(a) 200   (b) 5000   (c) 38   (d) 476   (e) 5900   (f) 16.87   (g) 347.9.

3 Write as ordinary numbers each of the following. Note that $10^1 \equiv 10$.
(a) 1×10^3 (b) 7.6×10^1 (c) 4.02 01   (d) 7.6 02
(e) 3.65×10^4 (f) 8.012E2   (g) 9.6 05   (h) 3.14×10^3.

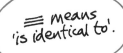
$\equiv$ means 'is identical to'.

4 Often standard form is combined with approximation.

Examples $319 \rightarrow 3.19 \times 10^2 \rightarrow 3.2 \times 10^2$ correct to 2 s.f.
$4000 \rightarrow 4.0 \times 10^3$ correct to 2 s.f.

Copy the following table, replacing all given lengths by numbers expressed in standard form correct to 2 s.f.

	Mean distance from Sun in km	Diameter in km
Sun	—	1 392 000
Mercury	57 900 000	4 880
Venus	108 200 000	12 104
Earth	149 600 000	12 756
Mars	227 900 000	6 787
Jupiter	778 300 000	142 800
Saturn	1 427 000 000	120 000
Uranus	2 869 600 000	51 800
Neptune	4 496 600 000	49 500
Pluto	5 900 000 000	6 000

5 In standard form, $400 \to 4 \times 10^2$, and $40 \to 4 \times 10^1$. Write 4 in standard form.

6 Example $\quad 3.4 \times 10^2 \times 8 \times 10^5 = 27.2 \times 10^7 \to 2.72 \times 10^8$ in standard form.

Write in standard form:
(a) $4.9 \times 10^3 \times 5 \times 10$ (b) $7.6 \times 10^2 \times 3 \times 10^3$
(c) $8.9 \times 10^4 \times 2 \times 10^2$ (d) $3.1 \times 10^5 \times 2.1 \times 10^5$
(e) $4.12 \times 10^3 \times 8 \times 10^4$ (f) $6.3 \times 10^2 \times 7 \times 10^3 \times 2 \times 10^8$.

7 What is the smallest and the largest number that could be written as:
(a) 1.0×10^6 (b) 1.00×10^6 (c) 1.000×10^6 (d) 1.0000×10^6
(e) $1.000\,00 \times 10^6$?

8 Use a scientific calculator to work question 6.

B Standard form: numbers below 1

$$7.8 \quad -02$$

The calculator display here shows 0.078 in standard form. The -02 tells us that the 7.8 should be shifted two columns to the right to give the true value.

This would be handwritten as 7.8×10^{-2}.

10^{-2} is the index way of writing the fraction $\dfrac{1}{10^2} = \dfrac{1}{100}$.

1 Each of the following shows a number in standard form. Copy them, replacing the * with the correct number.
(a) $0.082 \to * \times 10^{-2}$ (b) $0.0046 \to * \times 10^{-3}$ (c) $0.065 \to 6.5 \times *$
(d) $0.46 \to 4.6 \times *$.

2 Write as ordinary numbers:
(a) 8.06×10^{-2} (b) $6.09 \quad -01$ (c) 8×10^{-3} (d) 4.53×10^{-4}
(e) $1.35 \quad -04$.

3 Lyons Original Ready Brek has the following typical nutritional composition per 100 g.

Energy 1678 kJ	Vitamins: A, 0.0012 g	Niacin 0.027 g
Protein 12.2 g	B1, 0.0018 g B2, 0.0023 g	Iron 0.02 g
Fat 8.6 g	C, 0.042 g D, 0.000 017 g	Calcium 1.2 g
Carbohydrate 72 g		

Copy these details, but write each number in standard form.

*4 Write in standard form:
(a) 0.764 correct to 2 s.f. (b) 0.009 85 correct to 2 s.f.

*5 Change the following to standard form, to the stated degree of accuracy.
  (a) 786; 1 d.p. (b) 8000; 2 s.f. (c) 399; 1 s.f. (d) 24.989; 2 d.p.
  (e) 103.97; 3 s.f. (f) 60 991; 2 s.f. (g) 31.7×10^2; 3 s.f.
  (h) 431.6×10; 1 d.p. (i) 39.97×10^5; 2 d.p.

6 Example $\dfrac{6 \times 10^2 \times 2 \times 10^{-5}}{5 \times 10^3} = \dfrac{12 \times 10^{-3}}{5 \times 10^3} = 2.4 \times 10^{-6}$

  Notes: (i) Add indices when multiplying: $10^2 \times 10^{-5} = 10^{-3}$
  (ii) Subtract indices when dividing $10^{-3} \div 10^3 = 10^{-6}$.

Find in standard form:

  (a) $4.1 \times 10^{-3} \times 2 \times 10^2$ (b) $8.2 \times 10^{-2} \times 2 \times 10^2$

  (c) $1.2 \times 10^{-4} \times 1.2 \times 10^5$ (d) $4.1 \times 10^{-3} \times 3 \times 10^{-1}$ (e) $\dfrac{4 \times 10^2}{2 \times 10^{-3}}$

  (f) $\dfrac{2 \times 10^{-5}}{5 \times 10^{-6}}$ (g) $\dfrac{7 \times 10^4}{28 \times 10^{-2}}$ (h) $\dfrac{9 \times 10^4}{4.5 \times 10^5}$ (i) $\dfrac{6.2 \times 10^{-3} \times 2 \times 10^2}{4 \times 10^{-2}}$

  (j) $\dfrac{3.2 \times 10^{-8} \times 5 \times 10^{-6}}{4.8 \times 10^{-9}}$.

7 Use a scientific calculator to help you with the following questions.

  Example $1.76 \times 10^3 + 3.85 \times 10^9$
  Key: 1.76 EXP/EE 3 + 3.85 EXP/EE 9 =
  Note: You do not key in the multiplication signs.

  (a) $5.2 \times 10^8 - 7.1 \times 10^6$ (b) $6.95 \times 10^3 + 1.8 \times 10^5 - 3 \times 10^2$

  (c) $4.9 \times 10^4 \times 6.1 \times 10^7 - 3 \times 10^3$ (d) $\dfrac{1.4 \times 10^5 - 9.2 \times 10^3}{3 \times 10^9 - 2.5 \times 10^8}$.

---

8 As $10^{-3} = 1 \times 10^{-3} = 0.001 = \dfrac{1}{1000} = \dfrac{1}{10^3}$

  it follows that $10^{-2} = \dfrac{1}{10^2}$; $10^{-1} = \dfrac{1}{10}$; etc.

  Similarly $4^{-1} = \dfrac{1}{4}$ and $4^{-2} = \dfrac{1}{4^2} = \dfrac{1}{16}$.

  Write as fractions:
  (a) 3^{-1} (b) 3^{-2} (c) 16^{-1} (d) 2^{-3} (e) 3^{-4} (f) 20^{-2}.

9 Explain clearly why 0.6×10^{-2} is not the same as 0.60×10^{-2}

10 Explain why $2 \times 10^2 \times 3 \times 10^3 = 6 \times 10^5$, but $2 \times 10^2 + 3 \times 10^3 \neq 5 \times 10^5$.

11 Use a scientific calculator to answer question 6.

Monsieur Eiffel's marvellous tower

On 28 January, 1887, Gustave Eiffel, a French engineer, started to build his famous Parisian tower. The last rivet was hammered home on 10 March, 1889.

The tower starts 14 metres underground. After ten months' work it reached the first deck, 58 metres above ground. A further four months saw the second deck in place, twice as high. The third deck is at 276 metres. Above this are two very small platforms, the highest at 300.65 metres, from which one can see 80 km on a clear day. There used to be 1 710 steps from the ground to the highest deck. These were removed in 1983.

During its first year, 1 968 287 visitors paid six million francs to climb the tower, which covered three-quarters of its construction cost.

The tower is very stable and so well built that no rivet has ever had to be replaced. It is little affected by the wind, the strongest gale only moving it 12 cm out of line at the top, but a hot sun can move it 18 cm.

Every seven years, thirty steeplejacks spend eight months using 40 540 litres of paint to paint its 167 225 m² of ironwork, adding 45 tonnes to its weight.

Besides being a famous landmark, the tower has been used as a radio and television mast, as well as an exhibition stage for eccentrics who have ridden bicycles down it (!) and climbed its girders.

Once a pilot tried to 'thread the arches' (he failed!) and a tailor demonstrated a raincoat parachute (that failed too!).

Use the information opposite and your calculator to answer the following questions.

1   What fraction of the visible height of the tower is the underground section?

2   How many months did it take from the completion of the second deck to the completion of the tower?

3   What is the distance between the second and third decks?

4   On a clear day how many times further than one's height above the ground can one see from the top?

5   What was the average distance between the steps, in centimetres?

6   Explain why a hot sun causes the tower to lean over.

7   If no painting sessions have been missed, how many litres of paint have been put on the tower so far?

8   What is the weight of a litre of paint in kilograms?

9   How many centilitres of paint do the painters apply on average to each m^2?

10   What was the average entry fee paid by each visitor in the first year of the tower's construction?

11   What did the tower cost to construct?

12   Use the formula:
     time in seconds to fall = twice the height in cm divided by 981
     to find how long a stone dropped from the top takes to hit the ground.

13   Use the formula:
     velocity in km/h = $\sqrt{254 \times \text{distance fallen in metres}}$
     to work out the speed of a stone dropped from the top when it hits the ground.

A   Paying interest

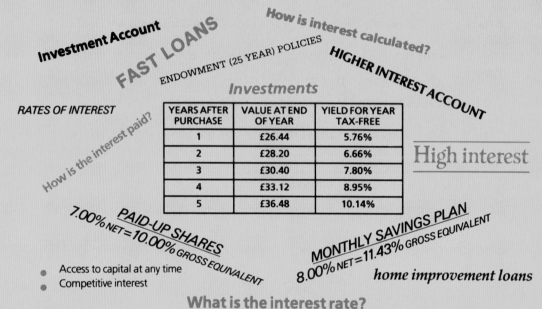

Investment Account

FAST LOANS

ENDOWMENT (25 YEAR) POLICIES

How is interest calculated?

HIGHER INTEREST ACCOUNT

RATES OF INTEREST

How is the interest paid?

Investments

YEARS AFTER PURCHASE	VALUE AT END OF YEAR	YIELD FOR YEAR TAX-FREE
1	£26.44	5.76%
2	£28.20	6.66%
3	£30.40	7.80%
4	£33.12	8.95%
5	£36.48	10.14%

High interest

7.00% NET = 10.00% GROSS EQUIVALENT

PAID-UP SHARES

MONTHLY SAVINGS PLAN

8.00% NET = 11.43% GROSS EQUIVALENT

- Access to capital at any time
- Competitive interest

home improvement loans

What is the interest rate?
The return is equivalent to a compound annual
interest rate of 7.85% over the full five years.

Interest is paid to someone who lends money. If you lend money to the Government through your Post Office Savings Bank, then the Government will pay you interest.

If the interest rate is $5\frac{1}{2}$% per annum (p.a.), then the Government will pay you £5.50 a year for every £100 you lend them.

If the interest is not added to the loan (that is, it is always 'withdrawn'), it is called **simple interest**.

If the interest *is* added to the loan, it is called **compound interest**. Most everyday-life interest is compound interest.

Examples   £100 loaned at 5% p.a. simple interest for 3 years gives £5 each year, making £15 interest altogether.

£100 loaned at 5% p.a. compound interest for 3 years gives £5 interest the first year, but 5% of £105 = £5.25 the second year, and 5% of £110.25 = £5.51 the third year, a total of £15.76 interest.

You may find it helpful to learn the formula:

$$\text{Simple interest} = \frac{P \times R \times T}{100}$$

where P is the principal (the initial amount lent)
      R is the interest rate p.a.
      T is the number of years for which the principal is lent.

For discussion

Lender	Borrower	Interest rate
Tom Smith	Government (PO Savings Bank)	5% p.a.
Building Society	Jill Brown (Mortgage)	13% p.a.
Ann Watson	Building Society (Share Account)	10% p.a.
Town Bank	Jack Tar (Bank Loan)	14% p.a.
Mary White	Town Bank (Deposit Account)	11% p.a.
Joy Jones	City Council (Local Authority Bonds)	15% p.a.

▷ Why does Tom lend his money to the Government?

▷ (a) Why does the Building Society lend money to Jill?
   (b) What is meant by 'a 100% mortgage'?
   (c) Where does the Building Society get the money that it lends to Jill?
   (d) Why does the Building Society charge Jill 13% interest but only pay Ann 10%?

▷ The City Council will not accept loans of less than £1000, nor for periods of less than one year. All interest is taxable. The Post Office Savings Bank will accept any amount over 50p for any time over 7 days. No tax is payable if less than £1400 is loaned.
   In what way is this reflected in the interests paid?

Using a calculator

To find the interest on £50 at 8%,
key: 50 ⊠ 8 %
or   50 ⊠ 8 % =
or   50 ⊠ 0.08 =

1 As £1 = 100p, then 1% interest is 1p in the £, and 5% interest is 5p in the £.

If Tom puts £50 in his Post Office Savings Bank Account for 1 year, how much interest will he receive?

2 13% interest is £13 in every £100.

Jill borrows £10 000 from the Building Society. How much interest will she pay in a year?

3 Ann Watson lends £500 to the Building Society through her Share Account. How much interest will they pay her at the end of the year?

4 Jack Tar borrows £800 from Town Bank. How much interest will he have to pay them in a year?

5 Mary White puts £75 into her Town Bank Deposit Account. How much interest will she receive after a year?

*6 Copy and complete the following table.

Principal (the amount loaned)	P	£10	£20	£35	£400	£350
Rate (the rate of interest p.a.)	R	5%	5%	5%	11%	10%
Interest (the amount paid in a year)	I					

P	£1000	£750	£650	£100	£200	£10 000	£600	£1600
R	9%	5%	5%	$7\frac{1}{2}$%	$10\frac{1}{2}$%	$10\frac{1}{2}$%	$10\frac{1}{2}$%	10%
I								

7 Find (a) to (l) in the following table.

Principal (the amount loaned)	P	£1500	£5000	£2000	£350	(e)
Rate (the rate of interest p.a.)	R	$8\frac{1}{2}$%	$13\frac{1}{4}$%	(c)	(d)	12%
Interest (the amount paid in a year)	I	(a)	(b)	£160	£24.50	£300

P	(f)	£400	(h)	(i)	£360	£150	(l)
R	$7\frac{1}{2}$%	(g)	11%	$10\frac{1}{2}$%	$9\frac{3}{4}$%	(k)	13%
I	£112.50	£32	£2.75	£262.50	(j)	£5.25	£1625

8 How much will Fred need to put into his Building Society account to gain £750 in a year if the interest rate is 10%?

9 How much interest will Joy Jones actually receive if she lends £3000 at 15%, but has to pay tax at 30% on the interest?

10 Jim buys a £4000 car on hire purchase for £150 deposit, then 12 monthly payments of £360. June buys a similar car, borrowing the money for one year from a bank at 11% interest. She agrees to pay the £4000 plus interest back in 12 equal monthly instalments.

(a) How much does Jim pay altogether for his car?
(b) How much will June have to pay her bank each month?
(c) Who pays less for their car, and by how much?

11 Write a brief essay on one, or both, of the following.

(a) Building Societies.
(b) You win £100 000 on the pools. In what different ways might you invest it to give a regular income? What are the advantages and disadvantages of each possibility?

B Compound interest

When the interest due to lenders is calculated, it is not usually sent to them. Instead, it is added to the amount they have loaned. This means that each interest payment is larger than the previous one (if the principal is not reduced). We say that the interest is 'compounded', hence compound interest.

Example Find the result of investing £1000 for 3 years at 10% compound interest.

Date	Details	Interest	Principal
31 Jan 1991	1st principal	—	£1000
31 Jan 1992	1st interest (10%)	£100	£1100
31 Jan 1993	2nd interest	£110	£1210
31 Jan 1994	3rd interest	£121	£1331

Using a calculator

To increase by $r\%$, you can multiply by $(100 + r)\%$.

Example To increase by 8%, multiply by 108%, or 1.08.

To decrease by $r\%$, you can multiply by $(100 - r)\%$.

Example To decrease by 8%, multiply by 92% or 0.92.

To multiply repeatedly, use the constant function on your calculator. This may be automatic, or may need to be programmed using either two presses of $\boxed{\times}$ or $\boxed{\times}$ then $\boxed{k}$.

Example Find the amount of £500 after 3 years at 7% compound interest.

Key: 1.07 $\begin{cases} \boxed{\times} \\ \boxed{\times}\ \boxed{\times} \\ \boxed{\times}\ \boxed{k} \end{cases}$ 500 $\boxed{=}\ \boxed{=}\ \boxed{=}$

Answer: £612.52

Note Questions often ask for the interest, not the amount. Remember to subtract the original principal from your answer. In the example the interest is £112.52.

The compound interest formula

Although calculators have made the compound interest formula of limited use, it is quicker if you have to work out the interest over many years.

The formula is
$$A = P(1 + 0.01R)^T$$

Example Find the compound interest on £30 000 at 9% for 25 years.
$$A = 30\,000 \times (1 + 0.09)^{25}$$

Key: 30 000 $\boxed{\times}$ 1.09 $\boxed{y^x}$ 25 $\boxed{=}$ Answer: £228 692.42   *Not a misprint!*

1 Find how much the following principals will amount to in 3 years if the interest is compounded.

	(a)	(b)	(c)	(d)	(e)
Principal	£3000	£400	£200	£250	£1000
Rate	10%	5%	7%	6%	7%

*2 Find how much the following principals will amount to if the interest is compounded.

	(a)	(b)	(c)	(d)
Principal	£1000	£100	£900	£4000
Rate	6%	5%	10%	5%
Time	2 y	2 y	3 y	3 y

3 Using a calculator to give each year's interest correct to the nearest penny, find the total amount for the following:

	(a)	(b)	(c)	(d)
Principal	£500	£80	£25	£10 000
Rate	7%	12%	$7\frac{1}{2}$%	$10\frac{1}{2}$%
Time	4 y	4 y	3 y	4 y

4 Bigtown Building Society pays savers 5% interest, correct to the nearest penny, every six months, this interest being compounded. If I put £500 into the Building Society for 3 years, calculate each of the six interest payments.

5 Ali reckons that the value of his new car will depreciate (go down) each year by about 5% of its previous year's value. If his car cost £10 000 when new, what would Ali expect it to be worth at the end of each of the next five years?

---

6 The formula $A = P(1 + 0.01R)^T$ gives the amount (A) which a principal (P) will realise in T years at R% per year compound interest.

Use a calculator to find, correct to the nearest 1p, the amount A for the following.

	(a)	(b)	(c)	(d)	(e)
P pounds	500	750	600	1000	30 000
R% p.a.	7%	10%	$12\frac{1}{2}$%	11%	13%
T years	5	8	10	4	6

7 (a) Jill wishes to buy a house and the City Building Society agree to lend her £25 000 at 15% compound interest for 25 years. If Jill made no payments until the 25 years were up, how much would she then owe the Society?

(b) The answer to part (a) should show you that this would be an impossible way to borrow the money. Instead, the Society would expect Jill either to pay all the interest due each year, and cover the £25 000 debt with life insurance (this is called an endowment mortgage); or to pay the interest and refund some of the loan each year, so that after 25 years she would owe them nothing.
If the society asks Jill to pay £303 each month for 25 years to discharge the debt completely, how much would she pay altogether?

(c) In reality, the interest paid is reduced by an income tax allowance, so the endowment mortgage payment would be about £210 a month, plus a life insurance premium. How much would the house really have cost her? (Remember that the house will almost certainly be worth a lot more than £25 000 in 25 years' time.)

8 Using the formula given in question 6 to help you, design a computer program to advise customers on their investments and loans.

14 Trigonometry: sines and cosines

For discussion

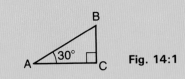

Fig. 14:1

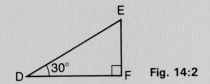

Fig. 14:2

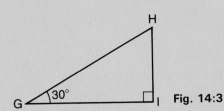

Fig. 14:3

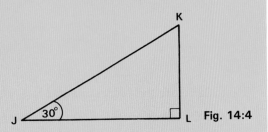

Fig. 14:4

Tangent and sine

o is the side *o*pposite the angle θ.

a is the side *a*djacent to the angle θ.

h is the *h*ypotenuse (opposite the right angle).

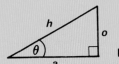

Fig. 14:5

$$\text{Tangent} \quad o = a \times \tan \theta \qquad \frac{o}{a} = \tan \theta$$

$$\text{Sine} \quad o = h \times \sin \theta \qquad \frac{o}{h} = \sin \theta$$

The following sentence may help you to remember the above facts:

One ancient teacher of history swore!

1 Example Calculate side o in Figure 14:6.

$o = h \times \sin \theta \rightarrow o = 12 \times \sin 28.7°$

Key: 12 $\boxed{\times}$ 28.7 $\boxed{\text{SIN}}$ $\boxed{=}$

Answer: $o = 5.76$ cm to 3 significant figures.

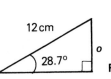

Fig. 14:6

Calculate correct to 3 s.f. the sides marked o in Figure 14:7.

(a)
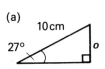

(b)
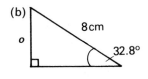

(c)
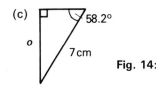

Fig. 14:7

83

2 Example Calculate angle θ in Figure 14:8.

$$\frac{o}{h} = \sin \theta \rightarrow \tfrac{7}{8} = \sin \theta$$

8cm / 7cm
θ
Fig. 14:8

Key: 7 $\boxed{\div}$ 8 $\boxed{=}$ $\boxed{\text{ARCSIN}}$
Answer: $\theta = 61.0°$ to the nearest tenth of $1°$.

Note: Your calculator may use $\boxed{\text{INV}}$ $\boxed{\text{SIN}}$ or $\boxed{\text{SIN}^{-1}}$ instead of $\boxed{\text{ARCSIN}}$.

(i) Draw the triangles in Figure 14:9 accurately to the sizes given.

(a)
6cm
3cm

(b)
4cm
6cm

(c)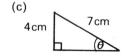
4cm 7cm
θ

(d)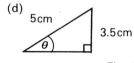
5cm
3.5cm
θ

Fig. 14:9

(ii) Calculate the angles marked θ, correct to the nearest degree.

(iii) Check your answers by measurement with a protractor.

*3 Example Calculate the side x in Figure 14:10.

$8^2 = x^2 + 3^2$ (Pythagoras' theorem)
$64 = x^2 + 9$, so $x^2 = 55$.
If $x^2 = 55$ then $x = \sqrt{55} = 7.4$ cm to the nearest 0.1 cm

8cm 3cm
$x$cm   **Fig. 14:10**

Use Pythagoras' theorem to calculate the third side of the triangles you drew in question 2. Check your answers by measurement.

*4 Use $o = h \times \sin \theta$ to calculate the side AB in each triangle in Figure 14:11. Remember that θ must be the angle opposite the side that you are trying to find. In some of the triangles, e.g. (a), you are told the size of this angle; in others, e.g. (b), you have to work it out using $\angle A + \angle C = 90°$.

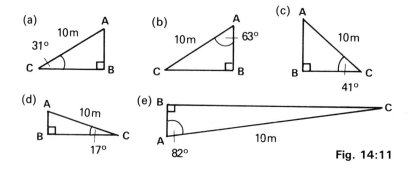

Fig. 14:11

*5 Calculate the sizes of the sides marked *x* in Figure 14:12.

(a)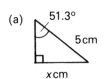

(b)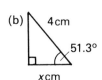

(c)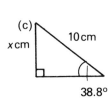

(d)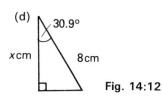

Fig. 14:12

*6 For Figure 14:13
(a) calculate AB using $o = a \times \tan \theta$.
(b) calculate AC using Pythagoras' theorem.

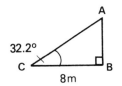

Fig. 14:13

*7 For Figure 14:14
(a) calculate YZ using $o = h \times \sin \theta$
(b) calculate XZ using $o = a \times \tan \theta$.

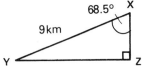

Fig. 14:14

*8 For Figure 14:15
(a) calculate $\angle R$ using the tangent function
(b) calculate PR using Pythagoras' theorem.

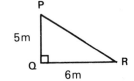

Fig. 14:15

9 For Figure 14:16
(a) calculate $\angle F$ using the sine function
(b) use your answer to part (a) to calculate $\angle E$
(c) calculate DF using Pythagoras' theorem
(d) calculate DF using $\angle E$ and the tangent function
(e) calculate DF using $\angle E$ and the sine function.

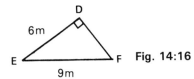

Fig. 14:16

10 The third function used in a right-angled triangle is the cosine.

The cosine of an angle is adjacent side over hypotenuse.

Learn the complete set of facts set out below.

$o = a \times \tan \theta$	$o = h \times \sin \theta$	$a = h \times \cos \theta$
$\dfrac{o}{a} = \tan \theta$	$\dfrac{o}{h} = \sin \theta$	$\dfrac{a}{h} = \cos \theta$

One ancient teacher of history swore at his class!

Fig. 14:17

11 (a) For Figure 14:18 find the length of side *a* correct to 3 s.f.
    (b) For Figure 14:19 calculate θ in degrees correct to the nearest tenth.

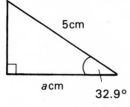

Fig. 14:18

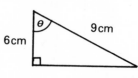

Fig. 14:19

You have probably realised that cosines are not essential to solve a right-angled triangle. Sines could always be used instead, by finding the other angle.

For questions 12 to 14 use sines, cosines, tangents, angle sum of a triangle and symmetry.

12 For Figure 14:20 find:
    (a) ∠BDM   (b) MC   (c) MB
    (d) MD   (e) ∠MCD   (f) ∠MBD
    (g) ∠MAC   (h) ∠MAB   (i) ∠MCA
    (j) ∠MBA.

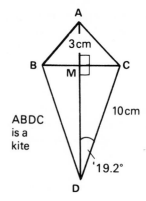

ABDC is a kite

Fig. 14:20

13 For Figure 14:21 find:
    (a) ∠HEG   (b) ∠FEH   (c) ∠F
    (d) EH to 3 s.f.   (e) HG
    (f) FH (using the answers to parts (b) and (d))
    (g) EF to 3 s.f.

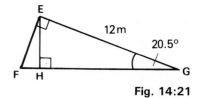

Fig. 14:21

14 For Figure 14:22 calculate all the lengths, and all the acute angles.

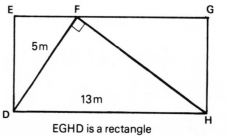

EGHD is a rectangle   **Fig. 14:22**

15 See Figure 14:23.

(a) Copy and complete:

(i) $\theta + \alpha = \ldots^\circ$ (ii) $\sin \theta = \dfrac{AB}{}$ (iii) $\cos \alpha = \underline{}$

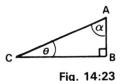

Fig. 14:23

(b) Using the results of part (a) state the value of θ if:
(i) $\sin 60^\circ = \cos \theta$ (ii) $\sin \theta = \cos 50^\circ$
(iii) $\sin 73.3^\circ = \cos \theta$ (iv) $\sin \theta = \cos 80.1^\circ$.

16 For Figure 14:24
(a) give three methods to find x without finding z first
(b) give six methods to find z once you know x.

15 cm   **Fig. 14:24**

17 Computers and trigonometry
Computers do not use degrees as their angle measure, they use radians. A radian is the angle subtended at the centre of a circle by an arc of the same length as the radius. As $2\pi r$ is the length of the circumference, this means that π **radians = 180°**. You should remember this fact. The sign for radian is a raised c.

$$1^c = \frac{180^\circ}{\pi} \quad \text{and} \quad 1^\circ = \frac{\pi^c}{180}$$

This will find the tangent of 37°:
```
1Ø PRINT TAN (37*PI/180)
```
You may need to define PI first by
```
LET PI = 4*ATN(1)
```

ATN is BASIC for arctan. Tan 45° = 1, so ATN(1) = 45° in radians, and 4*ATN(1) = 180° in radians = PI.

Some computers only have arctan (not arcsin or arccos).
To find arcsin e use:
$$\text{arcsin } e = \text{arctan} \left(\frac{e}{\sqrt{1 - e^2}} \right)$$

To find arccos e use:
$$\text{arccos } e = \text{arctan} \left(\frac{\sqrt{1 - e^2}}{e} \right)$$

These two formulae are obtained from the identities:

$$\tan \theta = \frac{\sin \theta}{\cos \theta} \quad \text{and} \quad \sin^2\theta + \cos^2\theta = 1$$

Try to work them out for yourself.

This will find the angle whose sine is 0.5:
```
1Ø PRINT ATN (0.5/SQR(1 − 0.5↑2))*180/PI
```

15 Expansion of quadratic brackets

A $(x + a)(x + b)$

$x(x + 3) \to x^2 + 3x$ [from $x(x + 3)$]

$2(x + 3) \to 2x + 6$ [from $2(x + 3)$]

So $(x + 2)(x + 3) \to (x + 2)(x + 3)$

$ \to x^2 + 3x + 2x + 6 \to x^2 + 5x + 6$

Similarly $(m - 3)(m + 2) \to (m - 3)(m + 2)$

$ \to m^2 + 2m - 3m - 6 \to m^2 - m - 6$

Note   The middle step should be done mentally when you have had some practice.

Expand

1 (a) $(a + 3)(a + 4)$ (b) $(a + 5)(a + 2)$ (c) $(a + 1)(a + 2)$.

2 (a) $(p + 5)(p - 3)$ (b) $(m + 6)(m - 2)$ (c) $(p - 5)(p + 2)$ (d) $(r - 7)(r + 4)$
   (e) $(p - 2)(p - 4)$ (f) $(a - 7)(a - 4)$.

3 (a) $(m + 3)^2$ [That is, $(m + 3)(m + 3)$]   (b) $(a + 4)^2$ (c) $(x - 2)^2$
   (d) $(x - 4)^2$.

*4 (a) $(b - 4)(b + 5)$ (b) $(a + 2)(a + 8)$ (c) $(a - 5)(a - 3)$ (d) $(a - 8)(a + 4)$.

*5 (a) $(r - 7)(r + 4)$ (b) $(p + 6)^2$ · (c) $(b - 3)^2$ (d) $(m - 7)^2$.

6 Example $(4 + x)(3 - x) \to 12 - 4x + 3x - x^2 \to 12 - x - x^2$

   Note   Do not attempt to change the order of the given terms.

   Write down the products of:

   (a) $(5 + x)(3 + x)$ (b) $(4 - x)(2 + x)$ (c) $(5 + x)(3 - x)$
   (d) $(2 + x)(7 - x)$ (e) $(3 - x)(2 - x)$ (f) $(4 - x)^2$

7 Expand:
   (a) $(x + a)(x + b)$ (b) $(x - a)(x + b)$ (c) $(x + a)(x - b)$ (d) $(x - a)(x - b)$

8 Use what you have learnt in this exercise to express the unshaded area in terms of x for each diagram in Figure 15:1.

(a) 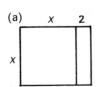   (b)   (c) 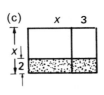   (d) 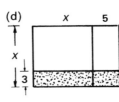   (e)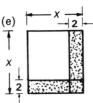

Fig. 15:1

9 Expand:
(a) $(x + 3)(x + a + 1)$ (b) $(x + 2)(x + a - 2)$ (c) $(x - 1)(x + a + 3)$

B $(ax + b)(cx + d)$

Example $(2x + 3)(4x - 5) \rightarrow 8x^2 - 10x + 12x - 15 \rightarrow 8x^2 + 2x - 15$

Expand

1 (a) $(3x + 5)(x + 2)$ (b) $(2x + 2)(3x + 8)$ (c) $(2x - 4)(3x + 8)$
  (d) $(3x - 5)(2x - 3)$.

2 (a) $(3x - 3)^2$ (b) $(a - 1)^2$ (c) $(8p - 3)^2$ (d) $(3q + 6)(3q - 6)$.

*3 (a) $(2x + 4)(3x + 5)$ (b) $(3x - 2)^2$ (c) $(2x - 4)(3x + 2)$ (d) $(4a - 5)(3a - 2)$.

*4 (a) $(2x + 3)^2$ (b) $(x - 4)(3x - 2)$ (c) $(4x - 5)(x + 7)$ (d) $(4x - 5)^2$.

5 (a) $(3m + 4n)(2m - 3n)$ (b) $(5a + 2b)(3a - 8b)$ (c) $(4a - 7b)(3a + 2b)$
  (d) $(3a - 2b)^2$.

6 Example $102^2 \rightarrow (100 + 2)(100 + 2)$
            $\rightarrow 10\,000 + 200 + 200 + 4 \rightarrow 10\,404$

  Use the above method to work out:
  (a) 105^2 (b) 81^2 (c) 84^2 (d) 109^2 (e) 78^2.

7 Figure 15:2 illustrates $(x + 3)(x + 1) \rightarrow x^2 + 4x + 3$.

	x	3
x	x^2	$3x$
1	x	3

Fig. 15:2

  Draw similar diagrams to illustrate:
  (a) $(x + 2)(x + 3)$ (b) $(x - 1)(x + 1)$ (c) $(x - 2)(x - 3)$.

16 Graphs: linear review; parabolas; reciprocal graphs

● You need to know . . .

● Coordinates

See the notes on page 1.

● Linear (straight-line) graphs

All straight lines can be expressed in equation form as $y = mx + c$, though the three terms may be moved around; e.g. $y = 2x$, $y = 3$, $y = 2x + 3$, $x + y = 2$, $2y + 3x = 4$ and $x = 2 - 7y$ are all equations of straight-line graphs.

Linear graphs are drawn by one of the following methods.

(a) Plotting method for $y + 2x = 3$

Choose three values for x (including zero) and find y for each, e.g.:

If $x = 0$ then $y + 0 = 3 \rightarrow y = 3$. Plot $(0, 3)$.
If $x = 2$ then $y + 4 = 3 \rightarrow y = -1$. Plot $(2, -1)$.
If $x = -1$ then $y - 2 = 3 \rightarrow y = 5$. Plot $(-1, 5)$.

See Figure 16:1.

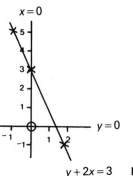

$y + 2x = 3$ Fig. 16:1

(b) Slope/crossing ($y = mx + c$) method for $y + 2x = 3$

When the equation is expressed in the form $y = mx + c$ then c gives the crossing point on the y-axis $(0, c)$ and m gives the slope (see Figures 16:2 and 16:3).

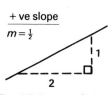

Fig. 16:2 +ve slope

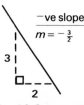

Fig. 16:3 −ve slope

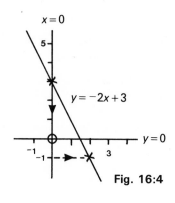

$y = -2x + 3$

Fig. 16:4

To use this method for $y + 2x = 3$ we first rearrange the terms to change it to $y = -2x + 3$. We now know that $m = -2$ and $c = 3$. Start from 3 on the y-axis, then go down and across to give a slope of -2. See Figure 16:4.

See also the use of linear graphs to solve simultaneous equations, page 8.

● Finding the equation of a linear graph

A straight line has the equation $y = mx + c$, where m is the slope and c is the crossing point on $x = 0$.

In Figure 16:5 the triangle under the sloping line shows that its slope is $-\frac{3}{4}$.

Remember: ＼ is a negative slope.
Bottom of triangle to bottom of fraction.

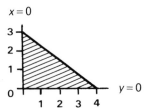

Fig. 16:5

For the line shown, $m = -\frac{3}{4}$ and $c = 3$, so its equation is $y = -\frac{3}{4}x + 3$.

Note that the triangle can be any size, usually the larger the better, but it is best to choose it so that its vertical and horizontal sides are integral if possible. Figures 16:6 to 16:8 show some examples of this.

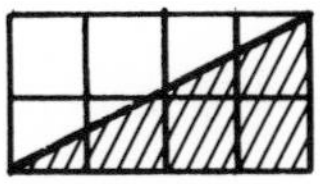

Slope $= \frac{2}{4} = \frac{1}{2}$

Good choice

Fig. 16:6

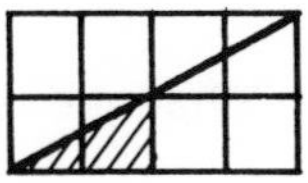

Slope $= \frac{1}{2}$

Fair choice

Fig. 16:7

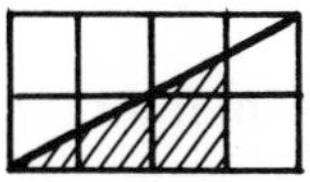

Slope $= \frac{1\frac{1}{2}}{3} = \frac{1}{2}$

Poor choice

Fig. 16:8

Test yourself

1 Draw and label x- and y-axes, each from -5 to 5. Plot the following points.
   A, (5, 5);   B, (5, -4);   C, (0, -4);   D, (5, 0);   E, (-2, -4);   F, (3, -4)

2 On your graph for question 1 draw the two straight lines through points A, D, B and through E, C, F, B. Label these lines with their equations.

   State the coordinates of the point which is equidistant from the origin and points D, B and C.

*3 On one set of axes from -5 to 5:
   (a) plot the graph whose equation is $y = x - 5$
   (b) plot the graph whose equation is $y = -2x$
   (c) plot the graph whose equation is $x + y = 3$.

4 On axes from 0 to 3, join the points (0, 1) and (3, 3). State the equation of the line that you have drawn.

5 Find, by drawing, the equations of the following straight lines.

	x-axis	y-axis	line passes through
(a)	0 to 4	0 to 3	(0, 2) and (4, 0)
(b)	0 to 3	0 to −2	(0, −2) and (3, 0)
(c)	0 to 4	−1 to 3	(0, −1) and (4, 2)
(d)	−1 to 2	−2 to 1	(−1, 1) and (2, −2)
(e)	−1 to 2	−3 to 2	(−1, −3) and (1, 1)
(f)	−2 to 2	−3 to 7	(−2, −3) and (2, 7)
(g)	−2 to 0	0 to 3	(−2, 3) and (0, 0)
(h)	−1 to 2	−3 to 2	(0, −2) and (1, 1)

6 When the equation is in the $y = mx + c$ form it is easy to state its slope, e.g. the slope of $y = -x + 7$ is -1 because m is -1.

Equations in other forms have to be changed to the $y = mx + c$ form if you are to find the slope without drawing.

Examples $y + 3x = 2 \rightarrow y = -3x + 2$; slope $= -3$
$y + 1 = -2x \rightarrow y = -2x - 1$; slope $= -2$
$4x = 3 + y \rightarrow 4x - 3 = y$; slope $= 4$
$y = 4 - \frac{1}{2}x \rightarrow y = -\frac{1}{2}x + 4$; slope $= -\frac{1}{2}$

Find the slope of:
(a) $y - 3x = 6$ (b) $y + \frac{1}{4}x = 1$ (c) $y - \frac{1}{4}x = 1$ (d) $y = 2 + 3x$
(e) $2 - y = 3x$ (f) $x = y + 8$ (g) $2x = 3 - y$ (h) $\frac{1}{2}x - y = 5$

7 **Example** $3y - 2x = 1 \rightarrow 3y = 2x + 1 \rightarrow y = \frac{2}{3}x + \frac{1}{3}$ (divide every term by 3)
Hence the slope of $3y - 2x = 1$ is $\frac{2}{3}$.

Find the slope of:
(a) $2y = 3x - 1$ (b) $3y = 2x + 1$ (c) $4y = 4x - 1$ (d) $3y = 6x$
(e) $\frac{1}{2}y = x$ (f) $\frac{1}{2}y = x + 2$.

8 The slope (m) of the line joining two points (x, y) and (X, Y) is $\dfrac{x - X}{y - Y}$. See Figure 16:9.

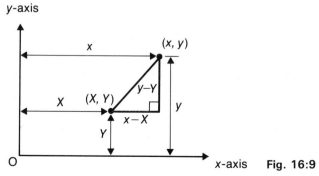

Fig. 16:9

From this and the general equation $y = mx + c$ it is possible to calculate the equation of a straight line graph from the coordinates of two points on it.

Example   Find the equation of the straight line through (7, 3) and (9, 1).

The slope $(m) = \dfrac{7 - 9}{3 - 1} = \dfrac{-2}{2} = -1$.

The equation is $y = -1x + c \rightarrow y = -x + c$.

As the line passes through (7, 3) we know that $X = 7$ when $Y = 3$.

Hence $y = -x + c \rightarrow 3 = -7 + c$, giving $c = 10$.

The equation is $y = -x + 10$.

Calculate the equations of the lines joining the points in question 5.

9   Investigate the plotting of points by a computer. Most computers use a simple PLOT X, Y command, although they usually only use the positive quadrant. You have to set up special instructions if you wish to move the origin away from the bottom left-hand corner of the screen. Computers differ too widely in their use of PLOT to give examples here.

Parabolas and reciprocal functions

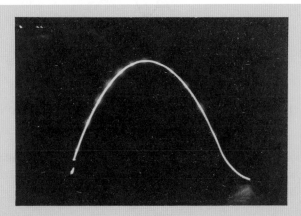

The path of a projectile, like this torch thrown in a dark room, is a parabola

Equations like $y = x^2$, $y = x^2 + 3$ and $y = 2x^2$ give **parabolas** when drawn as graphs.

Sometimes the equation is given in function notation, e.g. $y = f(x)$ where $f(x): x \rightarrow x^2$. This has the same meaning as $y = x^2$.

To draw the graphs, plot values of y for a series of values of x. (You are usually told which values of x to use.) It is best to work out the values in a table.

Example Draw the parabola $y = 2x^2 - 3$.

Values for x:

Working out:

x	-2	-1	0	1	2
$2x^2$	8	2	0	2	8
-3	-3	-3	-3	-3	-3

Add these two rows to find y.

Values for y:

y	5	-1	-3	-1	5

The points $(-2, 5)$, $(-1, -1)$, etc. are now plotted and joined with a smooth continuous curve. See Figure 16:10.

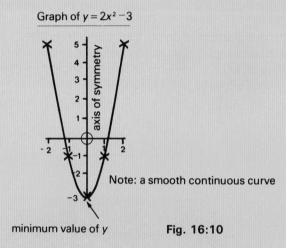

Graph of $y = 2x^2 - 3$

axis of symmetry

Note: a smooth continuous curve

minimum value of y Fig. 16:10

Equations like $y = \dfrac{3}{x}$ give a **reciprocal** graph. This is unlike other graphs you have met as it is in two parts.

$3 \div 0$ has no real meaning, but $3 \div x$ gets ever bigger as x gets smaller and smaller, so we say that the value of $\dfrac{3}{x}$ tends to infinity (∞) as x tends towards zero.

Example Plot the graph of $y = \dfrac{3}{x}$.

x	-5	-4	-3	-2	-1	0	1	2	3	4	5
y	-0.6	-0.75	-1	-1.5	-3	∞	3	1.5	1	0.75	0.6

See Figure 16:11.

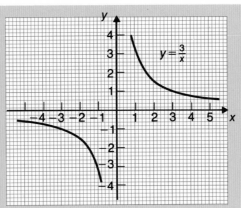

Fig. 16:11

1 (a) Copy and complete the table for $y = x^2$:

x	−4	−3	−2	−1	0	1	2	3	4
y	16					1			

(b) On 2 mm graph paper draw x- and y-axes. Use different scales on the two axes as follows: x from −4 to 4, 1 cm to 1 unit; y from 0 to 20, 1 cm to 5 units.

(c) Plot the coordinates from the table: $(−4, 16)$, $(−3, 9)$, etc.

(d) Join the points with a smooth curve.
Hints: Work from inside the curve, turning the paper as you go. Use your wrist as a pivot. Watch that you make the turning point curved, not pointed.

(e) Label your graph with its equation and *trace it* for use later in the exercise. (It is very important that you always remember to label your graphs with their equations.)

2 Copy and complete the following table, using the one that you drew up for question 1 to help you.

x	−4	−3	−2	−1	0	1	2	3	4
$y = x^2 + 4$	20	13			4	5			
$y = x^2 − 4$	12	5			−4	−3			
$y = x^2 + 9$	25								
$y = x^2 − 9$	7								

3 On 2 mm graph paper draw axes: x from −4 to 4, 1 cm to 1 unit; y from −10 to 25, 1 cm to 5 units. Plot on this grid the graph of $y = x^2$ together with all four graphs given in question 2, e.g. for $y = x^2 + 4$ plot $(−4, 20)$, $(−3, 13)$, etc. and for $y = x^2 − 4$ plot $(−4, 12)$, $(−3, 5)$, etc.

*4 (a) Check with your tracing of $y = x^2$ that all the graphs plotted in question 3 have the same shape.

(b) You will notice that $y = x^2 + 4$ crosses the y-axis at $y = 4$. Similarly $y = x^2 - 4$ crosses the y-axis at $y = -4$. Where should the graph of $y = x^2 + 3$ cross the y-axis?

(c) Copy and complete the table:

x	-4	-3	-2	-1	0	1	2	3	4
$y = x^2 + 3$	19								
$y = x^2 - 3$	13								
$y = x^2 + 2$	18								
$y = x^2 - 2$	14								

(d) Draw one pair of axes: x from -4 to 4, 1 cm to 1 unit; y from -5 to 20, 1 cm to 5 units. Plot on your grid the graphs of the equations in your table.

(e) Check that each graph crosses the y-axis at the expected point.

*5 Copy and complete the table:

x	-4	-3	-2	-1	0	1	2	3	4
$y = x^2$	16								
$y = -x^2$	-16								
$y = 2x^2$	32								
$y = -2x^2$	-32								
$y = 3x^2$		27							
$y = -3x^2$		-27							

*6 Draw one pair of axes: x from -4 to 4, 1 cm to 1 unit; y from -35 to 35, 1 cm to 5 units. Plot on your grid the graphs of the equations in the table for question 5.

*7 Draw up a table for $y = \frac{1}{2}x^2$, taking x from -4 to 4, then draw the graph of $y = \frac{1}{2}x^2$, choosing sensible scales.

8 Draw the graph of $y = \dfrac{1}{x}$ for values of x from -5 to 5.

9 (a) By considering the graphs drawn in question 3, state the coordinates of the crossing point on the y-axis for:

(i) $y = x^2 + 2$ (ii) $y = x^2 - 5$ (iii) $y = x^2 + a$.

(b) State the equation of the line of symmetry of the family of graphs $y = x^2 + a$.

10 Without using graph paper, and plotting no more than three points, sketch the graph of
(a) $y = x^2 + 1$ (b) $y = x^2 - 3$.

Show clearly where your graphs cross the y-axis.

11 On one pair of axes: x from -4 to 4, 1 cm to 1 unit; y from 0 to 35, 1 cm to 5 units, draw accurately the graphs of $y = x^2$, $y = 2x^2$ and $y = 3x^2$. (Ignore any values of y outside the given axes' ranges.)

12 On one pair of axes, x from -4 to 4, 1 cm to 1 unit; y from -35 to 0, 1 cm to 5 units, draw accurately the graphs of $y = -x^2$, $y = -2x^2$ and $y = -3x^2$.

13 In Figure 16:12, A, B, C and D are the graphs of the following equations. Which graph has which equation?

$$y = -\tfrac{1}{4}x^2$$
$$y = -\tfrac{1}{2}x^2$$
$$y = x^2$$
$$y = 4x^2$$

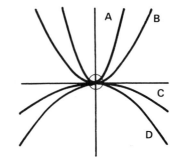

Fig. 16:12

14 Explain how a graph of $y = x^2$ could be used to find an approximate value for $\sqrt{7}$.

15 Draw, for values of x from -3 to 3 at 0.5 intervals, the graph of:

(a) $y = x^3$ (b) $y = -x^3$ (c) $y = \dfrac{1}{x^2}$ (d) $y = x^3 + 3x^2 - x + 1$

(e) $x^2 + y^2 = 9$.

17 Factorisation: common factors; difference of two squares

A   Common factors

If all the terms in an expression have a common factor then the common factor may be 'taken out' and written in front of a bracket.

Examples $3 + 6a \rightarrow 3(1 + 2a)$
$2a - ab \rightarrow a(2 - b)$
$3ax^2 + ax \rightarrow ax(3x + 1)$

Make sure that you take out the *highest* common factor.

1   Copy and complete:
(a) $7 - 14a \rightarrow 7(\quad - \quad)$ (b) $3xy + 4x \rightarrow x(\quad + \quad)$ (c) $16x - 12 \rightarrow 4(\quad - \quad)$
(d) $2x + 4xy \rightarrow 2x(\quad + \quad)$ (e) $3a - 2ab \rightarrow a(\quad - \quad)$ (f) $6ab + 9b \rightarrow 3b(\quad + \quad)$

*2   Copy and complete:
(a) $mx + my \rightarrow m(\qquad)$ (b) $ab + 2b \rightarrow b(\qquad)$ (c) $4a - 16 \rightarrow 4(\qquad)$
(d) $9a + 3b + 12c \rightarrow 3(\qquad)$ (e) $15ab - 10bc + 20bd \rightarrow 5b(\qquad)$.

*3   Copy and complete:
(a) $3cd + 6c \rightarrow \quad (d + 2)$ (b) $6ab + 10b \rightarrow \quad (3a + 5)$
(c) $5b - ab \rightarrow \quad (5 - a)$ (d) $2a + ab \rightarrow \quad (2 + b)$
(e) $4a + 6ab \rightarrow \quad (2 + 3b)$ (f) $6a - 9ab \rightarrow \quad (2 - 3b)$.

*4   Factorise:
(a) $6a - 6b$ (b) $7ab - 28$ (c) $4x - 8$ (d) $12 - 8a$ (e) $8b - 4c$
(f) $4a + 8b$ (g) $12 - 3a$ (h) $3bd + 12bc$.

Factorise the expressions in questions 5 to 13 where possible. Where an expression will not factorise, write 'No factors'.

5   (a) $3x - 6xy$ (b) $am - an$ (c) $16abc - 12ab$ (d) $3abx - 6aby$.

6   (a) $2x^2 - x$ (b) $3a^2 + 15a$ (c) $2x^2y - 2xy^2$ (d) $12m^2n - 18mn^3$.

7   (a) $ab - ca$ (b) $abc - 3bd$ (c) $12y^2 - 8y$ (d) $3ac - 7bd$.

8   (a) $4mnp + 6mp$ (b) $6mn^2 - 9m^2n$ (c) $5a^2b - 7c^2d$ (d) $2\pi r^2 + 2\pi rh$.

9   (a) $2a^2 + 3b^2$ (b) $24x^2 - 16x$ (c) $21h^2 - 14hn$ (d) $a^2b - ab^3$.

10   (a) $4a - 16a^2b$ (b) $3ab - 3a^3b^2$ (c) $amxy - bmdx$.

11   (a) $4m - 12n - 6b + 8d$ (b) $6a + 9b - 12c - 3$.

12 Example Factorise $3x - 3y + ax - ay$.

$3x - 3y + ax - ay \rightarrow 3(x - y) + a(x - y)$
Note that $(x - y)$ is itself now a common factor and may be 'taken out':
$3(x - y) + a(x - y) \rightarrow (x - y)(3 + a)$

Multiply $(x - y)(3 + a)$ to check the answer.

(a) $3x + 3y + ax + ay$ (b) $am + 5m + 3a + 15$ (c) $ab + b + 4a + 4$
(d) $5b - 10bc - 2d + 4cd$ (e) $cx + 2cy - dx - 2dy$
(f) $ap + 2bd + ad + 2bp$.

13 Example $\dfrac{6x + 6}{2xy + 2y} \rightarrow \dfrac{3(2x + 2)}{y(2x + 2)} \rightarrow \dfrac{3}{y}$

(a) $\dfrac{2x + 6}{xy + 3y}$ (b) $\dfrac{2am + 2ac}{6bm + 6bc}$ (c) $\dfrac{4a^2m + 4ap}{5abm + 5bp}$ (d) $\dfrac{6a^2p + 18ab}{9abp + 27b^2}$.

B   Difference of two squares

If two terms in an expression are both squares and are connected by a minus, then they may be split into 'sum times difference'.

Examples $a^2 - 16 \rightarrow (a + 4)(a - 4)$

$4x^2 - 25 \rightarrow (2x + 5)(2x - 5)$

This can be useful in arithmetic.

Examples $54^2 - 46^2 \rightarrow (54 + 46)(54 - 46) \rightarrow 100 \times 8 = 800$

Area of an annulus (e.g. washer) is $\pi R^2 - \pi r^2$.
$\pi R^2 - \pi r^2 \rightarrow \pi(R^2 - r^2) \rightarrow \pi(R + r)(R - r)$

Fig. 17:1

Use this 'difference of two squares' method to factorise the expressions in questions 1 to 4.

1 (a) $a^2 - 9$ (b) $25 - b^2$ (c) $1 - c^2$ (d) $81 - e^2$ (e) $1 - 25f^2$
   (f) $4c^2 - 49$.

*2 (a) $a^2 - 64$ (b) $9a^2 - 25$ (c) $16 - b^2$ (d) $e^2f^2 - 1$ (e) $a^2 - 64b^2$
   (f) $16 - 81b^2$.

3 Example $2a^2 - 18 \rightarrow 2(a^2 - 9) \rightarrow 2(a + 3)(a - 3)$

(a) $2a^2 - 32$ (b) $8 - 2x^2$ (c) $27 - 3b^2$ (d) $75 - 3b^2$.

4 (a) $a^3 - 9a$ (b) $18a - 2ab^2$ (c) $2\pi r^3 - 2\pi rh^2$ (d) $25x^2 - 36y^2$
   (e) $36x^2 - (x + 1)^2$ (f) $(x + 6)^2 - 36x^2$.

18 Arithmetic: basic skills; problems; earning a living

● You need to know . . .

● The metric system (SI)

Base units likely to be met in mathematics
Length: metre (m)
Mass (weight): kilogram (kg)
Time: second (s)

Prefixes in common use
mega (M) = 10^6 milli (m) = 10^{-3} ($\frac{1}{1000}$)
kilo (k) = 10^3
centi (c) = 10^{-2} ($\frac{1}{100}$)   micro (μ) = 10^{-6} ($\frac{1}{1\,000\,000}$)

Other units which may be used with SI
litre (best not abbreviated) = $1000\,cm^3$
tonne (best not abbreviated) = $1000\,kg$
hectare (best not abbreviated) = $10\,000\,m^2$

Some metric prefixes are used with these, e.g. the centilitre (cl) = $\frac{1}{100}$ litre = $10\,cm^3$, the millilitre (ml) = $\frac{1}{1000}$ litre = $1\,cm^3$, the megatonne.

Changing from one metric unit to another
Never insert zeros between figures. The figure in the units' column is rewritten in the correct column of the new unit.

Examples   (a)   108.9 mm → metres
The 8 in the units' column is 8 mm = $\frac{8}{1000}$ metre, so the 8 is rewritten in the thousandths' column, giving 108.9 mm → 0.1089 metres.

(b)   3.06 cm → metres
3.06 cm ─────────→ 0.0306 m
↓   ↓   3 cm = $\frac{3}{100}$ m   ↑

(c)   0.003 06 m → km
0.003 06 m ─────────→ 0.000 003 06 km
↓   ↓   0 m = $\frac{0}{1000}$ km   ↑

● Decimal fraction arithmetic

When adding or subtracting, be sure to keep the units' figures in a vertical line.

When multiplying, ignore zeros at the beginning or end of the numbers; multiply the resulting integers, then replace all omitted 'end' zeros; finally replace the decimal point so that there are as many figures after it as there were after the points in the original question.

Example   0.381 × 10 700 → 381 × 107 → 40 767 → 4 076 700 → 4 076.700 → <u>4076.7</u>

When dividing multiply both numbers by the power of 10 needed to change the divisor (the number you are dividing by) into an integer, then divide as usual. No further change in the position of the point is required.

Example $18.324 \div 0.09 \rightarrow \dfrac{18.324}{0.09} \xrightarrow{\times \text{ top and bottom by 100}} \dfrac{1832.4}{9} \rightarrow \underline{203.6}$

● Common fraction arithmetic

Common fraction to decimal fraction

Example $\frac{3}{5} \rightarrow 3 \div 5 \rightarrow 5\overline{)3.0}^{\,0.6} \rightarrow \underline{0.6}$

Decimal fraction to common fraction

Example $0.375 \xrightarrow[\text{thousandths' column}]{\text{last figure is in the}} \dfrac{375}{1000} \rightarrow \dfrac{375}{1000} \rightarrow \underline{\dfrac{3}{8}}$

Addition and subtraction

It is best to deal with the whole numbers first.

Examples $6\frac{3}{8} + 1\frac{1}{4} \rightarrow 7\frac{3}{8} + \frac{2}{8} \rightarrow \underline{7\frac{5}{8}}$

$4\frac{1}{3} - 2\frac{2}{5} \rightarrow 2\frac{5}{15} - \frac{6}{15} \rightarrow 2 - \frac{1}{15} \rightarrow \underline{1\frac{14}{15}}$

Multiplication of a fraction by an integer

Examples $\dfrac{2}{13}\cancel{8} \times \cancel{9}^{3} \rightarrow \underline{6}$

$2\frac{1}{6} \times 3 \rightarrow \dfrac{13}{\cancel{6}_2} \times \cancel{3}^{1} \rightarrow \dfrac{13}{2} \rightarrow \underline{6\frac{1}{2}}$

Fraction multiplied by fraction

Change all mixed numbers to improper (top-heavy) fractions first.

Example $3\frac{3}{4} \times 1\frac{1}{5} \rightarrow \dfrac{\cancel{15}^{3}}{\cancel{4}_2} \times \dfrac{\cancel{6}^{3}}{\cancel{5}_1} \rightarrow \dfrac{9}{2} \rightarrow \underline{4\frac{1}{2}}$

Fraction divided by integer

To divide by n, multiply by its reciprocal $\left(\dfrac{1}{n}\right)$.

Example $\frac{3}{4} \div 4 \rightarrow \frac{3}{4} \times \frac{1}{4} \rightarrow \underline{\frac{3}{16}}$

Division by a fraction

To divide by a fraction, multiply by its inverse.

Examples $3 \div \frac{1}{2} \rightarrow 3 \times \dfrac{2}{1} \rightarrow \underline{6}$

$2\frac{1}{2} \div 1\frac{2}{3} \rightarrow \dfrac{5}{2} \div \dfrac{5}{3} \rightarrow \dfrac{\cancel{5}^{1}}{2} \times \dfrac{3}{\cancel{5}_1} \rightarrow \dfrac{3}{2} \rightarrow \underline{1\frac{1}{2}}$

● **Divisibility**

A number divides exactly by:	2	3	5	6	9	10
if its digit-sum is:	any	3; 6; 9	any	3; 6; 9	9	any
and its last digit is:	even	any	0; 5	even	any	0

A number divides exactly by 4 if its last two digits divide exactly by 4.

A number divides exactly by 8 if its last 3 digits divide exactly by 8.

● **Arithmetic with directed numbers**

See the notes in Chapter 2 (page 6).

● **Approximation**

See the notes in Chapter 12 (page 70).

● **Prime numbers**

Primes have only two different factors; e.g. 19 is prime because its factors are 1 and 19; 9 is not prime because it has three factors, 1, 3 and 9.

To write a number as a product of prime factors:

Example $162 \rightarrow 2 \times 81 \rightarrow 2 \times 3 \times 27 \rightarrow 2 \times 3 \times 3 \times 9 \rightarrow 2 \times 3 \times 3 \times 3 \times 3$

This may be written:
```
2)162
3) 81
3) 27
3)  9
3)  3
    1
```

● **Highest common factor (HCF)**

A factor divides exactly into a number. The HCF is the highest factor that divides exactly into a set of numbers. For large numbers a prime factor method is useful.

Examples   The HCF of {12, 15, 18} is 3 (this can be done by just thinking about it).

To find the HCF of 168 and 180:

$168 \rightarrow 2 \times 2 \times 2 \times 3 \times 7$

$180 \rightarrow 2 \times 2 \times 3 \times 3 \times 5$

$HCF = 2 \times 2 \times 3 = \underline{12}$

● Lowest common multiple (LCM)

A multiple is made by multiplying by an integer. The LCM is the lowest number that is a multiple of each member of a given set of numbers.

Examples   The LCM of {6, 8, 12} is 24 (this can be done by just thinking about it).

To find the LCM of 18, 30 and 36:
As 36 is a multiple of 18, we need not think about the 18. All multiples of 30 end in a zero, therefore the answer is a multiple of 36 that ends in a zero and also divides exactly by 30. The answer is 180.

For large numbers a prime factor method is useful.

Example   Find the LCM of {18, 24, 64}.
$18 \rightarrow 2 \times 3 \times 3$
$24 \rightarrow 2 \times 2 \times 2 \times 3$
$64 \rightarrow 2 \times 2 \times 2 \times 2 \times 2 \times 2$
The prime factors of the LCM will consist of 2's and 3's. We need two 3's for 18 and six 2's for 64.
Hence the LCM is $2 \times 2 \times 2 \times 2 \times 2 \times 2 \times 3 \times 3 = 576$.

Test yourself

1 Add: 3000,   8.2,   0.49,   1.099.

2 Find the difference between 16 and 9.0974.

3 Find the product of 8.76 and 0.97.

4 $3.83819 \div 1.9$

5 $3\frac{5}{8} - 1\frac{3}{4}$

6 $1\frac{3}{4} - 7$

7 $2\frac{2}{3} \div 2\frac{2}{9}$

Questions 8 to 14 provide extra practice on questions like 1 to 7. Your teacher will tell you if you may omit them.

*8 (a) $2.6 + 300 + 0.49$ (b) $9.79 + 9009 + 8.19 + 0.099$.

*9 Find the difference between:
(a) 12 and 6.078   (b) 10 and 0.919.

*10 Find the product of:
(a) 0.3 and 0.4   (b) 0.1 and 0.07   (c) 10.3 and 0.75   (d) 9.79 and 89
(e) 3000 and 4.01.

*11 (a) $57.114 \div 1.9$ (b) $195.1313 \div 1.3$ (c) $103.2019 \div 1.7$
      (d) $0.208\,84 \div 2.3$.

*12 (a) $4\frac{7}{16} - \frac{3}{8}$ (b) $2\frac{4}{5} - \frac{3}{7}$ (c) $2\frac{5}{9} - 1\frac{5}{6}$ (d) $4\frac{5}{16} - 2\frac{7}{12}$ (e) $3\frac{23}{33} - 1\frac{8}{11}$.

*13 (a) $9 \div 2\frac{1}{2}$ (b) $6 \div \frac{1}{4}$ (c) $\frac{2}{3} \div 8$ (d) $1\frac{3}{5} \div 12$ (e) $3\frac{3}{5} \div 9$.

*14 (a) $2\frac{1}{2} \div 3\frac{3}{4}$ (b) $3\frac{3}{8} \div 2\frac{1}{4}$ (c) $2\frac{6}{11} \div 2\frac{7}{22}$ (d) $5\frac{1}{7} \div 6\frac{3}{4}$.

15 Rewrite {7.882, 691.398, 7108.8017} with the elements rounded to:
    (a) 2 significant figures   (b) 2 decimal places.

16 Write a number more than 100 which divides exactly by:
    (a) 2 and 3 but not 9   (b) 6 and 9   (c) 2, 3, 5, 6 and 9
    (d) neither 2, 3, 5, 6 or 9.
    Check your answers with a calculator.

17 (a) $4 - 12$ (b) 5×-6 (c) -4×-3 (d) $-8 - -5$ (e) $9 - 11$
    (f) -7×-3 (g) $9 - -2$ (h) $-6 + -3$.

18 Find the HCF and LCM of:
    (a) 3, 6 and 15   (b) 24, 32, 48 and 60.

19 In a sale all goods are '12p in the £ off!' What is the price in the sale of an article normally costing
    (a) £8   (b) £6.50   (c) £10.25?

20 Change the following to the units given in brackets.

    Example   708 mm (cm)   *Answer*: 70.8 cm

    (a) 35 mg (cg)   (b) 7.8 cm (mm)   (c) 350 m (km)   (d) 3000 cl (litres)
    (e) 5 tonnes (kg)   (f) 4.65 km (m)   (g) 0.75 cm (mm)   (h) 0.19 m (cm)
    (i) 0.5 km (cm)   (j) 1 litre (cm^3)   (k) 1 m^2 (cm^2)   (l) 1 m^3 (cm^3)

21 **Foreign currency**

Currency	Sell at rate	Buy at rate
USA dollars	$1.62	$1.72
Pesetas	Pta192	Pta205
Guilders	NLG3.32	NLG3.51
French francs	FRF9.89	FRF10.55
Lire	Lit2207	Lit2285
Deutschmarks	DM2.95	DM3.10

The chart shows the prices of foreign currency in an exchange bureau.

Ben Johnson arranged a tour of Europe, visiting France, Holland, Germany and Spain. He changed £150 for use in each of the countries he was visiting.

(a) How much of each currency did he receive?

(b) Ben was taken ill the day before he was due to leave, and had to cancel his holiday. He changed his foreign currency back into pounds sterling. How much did he lose in the two transactions?

22 A 12-hour clock loses 75 seconds a day (24 hours). How many days will it take to appear correct again after having been set to the right time?

23 Figure 18:1 shows a plan of the centre of Livsey.

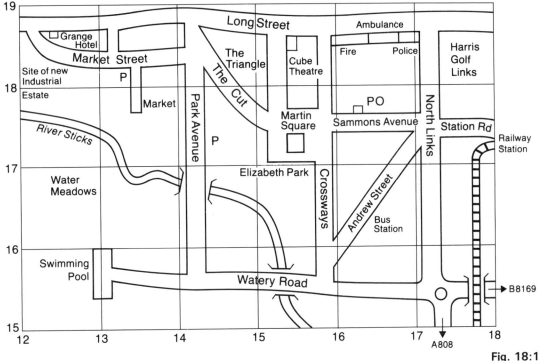

Fig. 18:1

(a) There is a bridge over the river at map reference 142168. What is the map reference of the other river bridge?

(b) State the grid reference of:
(i) the theatre   (ii) the post office   (iii) the B8169 railway bridge
(iv) the junction of Park Avenue with Watery Road.

(c) A car driver stops you outside the post office and asks for directions to the market. Help her.

Worksheet 18, which is an enlargement of Figure 18:1, may be used as coursework to plan a suitable traffic system for Livsey (one-way roads, traffic lights, stop/give-way junctions, etc.) and/or a bus service for the town centre.

24 Refer back to Figure 18:1. Fleur arrives at the railway station at 1000. She walks to the bus station, where she catches a bus to the Grange Hotel.

Figure 18:2 is a distance/time graph of her journey from the station.

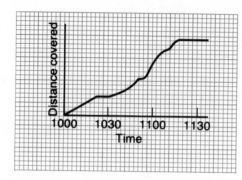

Fig. 18:2

Estimate:

(a) the time that Fleur arrived at the bus station
(b) the time that the bus left
(c) the time that the bus was held up in a traffic jam
(d) the time that Fleur got off the bus at the Grange Hotel
(e) the distance of the bus station from the railway station.

25 John observes the school playground from 8 to 4 one day, then draws Figure 18:3. Describe as fully as you can what happens when. (Use your imagination!)

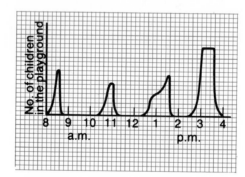

Fig. 18:3

26 Light travels at approximately 3×10^5 km/s.

(a) Find how far a spaceship travelling as a third of the speed of light would travel in an hour.

(b) How long would such a spaceship take from Earth to Saturn, a distance of 1.275×10^9 km?

27   A jar of water weighs 6.5 kg when full and 3.5 kg when half full. 1 cm³ of water has a mass of 1 g.

When the jar is a quarter full:
(a) what does it weigh   (b) how many litres does it contain?

28   Three carpenters and two apprentices together earn £900 a week. A carpenter's wage to an apprentice's is in the ratio 2:1. What does an apprentice earn a week?

29   A swimming-pool is 100 metres long, 60 metres wide and slopes along the length to give a steady increase in depth from 1 metre to 4 metres. How many litres of water will the pool hold? (Answer in standard form.)

30   A rectangular piece of paper is, to the nearest mm, 7.6 cm long and 2.8 cm wide. What is the maximum possible length, width, and area of the paper?

31   A roll of paper on a cylindrical former is 10 cm in diameter. The former is 2 cm in diameter and the paper is 0.1 mm thick.

(a) How many turns of paper are there?

(b) How long is the complete roll of paper? (Take $\pi = 3.1$.)

Earning a living

For discussion

▷ How long would it take an average wage earner to earn a million pounds?

▷ What is the difference between gross income and net income?

▷ How does the Government take money from the population?

▷ In what ways does the Government help people in need?

1   Work out the gross weekly income for:

(a) Isaac: 40 hours at £4 per hour, plus 6 hours overtime at time and a half

(b) Serina: basic salary of £100 plus 15% commission on sales of £1300

(c) Carl: paid piecework rate of 12p a bolt for the first 1000, then 20p a bolt. He machines 1200 bolts.

*2

```
┌─────────────────────────────────────────┐
│              PARCEL OFFICE                │
│                                           │
│                 Hours                     │
│        Mon to Thurs 0900–1700             │
│            Fri 0900–1530                   │
│           Sat & Sun closed                │
└─────────────────────────────────────────┘
```

Mary works in a parcel office during the hours shown. She has half an hour for lunch break each day.

(a) How many hours does she work
(i) on Monday   (ii) on Friday   (iii) in one week?

(b) What is Mary's gross weekly income if she is paid £2.97 per hour?

(NISEC)

*3   Copy and complete:

(a) James Coburn (machinist)
Basic hours (weekly): 40 at £4 per hour   £.........
Overtime (time and a half): 6 hours at £6   £.........
Total gross pay for week   £.........

(b) Rakput Singh (driver)
Basic hours (weekly): 38 at £6 per hour   £.........
Overtime (time and a half): 8 hours at £..... £.........
Total gross pay for week   £.........

(c) Serina Brown (manageress)
Basic wage (weekly):   £50.00
Commission at 10% on sales of £1500:   £.........
Total gross pay for week   £.........

(d) Marsha Bartlett (sole cutter)
Piecework rate £1.80 per 100
Pieces cut (w/e 15/5) 5000   £.........

*4

Tax allowances (1991/92)

Single person	£3295
Additional personal (single parent)	£1720
Additional personal (aged 65–74)	£1015
Additional personal (aged 75 +)	£1175
Additional married couple, both under 65	£1720
(paid to husband unless he earns less than allowance)	
one aged 65–74	£2355
one or both over 75	£2395

In 1991/92 Income Tax was charged at 25% on taxable income up to £23 700, then at 40%.

Taxable income = Gross income less allowances.

(a) Juliette is 18 and single. What is her tax allowance?

(b) Mr and Mrs Singh both work for wages. Mr Singh earns £15 000 a year. What is (i) his tax allowance, and (ii) her tax allowance?

(c) Mrs Goff works as a teacher, but Mr Goff is unemployed, so Mrs Goff claims the married couple's allowance. What is her tax allowance?

*5 Hazel earns £200 a week for 50 weeks a year. Of this, about £50 a week is deducted for Income Tax and National Insurance contributions. About how many years would Hazel have to work to pay for:

(a) a new hospital   (b) a Tornado fighter
(c) an ambulance   (d) a nurse's annual salary
(e) an army sergeant's annual salary
(f) a fire engine   (g) a tank?

Health Service

New hospital £20 000 000
X-ray machine £500 000
Body-scan machine £1 000 000
Ambulance £20 000
Nurse £12 000 p.a.

Fire Service

New fire station £1 500 000
Fire engine £75 000
Fireman £13 000 p.a.

Defence

Tornado fighter £17 000 000
Tank £1 500 000
Frigate £115 000 000
Army Sergeant £13 000 p.a.

Fig. 18:4

*6

National Insurance contributions (1991/92 rates)

Weekly pay	Contribution
Less than £43	Nil
£43 or more	2% on £43
	9% on balance

Note: men over 65 and women over 60 are exempted.

How much National Insurance will be paid by:
(a) Tariq, aged 18 with pay of £100
(b) Melanie, aged 61, with pay of £71
(c) Shandrum, aged 35, with pay of £300?

7 We now look at how an employer works out how much to deduct from his employee's pay.

Tax allowances are given in question 4.
National Insurance rates are given in question 6.

Example Asmat earns £978 per month.
She pays superannuation (towards a pension) of £78.24 a month. This is not taxed.
She is aged 21 and is single.

Her take home pay is worked out like this:

Allowances against income	
Superannuation	£78.24
Personal allowance £3295 ÷ 12	£274.58
Total allowances	£352.82

Taxable income	
£978 − £352.82	£625.18

Deductions from income	
Tax due 25% of £625.18	£156.30
Superannuation	£78.24

National Insurance
Annual income 12 × £978 = £11 736
2% on £43 × 52 = 2% on £2236
                = £44.72
9% on £9500   = £855.00
Monthly payment = £899.72 ÷ 12   £74.98

Total deductions from pay	£309.52

Net pay after deductions	
£978 − £309.52	£668.48

Read the above example carefully and check all the calculations.

8 Calculate, as in the example for question 7, the net monthly income for the following.

(a) Solomon, aged 25, single; monthly salary £925; superannuation payable, £64.75 per month

(b) Joe, aged 45, married; monthly salary £816; superannuation payable, £51.25 per month

(c) Gulam, aged 70, married (wife also 70), retired; monthly income £624.

---

9 Brian, aged 41, is self-employed.

(a) He makes a profit in the tax-year 1991/92 of £8565. He pays 17.5% of this as contribution to a PPP (personal pension plan). Calculate this contribution.

(b) Brian pays a flat rate contribution of £3.95 per week Class 2 National Insurance. How much does he pay in a year (52 weeks)?

(c) Because his profits are over £4750 he also has to pay Class 4 National Insurance. This is charged at 6.3% on the amount by which his profits exceed £4750. Calculate his Class 4 National Insurance.

(d) His tax allowances are made up of his personal allowance as a married man, his contribution to the PPP, and half his Class 4 contribution. What tax allowance does he receive?

(e) Calculate the amount of tax he has to pay.

(f) Calculate his net profit after paying income tax, National Insurance, and his PPP contribution.

10 Repeat question 9 for June, aged 30, who runs her own picture-framing business. In 1990/91 she made a profit of £6590. She is a single parent. She also pays 17.5% of her income to a PPP.

For discussion

Marks	Frequency
1 to 5	1
6 to 10	2
11 to 15	4
16 to 20	7
21 to 25	9
26 to 30	5
31 to 35	2
36 to 40	1

Mark	Cumulative frequency
5 or less	1
10 or less	1 + 2 = 3
15 or less	3 + 4 = 7
20 or less	7 + 7 = 14
25 or less	14 + 9 = 23
30 or less	23 + 5 = 28
35 or less	28 + 2 = 30
40 or less	30 + 1 = 31

Marks out of 40 for a class of 31 pupils

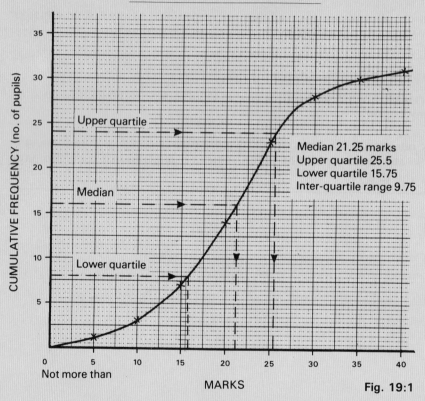

Median 21.25 marks
Upper quartile 25.5
Lower quartile 15.75
Inter-quartile range 9.75

Fig. 19:1

1 > What would you know about the test if the median had been: (a) 10 (b) 30?

2 > What would you know about the class if the quartiles had been at: (a) 5 and 35 (b) 30 and 35?

1 Table 1

Flowers on a stem	0	1	2	3	4	5	6	7	8
Frequency	4	5	5	7	10	9	6	4	1
Cumulative frequency	4	9	14						

Table 2

Letters per word	1	2	3	4	5	6	7	8	9
Frequency	2	4	20	16	9	4	7	2	1
Cumulative frequency	2	6							

Table 3

Number absent	0–9	10–19	20–29	30–39	40–49	50–59
Frequency	6	11	24	16	9	3

Table 4

Weight (nearest kg)	40–45	46–50	51–55	56–60	61–65	66–70	71–75
Frequency	5	11	19	26	18	13	8

(a) State the median number of flowers on a stem, the median number of letters in a word, the class in which the median number absent lies, and the class in which the median weight lies.

(b) Copy and complete all four tables to show the cumulative frequencies, then draw the cumulative frequency graphs ('ogives'). Show on your graphs for tables 3 and 4 the medians and the lower and upper quartiles, and also state the interquartile ranges.

*2 Number of absentees each day during an 80-day term:
16, 29, 41, 6, 24, 31, 19, 46, 30, 27, 22, 35, 34, 36, 11, 25, 38, 45, 26, 39, 36, 52, 12, 51, 24, 35, 47, 53, 28, 4, 37, 32, 44, 31, 15, 43, 20, 31, 29, 39, 22, 38, 42, 21, 38, 37, 34, 18, 33, 36, 34, 16, 42, 30, 28, 30, 37, 32, 20, 37, 27, 56, 43, 17, 57, 46, 33, 54, 47, 17, 39, 41, 48, 28, 35, 13, 31, 33, 21, 32.

(a) Complete a table for the above data:

Class	Tally	Frequency	Cumulative frequency
0–5 6–10 etc.			

(b) Draw a cumulative frequency curve to illustrate the data.

(c) Estimate from your curve the median number of days absent.

(d) Estimate the upper and lower quartiles and hence the interquartile range.

*3 Michelle has grown some tomato plants in a Growbag. As each tomato turns red she picks and weighs it. The weights to the nearest gram are:
45, 36, 57, 53, 74, 72, 38, 64, 78, 53, 41, 82, 65, 60, 51, 66, 68, 60, 53, 77, 55, 43, 49, 31, 80, 90, 77, 72, 65, 60, 61, 52, 41, 50, 49, 82, 94, 63, 69, 50, 55, 53, 42, 57, 63, 66, 71, 61, 44, 34, 30, 33.

(a) Copy and complete this cumulative frequency table:

Weight (g)	Tally	Frequency	Cumulative frequency
not above 40 40–50 50–60 etc.			

(b) Draw a cumulative frequency curve for the data.
Horizontal axis: Weight (not more than), from 40 g to 100 g
Vertical axis: Cumulative frequency, from 0 to 52

(c) Estimate from your curve the median tomato weight.

(d) Estimate the upper and lower quartiles, and hence the interquartile range.

4 In Figure 19:2, line (a) shows that 3 pupils scored 10 marks or less and 28 scored more than 10.

Write the information given by lines (b), (c) and (d).

5 **Example**   Using Figure 19:2, estimate how many pupils scored more than 80%.

80% of 40 marks is 32 marks.
Line (e) at 32 marks shows that 29 pupils scored 80% or less, so 2 pupils scored more than 80%.

Note: Be careful not to use the number on the vertical axis as your answer; line (e) meets this axis at 29, so 31 − 29 = 2 pupils gives the correct answer.

(a) Estimate how many pupils scored:
    (i) 50% or less   (ii) more than 50%   (iii) 70% or less   (iv) more than 70%.

(b) Estimate the score of the pupil who came:
    (i) 10th   (ii) 20th   (iii) 25th.

6 Using Figure 19:2, state an estimated pass mark if the percentage of the pupils who are to pass is:
(a) 80%   (b) 60%.

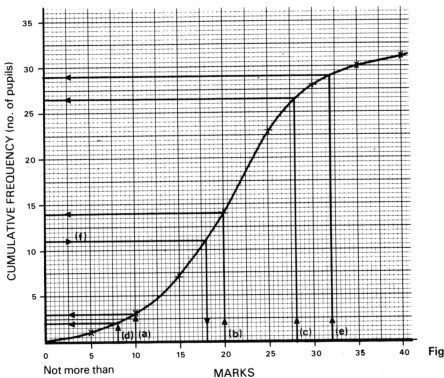

Marks out of 40 for a class of 31 pupils

CUMULATIVE FREQUENCY (no. of pupils)

MARKS

Not more than

Fig. 19:2

7 The following table shows the percentages of the population of the United Kingdom in various age ranges in 1901 and 1981.

Age range	under 11	11–20	21–30	31–40	41–50	51–60	61–70	71–80	80–110
% of 1901 population	22	20	18	14	11	7	5	2	1
% of 1981 population	15	16	14	13	11	11	10	7	3

(a) Draw the cumulative frequency curve for 1901, plotting points above 11, 21, 31, etc., then find:
  (i) the median age   (ii) the lower quartile   (iii) the upper quartile
  (iv) the interquartile range.

(b) Repeat part (a) for 1981, on the same axes.

(c) Comment on the differences between your two curves and two sets of answers. What differences would there be in the two societies?

---

8 Calculate the means for the data in question 1.

9 Find some test or exam results for different classes, and use statistical methods to compare the data. Write a report of your findings.

20 Inequalities and graph regions

• You need to know . . .

● Solving inequalities

Inequalities are solved like equations, although you have to be very careful when a letter is at the bottom of a fraction in the inequality (see question 8).

Example Solve $x + 5 > 8$.
If $x + 5 = 8$, then $x = 3$.
So if $x + 5 > 8$, then $x > 3$.

Example Solve $\dfrac{2x - 3}{4} \leqslant 9$.

If $\dfrac{2x - 3}{4} = 9$, then $2x - 3 = 36 \rightarrow 2x = 39 \rightarrow x = 19.5$.

So if $\dfrac{2x - 3}{4} \leqslant 9$, then $x \leqslant 19.5$.

● Graph regions

Figure 20:1 shows the line $y = -x + 2$.

For every point on this line the y-coordinate is equal to $-x + 2$, where x is the x-coordinate of the point.

Above the line, y is more than $-x + 2$.

Below the line, y is less than $-x + 2$.

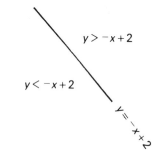

Fig. 20:1

Figure 20:2 shows the region

$\{(x, y); \quad x < 3; \ -x + 2 < y < x\}$.

to the left   above   below
of $x = 3$ $y = -x + 2$ $y = x$

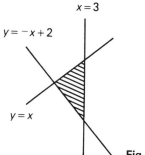

Fig. 20:2

1   State all possible values of n when n is an integer and:
(a) $1 < n < 4$ (b) $-2 < n < 0$ (c) $4 \leqslant n < 6$ (d) $4 > n \geqslant 8$
(e) $-6 \geqslant n \geqslant -9$.

2   Solve:

(a) $n + 3 > 8$ (b) $2b + 1 < 5$ (c) $2h - 7 \geqslant 4$ (d) $\dfrac{h + 3}{5} > 6$ (e) $\dfrac{2d - 1}{2} < 4$

(f) $e^2 < 4$ (answer in the form $a < e < b$)   (g) $n^2 \geqslant 9$ (two possible answers)

3 On axes from −4 to 4 each:

(a) draw the lines $x = 3$ and $y = -3$

(b) shade the region $\{(x, y): 0 < x < 3; -3 < y < 0\}$, that is, where $x > 0$ but $x < 3$ and $y > -3$ but $y < 0$

(c) draw the lines $x = -4$ and $y = 2$

(d) shade the region $\{(x, y): -4 < x < 0; 0 < y < 2\}$.

*4 Solve:

(a) $n + 2 \geqslant 6$ (b) $b - 7 > 15$ (c) $2b - 1 < 9$ (d) $3f + 7 \geqslant 1$ (e) $\dfrac{k - 1}{4} < 1$

*5 On axes from −4 to 4 each:

(a) draw the lines $x = 2$ and $y = 4$

(b) shade the region $\{(x, y): 0 < x < 2; 0 < y < 4\}$, that is, where $x > 0$ but $x < 2$ and $y > 0$ but $y < 4$.

(c) draw the lines $x = -4$ and $y = -2$

(d) shade the region $\{(x, y): -4 < x < 2; -2 < y < 0\}$, that is, where $x > -4$ but $x < 2$ and $y > -2$ but $y < 0$.

6 On axes from −3 to 3, shade the region defined by
$\{(x, y): x < 2; y > -1; -x < y < x\}$.

7 On axes from −3 to 3, shade the region defined by
$\{(x, y): x + 1 > y > 0; 2 > x > 1\}$.

---

8 (a) If $\dfrac{4}{x} = 4$, what is x?

(b) If $\dfrac{4}{x} > 4$, what is the range of values for x?

(c) Check your answer to part (b) by substituting several possible values for x.

(d) If $\dfrac{5}{x} = -5$, what is x?

(e) If $\dfrac{5}{y} < -5$, what is the range of values for y?

(f) Check your answer to part (e) by substituting several possible values for y.

(g) If $\dfrac{7}{x} > 2$, state the range of values for x.

(h) Solve $4 < \dfrac{3}{n} < 6$

9 Draw graphs to illustrate the following regions.

Note: To show $x \leqslant 3$, use a continuous line for $x = 3$.
To show $x < 3$, use a dotted line for $x = 3$ to show that $x = 3$ is *not* in the region.

(a) $\{(x, y): 1 \leqslant y \leqslant x + 1; \ x \leqslant 3\}$
(b) $\{(x, y): 0 \leqslant y \leqslant 2x - 1; \ 1 < x < 3\}$
(c) $\{(x, y): -2x + 1 \leqslant y \leqslant 0; \ x \leqslant 2\}$
(d) $\{(x, y): y \geqslant \frac{1}{3}x; \ -4 \leqslant x < -1\}$
(e) $\{(x, y): y \geqslant \frac{1}{2}x + 3; \ -1 < x \leqslant 2\}$
(f) $\{(x, y): 0 \geqslant y \geqslant -x - 2; \ 2 \geqslant x > 1\}$

10 A cabin on a fairground ride holds up to six people. The ride is considered dangerous, so the following safety regulations are enforced.

● A cabin must contain at least one adult and not more than three children.

● There must be at least one adult for every two children.

Letting x stand for the number of adults and y for the number of children, write four inequalities about x and/or y.

Plot the region defined by your inequalities on a grid, each axis from 0 to 6, then mark crosses on your grid to show all possible cabin loads.

21 Graphs: general parabola and equation solving

A The general parabola: $y = ax^2 + bx + c$

Curve sketching

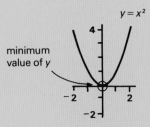

$y = x^2$

minimum value of y

Fig. 21:1

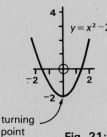

$y = x^2 - 2$

turning point

Fig. 21:2

maximum value of y

$y = -x^2$

Fig. 21:3

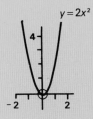

$y = 2x^2$

Fig. 21:4

$y = \frac{1}{2}x^2$

Fig. 21:5

$y = \frac{1}{2}x^2 + 1$

Fig. 21:6

All graphs of the family $y = ax^2 + c$ are symmetrical about the y-axis.

The value of c gives the crossing point on the y-axis.

The value of a affects the width of the curve and which way up it is: the lower the value of a, the wider the curve becomes (using the same axes scales); if a is negative, then the parabola has its turning point at the top (see Figure 21:3).

Draw a parabola with your wrist 'inside the curve', the way your hand pivots naturally.

For discussion

$y = x^2$ $\qquad$ $y = 4x^2$
$y = -2x^2$ $\qquad$ $y = -x^2$
$y = \frac{1}{2}x^2$ $\qquad$ $y = \frac{1}{4}x^2$

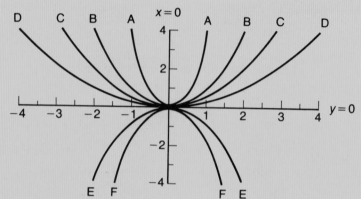

Fig. 21:7

1 (a) Copy and complete the tables for $y = 2x^2$ and $y = 2x^2 + 3$.

$y = 2x^2$

x	-3	-2	-1	0	1	2	3
x^2	9	4					
y	18	8					

$y = 2x^2 + 3$

x	-3	-2	-1	0	1	2	3
$2x^2$	18	8					
3	3	3					
y	21	11					

(b) Draw the graphs of $y = 2x^2$ and $y = 2x^2 + 3$ on one pair of axes. Scales: x from -3 to 3, 1 cm to 1 unit; y from 0 to 25, 1 cm to 5 units.

(c) Check the truth of the statement: 'The graph of $y = 2x^2 + 3$ is the same shape as the graph of $y = 2x^2$, but has its turning point at (0, 3) instead of at (0, 0)'.

2 (a) Copy and complete the tables for $y = \frac{1}{2}x^2$ and $y = \frac{1}{2}x^2 - 1$.

$y = \frac{1}{2}x^2$

x	-4	-3	-2	-1	0	1	2	3	4
x^2	16	9							
y	8	4.5							

$$y = \tfrac{1}{2}x^2 - 1$$

x	-4	-3	-2	-1	0	1	2	3	4
$\tfrac{1}{2}x^2$	8	$4\tfrac{1}{2}$							
-1	-1	-1							
y	7	$3\tfrac{1}{2}$		$-\tfrac{1}{2}$					

(b) Draw the graphs of $y = \tfrac{1}{2}x^2$ and $y = \tfrac{1}{2}x^2 - 1$ on the same axes. Scales: x from -4 to 4, 1 cm to 1 unit; y from -1 to 8, 1 cm to 1 unit.

(c) Write a statement like the one in question 1(c) about this pair of graphs.

3 Copy and complete the following tables for the given equations. Do not draw any graphs yet.

(a) $y = x^2 + 2x + 1$

x	-4	-3	-2	-1	0	1	2
x^2	16						
$2x$	-8						
1	1						
y	9	4		0			

(b) $y = x^2 - 2x + 2$

x	-2	-1	0	1	2	3	4
x^2	4						
$-2x$	4						
2	2						
y	10						

(c) $y = x^2 - 3x + 1$

x	0	$\tfrac{1}{2}$	1	$1\tfrac{1}{2}$	2	$2\tfrac{1}{2}$	3
x^2				$2\tfrac{1}{4}$			
$-3x$				$-4\tfrac{1}{2}$			
1				1			
y		$-\tfrac{1}{4}$		$-1\tfrac{1}{4}$			

(d) $y = 2x^2 + x + 1$

x	-2	-1	0	1	2
$2x^2$	8				
x	-2				
1	1				
y	7				

(e) $y = 1 + 2x - x^2$

x	-2	-1	0	1	2	3
1	1					
$2x$	-4					
$-x^2$	-4					
y	-7					

*4 Draw, very carefully, the graphs for the equations in question 3, using the scales given below. Make sure that your parabolas are smooth curves, with no sharp corners, bumpy bits, or 'feathers'!

Remember to label each graph with its equation.

Graph	x-axis	y-axis
(a)	-4 to 2, 1 cm to 1 unit	0 to 10, 1 cm to 2 units
(b)	-2 to 4, 1 cm to 1 unit	0 to 10, 1 cm to 2 units
(c)	0 to 3, 2 cm to 1 unit	-2 to 1, 2 cm to 1 unit
(d)	-2 to 2, 2 cm to 1 unit	0 to 12, 1 cm to 2 units
	Note: the lowest point is at $(-\frac{1}{4}, \frac{7}{8})$	
(e)	-2 to 3, 1 cm to 1 unit	-7 to 2, 1 cm to 1 unit

5 **Example** The axis of symmetry of the parabola $y = x^2 + 2x + 1$ in question 3(a) is $x = -1$, because the y-values are symmetrical about this x-value.

State the equations of the axes of symmetry for the other graphs in question 3. (See the note in question 4 about the minimum value of y for graph (d).)

6 (a) Draw up a table for $y = 2x^2 - x - 10$ for the integral values of x from -3 to 4.

(b) Using axes, x from -3 to 4, 1 cm to 1 unit; y from -12 to 20, 1 cm to 2 units, draw the graph of $y = 2x^2 - x - 10$.

(c) State the equation of the axis of symmetry of your graph.

(d) State the lowest possible value of y (its minimum value) if $y = 2x^2 - x - 10$. At what value of x does this occur?

7 Example Figure 21:8 shows the graph of the parabola $y = x^2 + 2x + 1$.

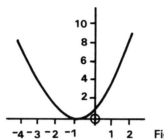

Fig. 21:8

As $(-1, 0)$ is a point on the parabola $y = x^2 + 2x + 1$, then when we substitute $x = -1$ into the equation the result must be 0.

We say that $x = -1$ is a solution of the equation $0 = x^2 + 2x + 1$ (usually written $x^2 + 2x + 1 = 0$).

(a) Draw your own copy of the parabola $y = x^2 + 2x + 1$, using the table you drew up in question 3(a) and the scales given in question 4. Remember to label the curve.

(b) Draw on your grid the line $y = 1$. Find the values of x at which this line crosses the parabola.

(c) Your answers to part (b) are the solutions of the equation $1 = x^2 + 2x + 1$ (or $x^2 + 2x = 0$). Try to explain briefly why this is.

(d) Draw on your grid the line $y = 4$. At what values of x does $y = 4$ cross $y = x^2 + 2x + 1$? Show why these values of x make the equation $x^2 + 2x = 3$ true.

(e) Draw on your grid the line $y = 6$. State, as accurately as you can, the values of x where $y = 6$ crosses $y = x^2 + 2x + 1$. State also the equation solved by these values of x.

(f) Repeat part (e) for the line $y = 8$.

(g) Draw on your grid the line $y = -1$. What must be true about the equation $x^2 + 2x = -2$?

8 (a) Draw the graph of $y = x^2 - 2x + 2$ (see questions 3(b) and 4(b)).

(b) Draw the following lines on your grid. For each line state the values of x where it crosses the parabola and state the equation that you have solved.
(i) $y = 1$ (ii) $y = 2$ (iii) $y = 5$ (iv) $y = 4$ (v) $y = 8$

9 State the equation solved by the x-coordinates of the crossing points of the following pairs of graphs. Do not draw the graphs.
(a) $y = 1$ and $y = x^2 - 3x + 2$ (b) $y = -1$ and $y = 2x^2 + 3x$
(c) $y = 2$ and $y = x^2 - x - 1$ (d) $y = 8$ and $y = 3x^2 - 2x + 7$
(e) $y = -2$ and $y = 2x^2 - 3x - 2$.

10 Draw five graphs of $y = x^2$ for values of x from -3 to 3 using the following five scales:
   (a) x, 1 cm to 1 unit; y, 1 cm to 1 unit
   (b) x, 1 cm to 1 unit; y, 1 cm to 2 units
   (c) x, 1 cm to 1 unit; y, 2 cm to 1 unit
   (d) x, 2 cm to 1 unit; y, 1 cm to 1 unit
   (e) x, 2 cm to 1 unit; y, 1 cm to 2 units

11 If all the axes in question 10 were re-numbered to 1 cm to 1 unit, without changing the drawn graphs, what would the equations of the graphs become?

B Using parabolas to solve quadratic equations

You should have completed Exercise 21A up to question 9 before starting this exercise.

A **quadratic equation** is one involving x^2. A very simple quadratic equation is $x^2 = 1$. Unlike the equations you have met before, a quadratic equation usually has two solutions. Both $x = 1$ and $x = -1$ make $x^2 = 1$ true.

Example   Figure 21:9 shows the graph of $y = x^2 - 3x + 1$.

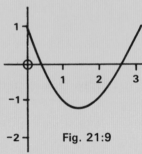

Fig. 21:9

Solve the equation $x^2 - 3x + 1 = 0$ (or $x^2 - 3x = -1$).

The parabola's equation, $y = x^2 - 3x + 1$, becomes the equation we have to solve, $x^2 - 3x + 1 = 0$, when $y = 0$. Therefore we find the solutions where the parabola crosses the line $y = 0$ (the x-axis). They are $x = 2.6$ and $x = 0.38$ approximately. (You often do not have exact answers to a quadratic equation. Sometimes there are no solutions: e.g. how can $x^2 + 1 = 0$?)

Example   Solve $x^2 - 3x + 2 = 0$ using the graph of $y = x^2 - 3x + 1$ (Figure 21:9).

First we change the left-hand side of the given equation to make it the same as the graph equation; that is, we have to change $x^2 - 3x + 2$ into $x^2 - 3x + 1$. We do this by subtracting 1:

$$x^2 - 3x + 2 = 0 \xrightarrow{\text{-1 from both sides}} x^2 - 3x + 1 = -1.$$

Now the solutions may be read where $y = -1$.

Answer: $x = 1$ and $x = 2$.

Check that $x^2 - 3x + 2 = 0$ when $x = 1$ and when $x = 2$.

1 Copy and complete:

Solve $x^2 - 3x = 0$ using the graph of $y = x^2 - 3x + 1$.
Change $x^2 - 3x$ into $x^2 - 3x + 1$ by adding 1.
Then $x^2 - 3x = 0 \xrightarrow{\text{+ 1 to both sides}} \ldots\ldots\ldots\ldots$
Read the solutions where $y = \ldots$ crosses the parabola.
Answer: $x = \ldots$ and $x = \ldots$

2 If you had drawn the graph of $y = 2x^2 + 8x - 5$, state the equation of the straight line you need to draw to solve:
(a) $2x^2 + 8x - 4 = 0$ (b) $2x^2 + 8x + 1 = 0$ (c) $2x^2 + 8x - 1 = 0$
(d) $2x^2 + 8x + 3 = 0$ (e) $2x^2 + 8x - 5 = 0$ (f) $2x^2 + 8x = 0$.

3 Draw the graph of $y = 2x^2 + 8x - 5$ for values of x from -5 to 1, using an x-axis scale of 2 cm to 1 unit. Use your graph to solve the equations given in question 2.

4 Draw on one grid, for values of x from -4 to 4, the graphs of $y = x^2$ and $y = -3x + 4$. State the equation solved by the crossing points of these graphs, and its solutions.

---

5 State the equation solved where $y = x^2$ crosses:
(a) $y = 2x + 1$ (b) $y = -2x + 1$ (c) $y = 3x - 2$
(d) $y = -2x - 4$ (e) $y = \frac{1}{2}x + 3$ (f) $y = \frac{1}{3}x - 1$.

6 Draw the graphs given in question 5 and hence solve the equations.

7 You can easily program a computer to give you the points to plot for a given equation of the type $y = ax^2 + bx + c$.

```
1Ø REM "PLOTME"
2Ø PRINT "Points to plot for parabola of form y = ax² + bx + c."
3Ø PRINT "Type value of a."
4Ø INPUT A
5Ø PRINT "Type value of b."
6Ø INPUT B
7Ø PRINT "Type value of c."
8Ø INPUT C
9Ø PRINT "Type smallest value for x."
1ØØ INPUT SX
11Ø PRINT "Type largest value for x."
12Ø INPUT LX
13Ø PRINT "Type x interval (e.g. 1 for −3, −2, −1, etc.)"
14Ø INPUT I
15Ø CLS   (Clear screen)
16Ø PRINT "y = ˄";A;"x↑2˄ + ˄";B;"x˄ + ˄";C
17Ø FOR X = SX TO LX STEP I
18Ø PRINT "Plot (˄";X;"˄'˄";A*X*X + B*X + C;"˄)"
19Ø NEXT X
```

22 Circles: arcs and sectors

A Arcs (radians)

To find the length of an arc, first find what fraction of the circumference it is by considering the angle it subtends at the centre.

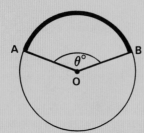

Fig. 22:1

In Figure 22:1   arc AB = $\dfrac{\theta}{360°}$ × circumference = $\dfrac{\theta}{360}$ × π × diameter

Note: θ is a Greek letter, pronounced 'theta'.

Example   In Figure 22:2, $\theta = 50$ and the diameter is 36 cm.

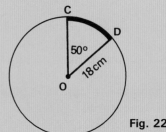

Fig. 22:2

$$\text{Arc CD} = \frac{50}{360} \times \pi \times 36 \rightarrow \frac{5\cancel{0}}{{}_1\cancel{360}} \times \frac{22}{7} \times \cancel{36}^1 = \frac{110}{7} \rightarrow 15\tfrac{5}{7} \text{ cm}$$

1 Find the length of each marked arc in Figure 22:3.

(a) 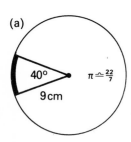   (b) 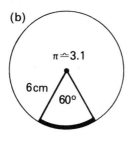   (c) 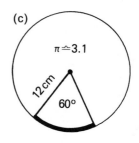   (d)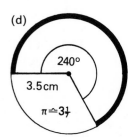

Fig. 22:3

*2 State the values of (a) to (l) in this table.

Length of arc	60 cm	3 cm	20 cm	7 cm	10 cm	5 cm
Circumference	120 cm	12 cm	80 cm	21 cm	60 cm	25 cm
Arc as fraction of circumference	(a)	(c)	(e)	(g)	(i)	(k)
Angle at centre	(b)	(d)	(f)	(h)	(j)	(l)

*3 The formula given in the introduction can be expressed as $A = \dfrac{\theta}{360} \times C$, where A is the length of the arc and C is the circumference of the circle. Show that this formula can be changed to $C = \dfrac{A}{\theta} \times 360$.

4 Use the formula given at the end of question 3 to find the circumference of the circle in which an arc 6 cm long subtends an angle of 54° at the centre.

5 Change $A = \dfrac{\theta}{360} \times C$ to make θ the subject. Hence find the angle (θ) subtended by an arc (A) 22 cm long, in a circle of radius 10.5 cm. (Note: First find C using $C = \pi d$, taking $\pi = \frac{22}{7}$.)

6 (a) Using D for diameter and A for arc, the arc formula becomes $A = \dfrac{\theta}{360} \times \pi \times D$.

Rewrite this formula to make the subject:
(i) D (ii) θ.

(b) In a circle of what diameter does an arc of length 15.5 cm subtend an angle of 200° at the centre? (Take $\pi = 3.1$.)

(c) What angle is subtended at the centre of a 3.5 cm radius circle by a 5.5 cm arc? (Take $\pi = 3\frac{1}{7}$.)

7 When the length of arc equals the radius of the circle, the angle subtended at the centre is 1 radian (1ᶜ).

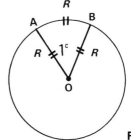

Fig. 22:4

In Figure 22:4, arc $AB = R$, $\theta = 1^c$, and the circumference $= 2 \times \pi \times R$. Using the arc formula in the introduction this gives

$$R = \frac{1^c}{360°} \times 2 \times \pi \times R \rightarrow R = \frac{1^c}{180°} \times \pi \times R \rightarrow$$

$$R = \frac{\pi^c}{180°} \times R$$

Hence π **radians** = **180°.** This important fact should be learnt.

(a) Use a calculator to find 1 radian in degrees.

(b) Show that when angle θ is measured in radians, the arc formula becomes **arc = θ × radius.**
Hence find the length of arc subtending 3^c in a circle of radius 8 cm.

---

8 Computers usually use radian measure for angle calculations. Write a BASIC program line to convert an angle from degrees (D) to radians (R).

9 In Figure 22:5, h is the height of the cone, and l is the slant height. Figure 22:6 shows the net of the cone.

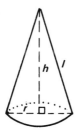 Fig. 22:5

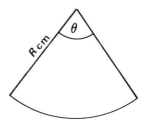 Fig. 22:6

Calculate R in cm correct to 3 s.f. and θ in radians and in degrees (to the nearest 1°) if the cone is to be 8 cm high with base radius 5 cm. (Take π = 3.14.)

Make the cone to check your answer.

B   Sectors

In Figure 22:7, P is the major sector and Q is the minor sector.

Area of Q $= \dfrac{\theta^{\circ}}{360^{\circ}} \times$ area of circle

$\qquad\qquad = \dfrac{\theta}{360} \times \pi \times r^2$

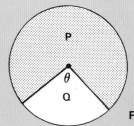 Fig. 22:7

1 For each part of Figure 22:3 (page 126) find the area of the sector containing the thicker arc.

*2 Calculate the total perimeter and the area of a sector which subtends an angle of 200° at the centre of a 10 cm radius circle. (Take π = 3.1.)

3 Show that if S represents the area of the sector, then the formula given in the introduction can be changed to

$$r = \sqrt{\dfrac{S \times 360}{\pi \times \theta}}.$$

4 What is the radius of the circle in which a sector of area 46.5 cm² subtends 54° at the centre? (Take π = 3.1.)

5 (a) Remembering that π radians = 180° (see Exercise 22A, question 7), show that if θ is measured in radians the formula given in the introduction becomes

$$\text{sector area} = \frac{\theta R^2}{2}.$$

(b) What is the area of the sector subtending 2.5^c at the centre of a 3 cm radius circle?

(c) What is the angle in radians subtended at the centre of a 4 cm radius circle by a sector of area 50 cm²?

---

6 Calculate the total surface area of a cone of height 10 cm and base radius 3 cm. (Take π = 3.14.)

7 Prove that the curved surface area of a cone is $\pi r l$, where l is the slant height and r is the base radius.

8 Write a computer program to calculate the length of an arc and the sector area, given the radius of the circle and the angle in degrees subtended by the arc at the centre.

9 The volume of a cone is $\frac{1}{3}\pi r^2 h$, where r is the radius of the base circle and h is the vertical height.

A manufacturer decides to market Sphinx Phizz drinks in conical containers that hold 350 ml when completely full. The top point can be broken off and a straw inserted to enjoy the Phizz.

What size should they make the container if it is to use the smallest amount of aluminium in its construction?

A Similar shapes

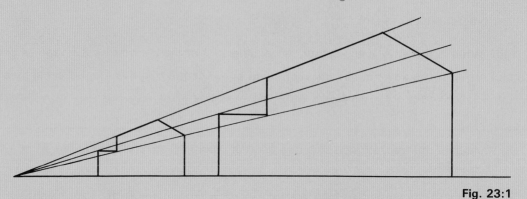

Two shapes are similar when one is an exact enlargement of the other.

Fig. 23:1

When two shapes are similar, their corresponding (in the same position) sides are in the same ratio, and their angles are the same sizes. For a triangle, and only for a triangle, it is sufficient to know *one* of these two facts to know that the shapes are similar.

In Figure 23:2, the two shapes have angles of the same sizes, but they are not similar.

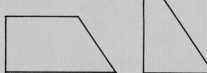

Fig. 23:2

In Figure 23:3, the two shapes have their sides in the same ratio (2:1) but they are not similar.

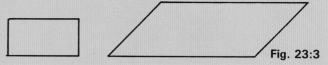

Fig. 23:3

The triangles in Figure 23:4 are similar because their angles are the same sizes. By writing the equal angles over each other, $\frac{A\ B\ C}{D\ E\ F}$, then covering up one column at a time we obtain the ratio of the sides:

$$\frac{BC}{EF} = \frac{AC}{DF} = \frac{AB}{DE} = \text{the scale factor of the enlargement.}$$

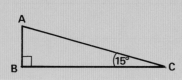
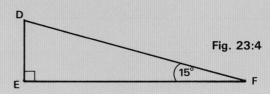

Fig. 23:4

Example Calculate the unknown lengths in Figure 23:5.

Fig. 23:5

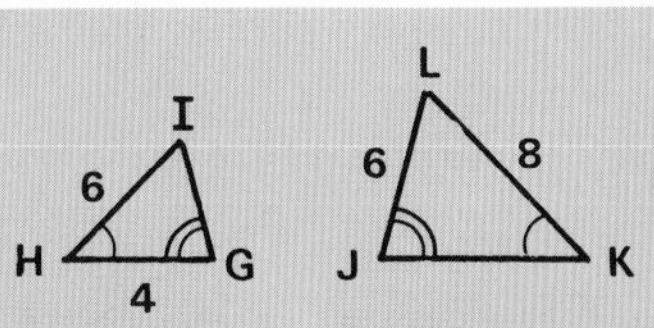

First find the scale factor of the enlargement. To do this, identify two corresponding sides where lengths are both known. Corresponding sides are opposite the same angle in both shapes. In Figure 23:5, HI and LK are the required corresponding sides. The scale factor is $\frac{8}{6}$ (or $\frac{6}{8}$).

Now decide which shape is the bigger and which the smaller. (It is a good idea to write B and S inside your copy of the diagram.)

To find JK
Find the side which corresponds to JK in the other shape. It is HG, as both are opposite the blank angle. Then JK is bigger than HG by the scale factor $\frac{8}{6}$, so
JK = $4 \times \frac{8}{6} = 5\frac{1}{3}$ cm.

To find IG
Find the side which corresponds to IG in the other shape. It is LJ, as both are opposite the one-arc angle. Then IG is smaller than LJ by the scale factor $\frac{6}{8}$, so
IG = $4 \times \frac{6}{8} = 4\frac{1}{2}$ cm.

1 Calculate the unknown sides in each pair of similar triangles in Figure 23:6. Dimensions are cm.

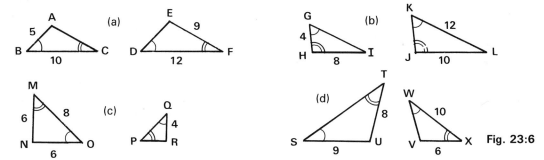

Fig. 23:6

2 Calculate the unknown sides in the pairs of similar triangles in Figure 23:7. Dimensions are cm.

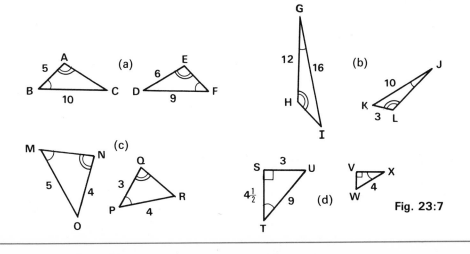

Fig. 23:7

131

3 Calculate by similar triangles the unknown sides in Figure 23:8. Dimensions are cm.

(a)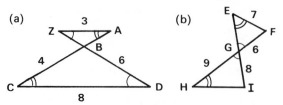

(b)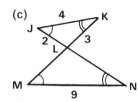

(c)

Fig. 23:8

4 In Figure 23:8(a), why must ZA be parallel to CD?

5 Copy Figure 23:9. Mark the angles that you know must be equal, then calculate the unknown lengths. Dimensions are cm.

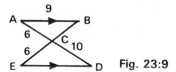

Fig. 23:9

6 Copy Figure 23:10. Mark the angles that you know must be equal, then calculate all unknown lengths. Dimensions are cm.

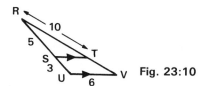

Fig. 23:10

7 Figures 23:11 and 23:12 illustrate the **midpoint theorems**.

In Figure 23:11, **the line from the midpoint of one side of a triangle, parallel to another side, bisects the third side.**

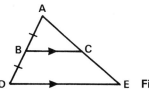

Fig. 23:11

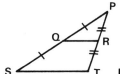

Fig. 23:12

In Figure 23:12, **the line joining the midpoints of two sides of a triangle is parallel to, and a half of, the third side.**

Draw, any size, copies of Figures 23:11 and 23:12, then check by measurement that the two theorems are true for *your* diagrams. (The formal proofs are given in Question 4 on page 136.)

8 In a triangle ABC, AB = 6 cm, BC = 8 cm, and AC = 7 cm. X is the midpoint of AB, and Y is on AC such that XY // BC.

(a) Calculate the lengths of AY and XY.

(b) Show that △s AXY and ABC are similar, and that $\dfrac{AX}{AB} = \dfrac{AY}{AC} = \dfrac{XY}{BC}$.

9 WXYZ is a quadrilateral. P, Q, R and S are the midpoints of the sides. Show that PQRS is a parallelogram.

10 ABCD is a kite. P, Q, R and S are the midpoints of the sides. Show that PQRS is a rectangle.

B Congruent triangles

Congruent shapes are exactly the same shape and size.

They can be reflections, rotations, or translations of each other, but cannot be enlargements (except by scale factor 1 and −1).

To investigate

How many different (not congruent) triangles can be drawn to fit each of the following descriptions?

(a) One side 4 cm, one side 3 cm

(b) Two sides 4 cm, one side 6 cm

(c) One side 3 cm, one side 4 cm, one angle 40°

(d) One side 4 cm, one angle 30°, one angle 80°

(e) One angle 50°, one angle 90°

(f) One angle 90°, one side 4 cm, one side 6 cm

(g) One side 5 cm, one side 3 cm, one angle 120°

(h) One angle 90°, hypotenuse 6 cm, one side 4 cm

(i) One side 3 cm, one side 7 cm, one side 4 cm

(j) One side 2 cm, one side 4 cm, one side 7 cm.

Your investigation should have shown you that there are four sets of facts about a triangle which define it uniquely. In each case three measurements must be known.

(1) **Three sides** (Figure 23:13)

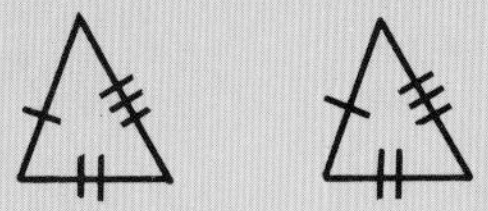

(2) **Two sides, included angle** (Figure 23:14)

 (*Included* means 'between the sides'. If the angle is acute, but not included, there are two possible triangles. This is called the **ambiguous case**.)

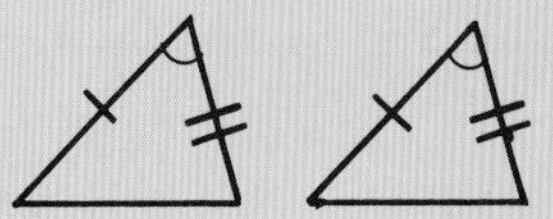

(3) **Right angle, hypotenuse, side** (Figure (23:15)

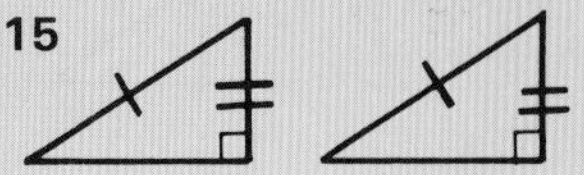

 (The *hypotenuse* is the side opposite the right angle.)

Fig. 23:13

Fig. 23:14

Fig. 23:15

(4) **Two angles, corresponding side** (Figure 23:16)

(*Corresponding* means in the same position: opposite the same angle.)

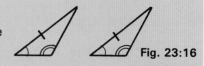

Fig. 23:16

Example In Figure 23:17, △s $\begin{matrix} ABC \\ CDA \end{matrix}$ are congruent (3 sides).

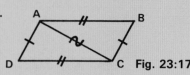

Fig. 23:17

Note: AC is the third side. It is **common** to both triangles, therefore equal in both. We mark a common side with a wavy line.

From $\begin{matrix} ABC \\ CDA \end{matrix}$:

covering up $\begin{matrix} A \\ C \end{matrix}$ gives BC = DA

covering up $\begin{matrix} B \\ D \end{matrix}$ gives AC = CA

covering up $\begin{matrix} C \\ A \end{matrix}$ gives AB = CD.

1 Where the following pairs of triangles (Figure 23:18) are congruent, write the equal angles and sides over each other and give the case of congruency. If the triangles are not congruent, explain briefly why not.

Note: The triangles are often drawn deliberately to appear not congruent when they are, and vice versa. Only take sides and angles as equal if they are marked equal.

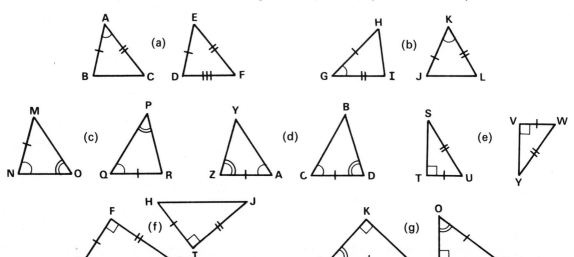

Fig. 23:18 continued ▶

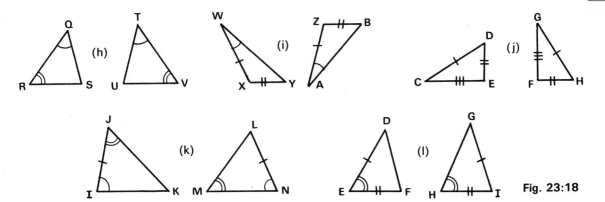

Fig. 23:18

*2 Construct accurately the following pairs of triangles. It will help if you roughly sketch the triangles first. Say why each pair are or are not congruent.

(a) AB = 3 cm; BC = 4 cm; AC = 2 cm
    DE = 2 cm; EF = 3 cm; DF = 4 cm

(b) HI = 4 cm; ∠H = 30°; HG = 5 cm
    JK = 5 cm; ∠K = 30°; KL = 4 cm

(c) ON = 6 cm; ∠O = 60°; NM = 5.5 cm
    QR = 6 cm; ∠Q = 60°; PQ = 5.5 cm

(d) SU = 3 cm; ∠U = 90°; ST = 5 cm
    VW = 3 cm; ∠V = 90°; WX = 5 cm

(e) AZ = 4 cm; ∠Z = 60°; ∠A = 45°
    BC = 4 cm; ∠C = 60°; ∠D = 45°

(f) QR = 5 cm; ∠Q = 45°; SR = 4 cm
    TU = 5 cm; ∠T = 45°; US = 4 cm

(g) IJ = 4 cm; ∠J = 60°; HI = 3 cm
    AG = 4 cm; ∠G = 60°; AE = 3 cm

3 Give reasons for the following pairs of triangles (Figure 23:19) being congruent or not. Where they are congruent, write the equal angles over each other, as in question 1.

(a)
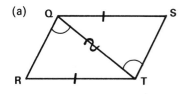

(b)
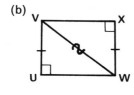

(c)
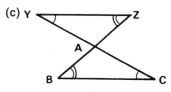

(d)
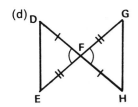

(e)
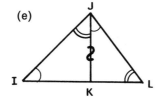

(f)
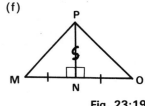

Fig. 23:19

4 **Example** *Given* Figure 23:20, in which AB // DC and AB = DC.
To prove BC // AD, making ABCD a parallelogram.

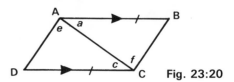

Fig. 23:20

Proof In △s ABC and ADC,
AB = DC (given)
AC is common
$a = c$ (alternate angles, AB // DC)
∴△s $\begin{matrix} ABC \\ CDA \end{matrix}$ are congruent (2 sides, included angle)
∴$e = f$ (angles congruent triangles)
∴AD // BC (e and f are alternate *and* equal)

(a) Prove that in Figure 23:21 EF = HG and
EH = FG.

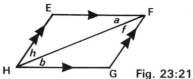

Fig. 23:21

(b) Prove that in Figure 23:22 IJ // LM.

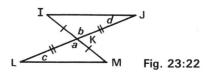

Fig. 23:22

(c) In Figure 23:23, ABCD and BEFG are
squares.
(i) Why must ∠ABE = ∠FBC?
(ii) Prove that △s ABE and CBF are
congruent.
Note: This is part of the Euclidean proof
of Pythagoras' theorem.

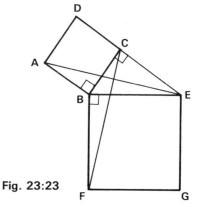

Fig. 23:23

5 In △ABC, AB = AC. AD is drawn perpendicular to BC, D lying on BC.

(a) Prove that ∠B = ∠C.

(b) State what other equalities are true in △ABC.

6 Assuming nothing more about a parallelogram than that it is a quadrilateral with both pairs of opposite sides parallel, prove that the opposite sides and opposite angles of a parallelogram are equal.

7 Prove that a quadrilateral with both pairs of opposite sides equal must be a parallelogram.

8 In Figure 23:24, prove by congruent triangles that BQ = PC.

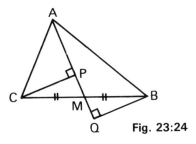

Fig. 23:24

9 Prove by congruent triangles that a quadrilateral with one pair of sides both equal and parallel must be a parallelogram.

10 ABCD is a rectangle. An isosceles triangle BCE is drawn outside the rectangle, with BE = CE. Prove that AE = DE.

11 The diagonals HJ and IK of parallelogram HIJK cross at M. Prove that the area of △HMK equals the area of △JMI. (Note: This is often just written: Prove △HMK = △JMI.)

12 K, L and M are the midpoints of the sides of any triangle PQR. Prove that:
(a) △KLM is similar to △PQR   (b) △KLM = $\frac{1}{4}$△PQR.

13 ABCD is a parallelogram in which ∠BAC = 90°. BC is produced to E such that BC = 2CE and ∠DEC = 90°. Prove that ∠B = 45°.

14 Find the rest of the proof of Pythagoras' theorem referred to in question 4(c).

$3a^2$ means $3 \times a^2$, so that if $a = 4$, $3a^2 \rightarrow 3 \times 16 = 48$.

$3a^2b^3 \times 2ab^4 \rightarrow 6a^3b^7$. You may use the rule 'add the indices when multiplying powers of the same letter', or think of the terms written out in full:

$3a^2b^3 \times 2ab^4 \rightarrow 3 \times a \times a \times b \times b \times b \times 2 \times a \times b \times b \times b \times b$

3×2 is 6; the three a's multiply to give a^3; the seven b's multiply to give b^7.

1 If $a = 1$, $b = 3$, $c = 4$ and $h = 0$, find the value of:
   (a) $2a^3$ (b) $2b^2$ (c) a^3h^2 (d) ab^2h (e) $2b^2 - c^2$ (f) $b^3 - 4b^2h^3$.

2 Simplify:
   (a) $a^4 \times a^3$ (b) $b \times b^2$ (c) $2b \times 2b$ (d) $3a^2 \times 2a^3$ (e) $a \times b$
   (f) $a^3 \times 4b^2$.

3 Simplify:
   (a) $4c^3 \times 3c^5$ (b) $3c^2 \times 5d^2$ (c) $2a^2 \times 3ab^2$ (d) $4m^3n^2 \times 3mn^3$.

4 **Example**   Simplify $4a^5b^3c \div 8a^2bc^3$.

$$\frac{4a^5b^3c}{8a^2bc^3} \rightarrow \frac{{}^1\cancel{4} \times \cancel{a} \times \cancel{a} \times a \times a \times a \times \cancel{b} \times b \times b \times \cancel{c}}{{}_2\cancel{8} \times \cancel{a} \times \cancel{a} \times \cancel{b} \times \cancel{c} \times c \times c}$$

Having cancelled as much as possible, this leaves $\dfrac{a^3b^2}{2c^2}$.

Or: Using the 'subtract indices' rule:

$$\frac{4a^5b^3c}{8a^2bc^3} \rightarrow \frac{1a^{5-2}b^{3-1}}{2c^{3-1}} \rightarrow \frac{a^3b^2}{2c^2}$$

Note: The c term is at the bottom in the answer because the bigger power of c (c^3) was at the bottom to start with.

Simplify:
   (a) $\dfrac{a^4}{a^3}$ (b) $\dfrac{a^8}{a^4}$ (c) $\dfrac{a^4}{a}$ (d) $\dfrac{a^3}{a^3}$ (e) $a^6 \div a^4$.

5 Simplify:
   (a) $a^6 \div a^6$ (b) $a^3 \div a^5$ (c) $a^2 \div a^6$ (d) $a \div a^6$.

*6 Simplify:
   (a) $\dfrac{a^5}{a^3}$ (b) $\dfrac{2a^6}{a}$ (c) $\dfrac{3a^3}{15a^2}$ (d) $\dfrac{24b^3c}{6bc}$ (e) $\dfrac{2a^2c^3}{3c^3d^2}$.

*7 Substitute the values $a = 2$, $b = 5$, $c = 4$ and $d = 3$ into your *answers* to question 6.

*8 Example $c^3(c^4 + 2) \rightarrow c^7 + 2c^3$

Multiply:
(a) $x^2(x^3 + 3)$ (b) $x^3(x - 5)$ (c) $x^3(x^2 - x)$.

9 The value of a^0

$a^x \div a^x$ must equal 1, but using the subtraction of indices rule, $a^x \div a^x \rightarrow a^{x-x} = a^0$. Hence the fact that

$$a^0 = 1$$

Find the value of:
(a) 3^0 (b) 8^0 (c) c^0 (d) $4a^0$ (e) $3b^0$.

10 Example $(2a^2)^3 \rightarrow 2a^2 \times 2a^2 \times 2a^2 \rightarrow 8a^6$

Learn: $$(x^m)^n \rightarrow x^{mn}$$

Simplify:
(a) $(3a)^2$ (b) $(-a)^3$ (c) $(3ac)^3$ (d) $(-4)^3$ (e) $(-ab)^3$ (f) $(3a^2)^4$

(g) $(2a^2b)^2$ (h) $\left(\dfrac{1}{b^2}\right)^3$ (i) $\left(\dfrac{2a}{3b}\right)^3$ (j) $\left(\dfrac{a^2}{b^3}\right)^2$

11 $x^{\frac{1}{2}}$ is another way of writing $\sqrt{x}$ because $x^{\frac{1}{2}} \times x^{\frac{1}{2}} = x^{\frac{1}{2}+\frac{1}{2}} = x$.

Similarly $x^{\frac{1}{3}} \times x^{\frac{1}{3}} \times x^{\frac{1}{3}} = x$, so $x^{\frac{1}{3}}$ is the cube root of x, $\sqrt[3]{x}$.

Learn: $x^{\frac{1}{n}}$ is the same as $\sqrt[n]{x}$.

A fractional index gives a root.

Find:
(a) $9^{\frac{1}{2}}$ (b) $25^{\frac{1}{2}}$ (c) $27^{\frac{1}{3}}$ (d) $125^{\frac{1}{3}}$ (e) $16^{\frac{1}{4}}$.

Your calculator may mark its root key using the above notation. Look back to Chapter 9, page 51, for more information on this.

12 As 8^2 means '8 squared', and $8^{\frac{1}{3}}$ means 'the cube root of 8', it follows that $8^{\frac{2}{3}}$ means the cube root of 8 squared, that is, $2^2 = 4$.

Always find the root first, then the power; this keeps the numbers smaller.

Find:
(a) $27^{\frac{2}{3}}$ (b) $16^{\frac{3}{4}}$ (c) $4^{\frac{3}{2}}$ (d) $9^{\frac{3}{2}}$ (e) $8^{\frac{5}{3}}$ (f) $25^{1\frac{1}{2}}$ (g) $4^{2\frac{1}{2}}$.

13 By subtracting indices, $a^2 \div a^4 = a^{-2}$.

By cancelling, $a^2 \div a^4 \rightarrow \dfrac{a^2}{a^4} \rightarrow \dfrac{1}{a^2}$

Therefore $a^{-2} = \dfrac{1}{a^2}$.

Similarly $a^{-1} = \dfrac{1}{a}$ and $49^{-\frac{1}{2}} = \dfrac{1}{\sqrt{49}} = \frac{1}{7}$.

Learn: x^{-n} is the same as $\dfrac{1}{x^n}$.

A negative index gives 'one over'.

Find:
(a) 4^{-1} (b) 3^{-1} (c) 8^{-1} (d) 1^{-2} (e) 2^{-2}.

14 Simplify:

(a) $8^{-\frac{1}{3}}$ (b) $4^{-\frac{1}{2}}$ (c) $36^{\frac{1}{2}}$ (d) $36^{-\frac{1}{2}}$ (e) $25^{\frac{1}{2}}$.

15 **Example**   Evaluate $8^{-\frac{2}{3}}$

Negative index $\Rightarrow$ one over. Hence $8^{-\frac{2}{3}} \rightarrow \dfrac{1}{8^{2/3}}$.

Index $\frac{1}{3}$ $\Rightarrow$ cube root. Hence $\dfrac{1}{8^{2/3}} \rightarrow \dfrac{1}{2^2} \rightarrow \dfrac{1}{4}$.

Simplify:
(a) $27^{-\frac{2}{3}}$ (b) $16^{\frac{3}{4}}$ (c) $16^{-\frac{3}{4}}$ (d) $9^{-\frac{3}{2}}$ (e) $8^{\frac{5}{3}}$.

16 Simplify:

(a) $4^{-1\frac{1}{2}}$ (b) $16^{-1\frac{1}{2}}$ (c) $125^{-\frac{2}{3}}$ (d) 100^{-3} (e) $64^{\frac{2}{3}}$.

---

17 Simplify:
(a) $(3a)^{-2}$ (b) $3a^{-2}$ (c) $(2a)^{-1}$ (d) $2a^{-1} \times 2a^3$ (e) $(2a)^{-4}$

(f) $4^{1\frac{1}{2}}$ (g) $2a^{\frac{1}{2}} \times 3a^{\frac{1}{2}}$ (h) $\sqrt[3]{2^6}$ (i) $9^{-\frac{1}{2}}$ (j) $(36a^2)^{\frac{1}{2}}$

(k) $3^{-3} \times 3^4$ (l) $\sqrt{1\frac{9}{16}}$ (m) $\sqrt{6\frac{1}{4}}$ (n) 1^{-1} (o) $2^{\frac{1}{2}} \times 2^{\frac{3}{2}}$ (p) $0.04^{\frac{1}{2}}$

(q) 7^0 (r) $0.027^{\frac{2}{3}}$ (s) $3^a \times 3^{-a}$ (t) $8a \times (2a)^{-3}$.

18 Investigate graphs of the family $y = ax^{-n}$.

25 Similar shapes: ratio of area and volume

A Lengths and areas of similar shapes

For discussion

The three photographs and their frames shown in Figure 25:1 are mathematically similar shapes. The smallest uses 24 cm of moulding and contains 32 cm² of glass. Discuss the lengths of moulding and the areas of glass for the other frames.

5 cm

10 cm

12 cm

Fig. 25:1

1 The pet food manufacturer Petco promises that for every three Petco can-labels sent to them they will donate 2p to the RSPCA.

(a) How much will Petco donate if I send them 30 labels?

(b) How many labels must I send for a donation of £1?

2 Two different scale models of a railway engine are available. One model fits a 20 mm wide track; the other fits a 25 mm wide track. Show that the models' lengths are in the ratio 4 : 5, then calculate the length of the longer engine if the smaller is 14 cm long.

3 Two squares have sides of 2 cm and 5 cm. Write as simply as possible the ratio of:
(a) their perimeters   (b) their diagonals   (c) their areas.

4 Draw two similar rectangles with sides in the ratio 2 : 3, making the smaller one 2 cm long and 1 cm wide. By drawing or otherwise, find the ratio of their areas.

5 A piece of paper has an area of 11 cm². What is the area of a similar-shaped piece of paper if it is twice as long?

6 A square has an area of 10 cm².

What is the area of a square with its sides:

(a) twice the first   (b) three times the first   (c) four times the first?

7 A lawn is a rectangle 5 yards long and 4 yards wide.

(a) What is the length and the width of a larger but similar-shaped lawn if its dimensions are in the ratio 2 : 1 with the first?

(b) If the first lawn needs 1 bag of fertilizer at the advised rate, how many bags will the second need at the same rate?

8 A window is made up of two panes of glass, similar in shape but one three times the other in length. If the larger pane costs £18, what will the smaller cost?

*9 Two tables are the same shape but one is four times as long as the other. If the larger has an area of 64 ft², what is the area of the smaller?

*10 A plan of a garden has an area of 50 cm². If it is drawn to a lengths' scale of 1 : 100, what is the area of the real garden in cm²?

*11 Change your answer to question 10 to square metres.
(1 m² = 1 m × 1 m = 100 cm × 100 cm)

*12 I paint half a wall in 15 minutes. How long should I take to paint the whole wall?

*13 A window of height 1 m contains 4000 cm² of glass. A similar-shaped window is 50 cm high.

(a) What is the lengths' ratio of the first window to the second, as simply as possible?

(b) What is the areas' ratio?

(c) What is the area of the glass in the smaller window?

*14 A door is drawn to a scale where 2 cm represents 20 cm.

(a) What is the lengths' ratio, as simply as possible?

(b) If the drawn door has an area of 60 cm², what is the area of the real door?

15 A 'Tower of Hanoi' set has five discs, all the same thickness. The largest is twice the diameter of the smallest, which weighs 50 g. What does the largest weigh?

16 How many times as much paint is needed to paint an 8 cm-side cube as a 4 cm-side cube?

17 The triangles in Figure 25:2 are similar.

What is the ratio of their areas?

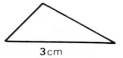

3 cm   1 cm   **Fig. 25:2**

18 How many times as much paint is needed to paint a 10 cm-radius sphere as to paint a 2 cm-radius sphere?

19 A lawn 7 m by 12 m takes 10 minutes to mow. About how long should it take to mow a lawn 14 m by 24 m?

20 A machine stamps out circular discs from sheet steel of a standard gauge (thickness). If a 5 mm-radius disc weighs 50 g, what does a 1 cm-radius disc weigh?

21 A piece of paper 40 mm by 10 mm is cut into four equal rectangles. What is the area of each rectangle?

22 A projector enlarges a slide of area 6 cm² to an area of 600 cm². If a tree is 15 mm tall on the slide, how tall is it on the screen?

23 One box of carpet tiles is sufficient for 10 m² of floor. How many boxes would I need for 40 m² of floor?

24 The three tiers of a wedding cake are to be similar shapes with sides in the ratio 5:4:3. The largest tier is 30 cm square and 10 cm deep.

(a) Calculate the sizes of the other two tiers.

(b) Each cake is covered with the same thickness of marzipan and icing. The bottom tier needs 250 g of marzipan and 100 g of icing. How much of each is needed for the other tiers?

25 The plans of an office block are made to a scale of 1:50. One room is shown to be 13.4 cm wide and 15.2 cm long on the plan. What will be its true size, in metres?

26 Express these map ratios in their simplest form.

Example   3 cm represents 450 m → 3 cm represents 45 000 cm → 3:45 000 → 1:15 000

(a) 1 cm represents 500 m   (b) 4 cm represents 600 m   (c) 5 cm represents 1 km

27 A map is drawn to a scale 1:100 000.

(a) What length in km does 1 cm on the map represent?

(b) A forest measures 1 cm by 2.4 cm on the map. What are its real measurements in km?

28 For the pairs of similar shapes in Figure 25:3, state the areas (a), (b) and (c).

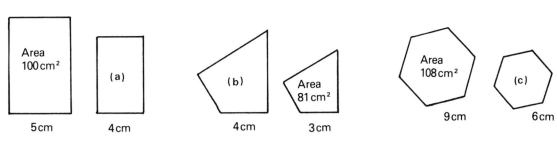

Fig. 25:3

29 A photograph is 9 cm long and has an area of 54 cm². What is the area of an enlargement of the photograph which is 12 cm long?

30 A circle has an area of 12 cm². What is the area of a circle with a radius:
(a) twice as big   (b) three times as big   (c) half as big?
(Note: Do not use the area of a circle formula.)

31 Two similar polygons have areas of 810 cm² and 160 cm² respectively. If one side of the larger polygon is 9 cm long, find the length of the corresponding side on the smaller polygon.

---

32 For maps and plans the ratio is usually in the form 1 : n, called the *representative fraction* (RF).

> **Example**   The RF of a map is 1 : 60 000.
>   This means 1 cm represents 60 000 cm = 600 m.

Find the actual distances represented by the given distances on a map with the given RF
(a) 3 cm, RF = 1 : 1000   (b) 5 cm, RF = 1 : 10 000
(c) 9 cm, RF = 1 : 20 000   (d) 7 cm, RF = 1 : 100 000
(e) 7 mm, RF = 1 : 25 000   (f) 4.6 cm, RF = 1 : 50 000.

33 An Ordnance Survey map, RF 1 : 50 000, measures 80 cm by 80 cm.

(a) What ground distances do these measurements represent?

(b) The map is subdivided into squares of 2 cm sides and of 20 cm sides. What distances do these measurements represent?

(c) What ground area is represented by: (i) the map   (ii) the small squares   (iii) the large squares?

34 Find the real areas, in km², represented by the following areas on maps with the given RF.
(a) 25 cm²; RF 1 : 10 000   (b) 46 cm²; RF 1 : 20 000.

B   Ratio of volumes

The ratio of the volumes of similar solids is the cube of the ratio of their corresponding lengths.

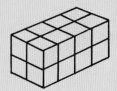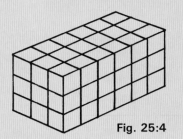

Fig. 25:4

For discussion

Examples (a) A vase, similar in shape to the one in Figure 25:5 but twice as tall, holds 2 litres. Find the dimensions of this vase, and the capacity of the vase drawn in Figure 25:5.

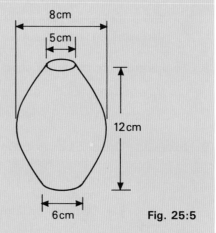

Fig. 25:5

(b) Lead shot is made as spheres of various radii. A 1 mm radius sphere weighs 50 mg. Find the weight of other shot, up to a radius of 10 mm.

1 A plastic cube of side 1 cm weighs 1 g. State the weight of a cube made from the same plastic with side:
(a) 2 cm   (b) 3 cm   (c) 4 cm   (d) 10 cm.

2 Two similar jugs have heights of 3 cm and 6 cm. The smaller has a base radius of 5 cm. The larger has a volume of 480 cm³.

(a) What is the base radius of the larger jug?

(b) What is the volume of the smaller jug?

3 A block is 1 cm wide, 2 cm long and 3 cm high. State the dimensions of a similar block made from the same material, but eight times as heavy.

4 Two similar cuboids have their lengths in the ratio 3 : 5. The larger has a volume of 250 cm³.

(a) State the ratio of the volumes of the two cuboids.

(b) Calculate the volume of the smaller cuboid.

5 A sphere of lead weighs 100 g. Calculate the weight of a sphere of lead of:
(a) twice the radius   (b) three times the radius   (c) ten times the radius
(d) half the radius   (e) one tenth the radius.

*6 A packet of washing powder weighs 5 kg. What would be the weight of a similar shaped packet:
(a) twice as tall   (b) three times as tall?

*7 A marble model of a marble statue weighs 12 kg. The original statue is ten times the height of the model. What is its weight?

8 A glass marble weighs 30 g and is 10 mm in diameter.

    (a) How much will eight of the marbles weigh?

    (b) The eight marbles are melted down and recast into one large one. Write down its radius. (No working is necessary.)

9 Two bottles are of similar shapes. The one which is 30 cm tall holds 1 litre when full.

    (a) How much does the other, 15 cm tall, hold when full?

    (b) If a similar bottle is made to hold 1 ml, how tall is it?

10   Example The two boxes in Figure 25:6 are similar solids.
The ratio of their lengths is $3:5$.
The ratio of their volumes is therefore $3^3:5^3 = 27:125$.
The larger is $\frac{125}{27} = 4\frac{17}{27}$ times as large in volume, but only
$\frac{5}{3} = 1\frac{2}{3}$ times as large in lengths.

$$\text{Volume of smaller} = \frac{27}{125} \times \text{volume of larger}$$

$$= \frac{27}{125} \times 75 \text{ cm}^3 = 16.2 \text{ cm}^3.$$

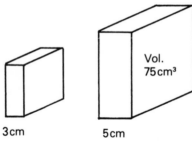

3cm   5cm   **Fig. 25:6**

Vol. 75cm³

For each pair of similar solids in Figure 25:7
(i) state the lengths' ratio
(ii) calculate the unknown volume.

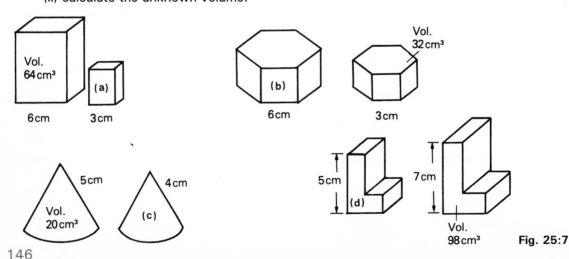

Fig. 25:7

11 The middle-size gnome in Figure 25:8 weighs 5 kg. What are the weights of the others?

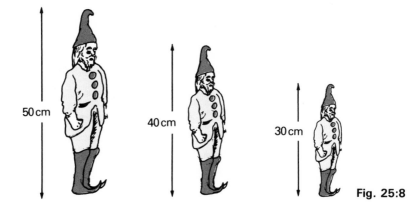

50 cm   40 cm   30 cm

Fig. 25:8

12 The fish in Figure 25:9 are all approximately similar. The smallest one provides about 250 calories. How many calories, to the nearest 10, would the other fish provide?

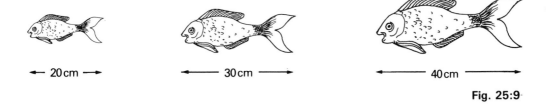

◄— 20 cm —►   ◄— 30 cm —►   ◄— 40 cm —►

Fig. 25:9

13 A sweet company markets its products in boxes of similar shapes. The 9 cm-long box holds 160 grams. What length box is needed to hold 540 grams, and how many times as much card will be needed to make it?

14 Ali can just lift 100 kg. Slabs of metal need to be lifted. They are various rectangular shapes, but all have length-to-width radio 2 : 1, and all have the same thickness. A 30 cm by 15 cm slab weighs 10 kg. What size is the largest slab that Ali can lift?

15 Two similar bottles hold 1.35 litres and 3.2 litres. The larger bottle has a radius of 4 cm and uses 5p's worth of glass.

(a) Calculate the radius of the smaller bottle.

(b) Calculate the cost of the glass to make the smaller bottle, if both bottles use the same thickness of glass.

16 A baby weighs 3.5 kg and is 50 cm long. If babies were similar 'shapes' to adults, what would be the weight of an adult, 180 cm tall, (a) in kg, and (b) in stones? (6 kg ≃ 1 stone) Discuss your answer.

17 Kuvrup paint cans are similar shapes. Figure 25:10 shows a 1 litre can.

How high is:
(a) the $2\frac{1}{2}$ litre can   (b) the 5 litre can?

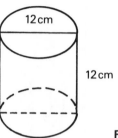

Fig. 25:10

18 Gog was an evil giant. He was 14 feet tall.

(a) Comparing him with a man of height 6 feet (assuming similar shapes), find:
  (i) the ratio of the heights
  (ii) the ratio of the cross-sectional area of the bones (the cross-sectional area determines the strength of bones)
  (iii) the ratio of the body volumes

(b) How many times more weight per unit area did Gog's bones have to withstand than the man's bones?

(c) Calculate Gog's weight if an average 6-feet tall man weighs 12 stone 12 pounds (1 stone = 14 pounds).

Using your calculator

The Nile

For 4145 miles, from 8594 feet up in Burundi to the Mediterranean, the Nile brings life and spectacle to nine African countries. At Khartoum, 1850 miles from the sea, the White Nile is joined by the Blue Nile, a thunderous river that provides six-sevenths of the total water that reaches the sea.

Without the Nile, Egypt, a country of 390 000 square miles, would be a barren desert. Of Egypt's 44 million people, 97% live on the 4% of its land watered by the Nile. Cairo, with ten million people, the largest city in Africa, lies 4000 miles from the source of the Nile at the start of the delta, 150 miles wide when it reaches the sea. Half of Egypt's population live in this delta.

For thousands of years Egypt was at the mercy of the annual flooding of the Nile, but between 1960 and 1970, 41 000 workmen built the Aswan Dam, $2\frac{1}{2}$ miles wide and 364 feet high, at a cost of £560 million. Now the flood waters, held back to make Lake Nasser, are released gradually, generating 8000 million kilowatt-hours of electricity annually, 70% of Egypt's needs. Surplus water is piped up to 30 miles inland, reclaiming millions of acres of desert. In the first ten years of the dam's life, Egypt's food production rose by 35%, with a bonus of 30 000 tons of fish being caught annually in the lake.

Helped by the dam and strikes of oil, Egypt's economy is improving rapidly, though in 1983 its average per capita income was still only £226 per annum.

Use this information and your calculator to answer the following questions.

1   How far is it from the source of the White Nile to Khartoum?

2   What percentage of the Nile, when it reaches the sea, started as the White Nile?

3   What fraction of the circumference of the Earth is the Nile? (Earth's radius = 6380 km. Take 5 miles = 8 km.)

149

4 About how many Egyptians live on land not watered by the Nile?

5 About how many hectares are watered by the Nile? (1 hectare = 10 000 m². Take 5 miles = 8 km.)

6 What is the area of the Nile delta? (Assume it is an isosceles triangle.)

7 How many kilowatt-hours of electricity does the dam generate each day? (Answer in standard form.)

8 How many kilowatt-hours of electricity does Egypt need each year? (Answer in standard form.)

9 How many man-hours did it take to build the Aswan Dam? (Assume each man worked 8 hours a day, and that work continued 'round the clock'.)

10 What percentage of the total income of all Egypt's population did the dam cost?

11 What is the area of one face of the dam in m²? (8 km ≃ 5 miles, and 1 m = 3.28 ft.)

A   Surface areas

Areas of plane figures

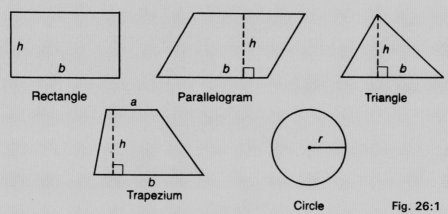

Rectangle

Parallelogram

Triangle

Trapezium

Circle   Fig. 26:1

Rectangle/Parallelogram	Base times height: $A = bh$
Triangle	Half base times height: $A = \frac{1}{2}bh$
Trapezium	Half the sum of the parallel sides times the distance between them: $A = \frac{1}{2}(a + b)h$
Circle	*Pi* times the square of the radius: $A = \pi r^2$

Surface areas of solids

Cylinder   Curved surface area is circumference of base circle times height of cylinder: πdh

Total surface area is curved surface area plus the areas of the top and bottom circles: $\pi dh + 2\pi r^2$

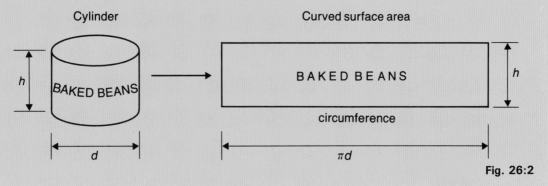

Cylinder

Curved surface area

BAKED BEANS

BAKED BEANS

circumference

πd

Fig. 26:2

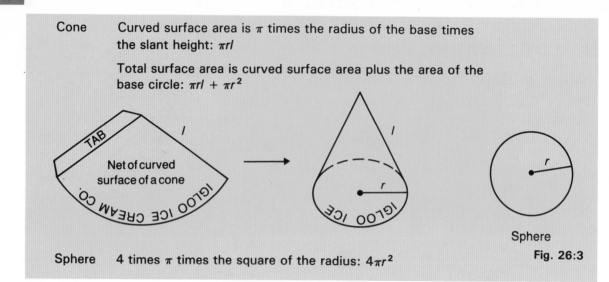

Cone Curved surface area is π times the radius of the base times the slant height: π*rl*

Total surface area is curved surface area plus the area of the base circle: π*rl* + π*r*²

Net of curved surface of a cone

Sphere

Fig. 26:3

Sphere 4 times π times the square of the radius: 4π*r*²

Use a calculator for this exercise. Take π = 3.1416 or use the π key.
Give answers correct to 3 significant figures, where appropriate.

1 Find the areas of the plane shapes in Figure 26:4.

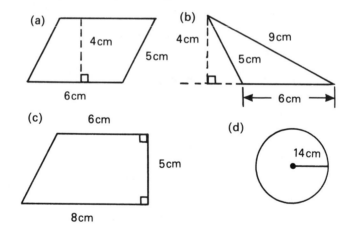

(a) 4cm 6cm 5cm

(b) 4cm 9cm 5cm 6cm

(c) 6cm 5cm 8cm

(d) 14cm

Fig. 26:4

2 A cylindrical tin has a radius of 10 cm and a height of 5 cm. Calculate:
(a) the curved surface area (b) the area of one circular end
(c) the total surface area.

3 Calculate the curved surface area and the base area for a cone with:
(a) radius 7 cm, slant height 16 cm
(b) radius 9 cm, slant height 21 cm
(c) diameter 7 cm, slant height 8 cm.

4 Calculate the surface area of a sphere with:
(a) radius 1 cm (b) radius 5 cm.

*5 Find the areas of the plane shapes in Figure 26:5.

(a)

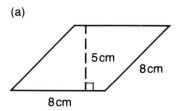

5 cm
8 cm
8 cm

(b)

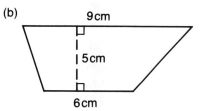

9 cm
5 cm
6 cm

(c)

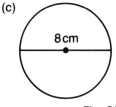

8 cm

Fig. 26:5

*6 Repeat question 2 for a tin of radius 5 cm and height 10 cm.

7 A cone has a curved surface area of 1320 cm² and a radius of 35 cm. Calculate the slant height.

8 A sphere has an area of 1519.76 cm². What is its radius?

---

9 A cylindrical tank has to be lagged over its top and sides. It has a diameter of 0.75 metres and a height of 1.3 metres. What is the cost at £5.60 per m²?

10 A cylinder has a curved surface area of 990 cm² and a height of 15 cm. Calculate:
(a) the circumference of a circular end
(b) the radius of the cylinder.

11 Figure 26:6 shows a cross-section of a plumb-bob. It is made from a 1 cm-diameter brass rod. Calculate the curved surface area, correct to 2 d.p., of:
(a) the hemisphere   (b) the cylinder
(c) the cone
(d) the complete plumb-bob.

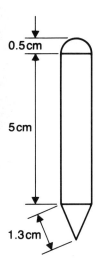

0.5 cm

5 cm

1.3 cm

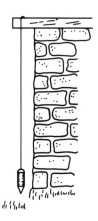

Fig. 26:6

12 In Figure 26:7, r represents the base radius of a cone, with l the slant height and h the vertical height.

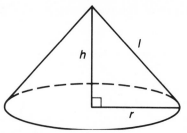

Fig. 26:7

The formula $l^2 = h^2 + r^2$ (Pythagoras' theorem) may be used to calculate the slant height of a cone if the base radius and vertical height are given.

Calculate, correct to 3 s.f., the total surface area of a cone with:
(a) vertical height 9 cm, radius 8 cm
(b) vertical height 12 cm, radius 7 cm.

13 Make a model of the two cones in question 12.

B Volumes

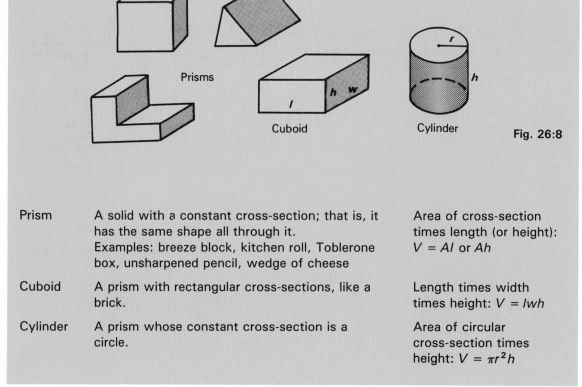

Fig. 26:8

Prism	A solid with a constant cross-section; that is, it has the same shape all through it. Examples: breeze block, kitchen roll, Toblerone box, unsharpened pencil, wedge of cheese	Area of cross-section times length (or height): $V = Al$ or Ah
Cuboid	A prism with rectangular cross-sections, like a brick.	Length times width times height: $V = lwh$
Cylinder	A prism whose constant cross-section is a circle.	Area of circular cross-section times height: $V = \pi r^2 h$

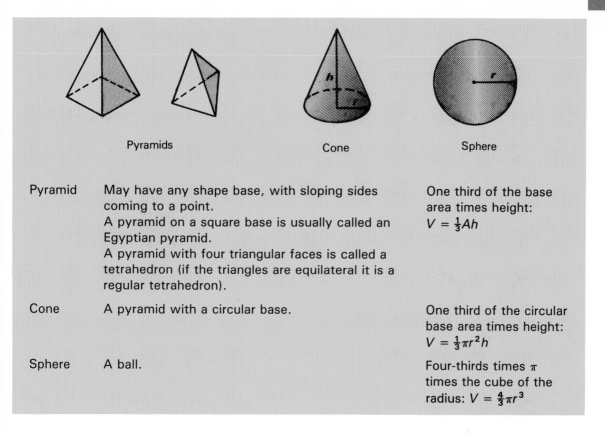

Pyramid	May have any shape base, with sloping sides coming to a point. A pyramid on a square base is usually called an Egyptian pyramid. A pyramid with four triangular faces is called a tetrahedron (if the triangles are equilateral it is a regular tetrahedron).	One third of the base area times height: $V = \frac{1}{3}Ah$
Cone	A pyramid with a circular base.	One third of the circular base area times height: $V = \frac{1}{3}\pi r^2 h$
Sphere	A ball.	Four-thirds times π times the cube of the radius: $V = \frac{4}{3}\pi r^3$

In all this exercise you should give answers correct to 3 significant figures, where appropriate.

Take π as 3.1416 or use the π key.

1 Find the volumes of the solids in Figure 26:9.

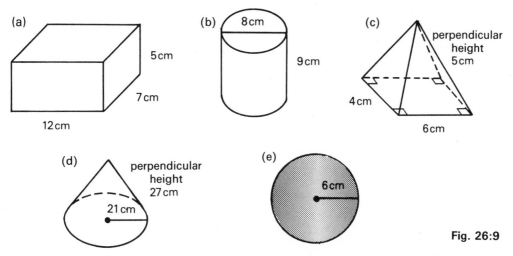

Fig. 26:9

*2 Find the volumes of the solids in Figure 26:10.

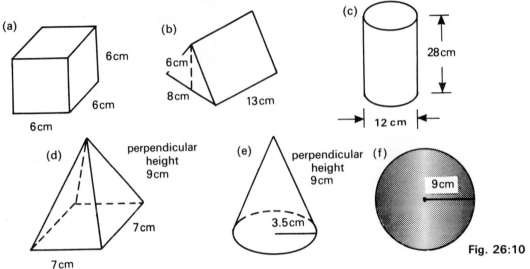

Fig. 26:10

*3 A cylindrical barrel of radius 35 cm and height 120 cm is filled with cider. Taking $\pi = \frac{22}{7}$ find the volume of cider in the barrel in (a) cm³ and (b) litres. (Note: 1 litre = 1000 cm³.)

4 Figure 26:11 shows the plans and elevations of four solids. Calculate the volume of each solid in cm³.

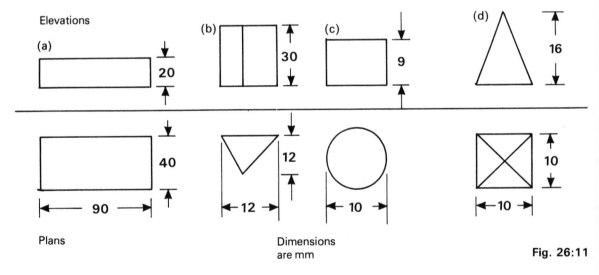

Fig. 26:11

5 An oil company drilled down 7000 m using a drill of 5 cm radius. How many m³ of earth and rock were removed? (Take $\pi = \frac{22}{7}$.)

6 Find the total surface area and the volume of a cylinder of radius 12 cm and height 23 cm.

7 Find the total surface area and the volume of a cone which fits exactly into the cylinder of question 6.

8 How many cans of radius 8 cm and height 30 cm can be filled from a drum of radius 40 cm and height 1.2 m? (Do not substitute a value for π; cancel it out instead.)

9 A cylinder of metal, 20 cm long and of 2 cm radius, is drawn out into wire of 2 mm diameter. How long is the wire? (Do not substitute for π.)

10 A cylindrical tank of diameter 1 m and height 126 centimetres leaks through a rust hole at the rate of 5 litres per hour. How long will it take to lose half the contents of a full tank?

---

11 A lead rod, 20 cm in diameter and 32 cm long, is melted down to make spherical shot of radius 1.5 mm.

    (a) Calculate the dimensions of the rod in millimetres, then the volume of the rod in mm^3.

    (b) Calculate the volume of one piece of shot.

    (c) How many shot may be made from the rod, to the nearest hundred?

12 A brass rod, 12 cm radius and 16 cm long, is to be melted down and re-cast into 4 cm-long rods of 3 cm radius. How many rods can be made?

13 How many packets of butter 10 cm by 7 cm by 4 cm could be packed in a box 96 cm by 84 cm by 45 cm?

14 Figure 26:12 represents a boiler consisting of a cylinder with hemispherical ends. Calculate its volume.

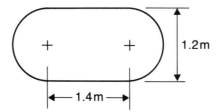

    1.2m

    1.4m   **Fig. 26:12**

15 Water flows through a 7 cm-radius pipe at the rate of 3 metres per second. How many litres will the pipe discharge in 1 minute?

16 A manufacturer wants to make half-litre cylindrical cans using as little metal as possible. By drawing a graph, or otherwise, find what the dimensions of the cans should be.

A Solid symmetry

For discussion

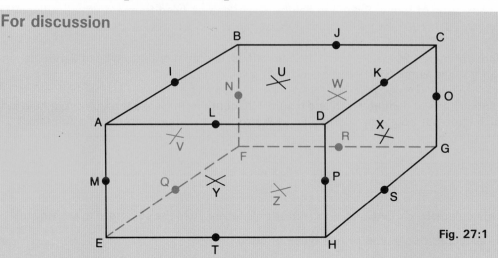

Fig. 27:1

Figure 27:1 shows a cuboid ABCD is a square.
● are the midpoints of edges; X are the centres of faces.
Red lettered points are seen 'through' the cuboid.

> **Planes of symmetry (reflection symmetry)**
> In the cuboid shown in Figure 27:1, BDHF is a plane of symmetry (see Figure 27:2), and IKSQ is another (see Figure 27:3).

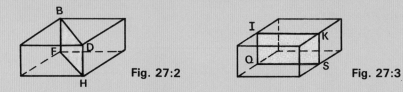

Fig. 27:2

Fig. 27:3

A plane of symmetry acts as a mirror.

(a) Why is ADGF in Figure 27:1 not a plane of symmetry?

(b) State the two diagonal planes of symmetry, and the three planes of symmetry parallel to the faces, for the cuboid in Figure 27:1.

> **Axes of symmetry (rotational symmetry)**
> In Figure 27:1, UZ is an axis of symmetry (see Figure 27:4). The cuboid in Figure 27:1 has five axes of symmetry. Name each of them.

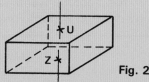

Fig. 27:4

The symmetry number of a solid is the number of ways that it can be put into a mould of itself. The cuboid in Figure 27:1 has symmetry number 8.

The models on worksheets 27A–M will be helpful in studying this topic.

1 For the solids in Figure 27:5 state the planes of symmetry and the axes of symmetry. Also state the symmetry numbers.

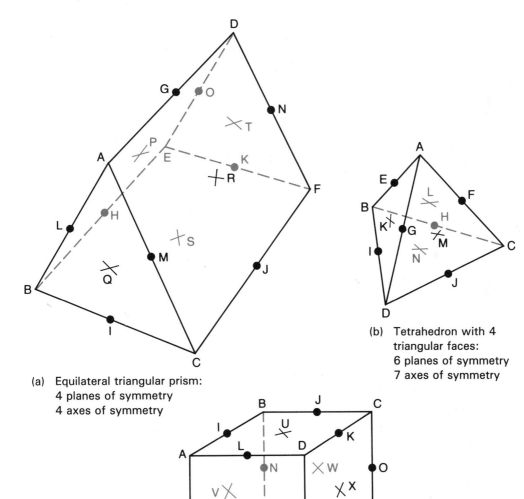

(a) Equilateral triangular prism:
    4 planes of symmetry
    4 axes of symmetry

(b) Tetrahedron with 4
    triangular faces:
    6 planes of symmetry
    7 axes of symmetry

(c) Cube: 9 planes of symmetry
    13 axes of symmetry   **Fig. 27:5**

> **2** Investigate the symmetry of:
>   (a) a regular pentagonal prism
>   (b) a regular hexagonal prism
>   (c) a frustum of a square-based pyramid.

B   Mensuration of solids

When answering questions about solids, spend some time trying to see the two-dimensional object drawn on the paper as a real three-dimensional solid. You may even be able to make a simple model of it from a piece of paper.

Calculations are always made using plane shapes (often triangles) and it is sensible to draw these triangles separately (and fairly accurately).

1 Figure 27:6 shows a square-based pyramid. All edges are 6 cm long.

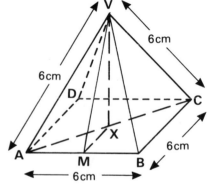

Fig. 27:6

(a) How many (i) faces, (ii) vertices (corners), and (iii) edges, has the solid?

(b) In Figure 27:6 there are 9 right angles, although none of them looks like a right angle. Find them all, e.g. ∠VMA.

(c) Sketch the following triangles, showing the right angles as true ones, and marking any known lengths. The first is shown as an example in Figure 27:7.
  (i) △ABC   (ii) △ADC   (iii) △VAM
  (iv) △VMB (v) △VAX (vi) △VXM

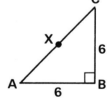

Fig. 27:7 True shape of △ABC

(d) Use Pythagoras' theorem to help you calculate, correct to 3 significant figures:
  (i) AC (use △ABC)   (ii) AX   (iii) XM   (iv) VM (use △VAM)
  (v) VX (use △VXM).

2 Referring to Figure 27:6, and using the triangles drawn for question 1(c), calculate to the nearest 0.1°:
  (a) ∠BAC   (b) ∠CAD   (c) ∠VAM   (d) ∠MVA   (e) ∠VBM   (f) ∠BVM
  (g) ∠VAX   (h) ∠AVX   (i) ∠VMX   (j) ∠XVM.

*3   Repeat question 1(d) for a square-based pyramid with all edges 7 cm long.

*4   Repeat question 2 for the 7 cm-sided pyramid.

5   An ant crawling straight across a table top bumps into a matchbox. It climbs over the box, keeping as far as possible to its planned route. The box is 5 cm by 3 cm by 2 cm.

   (a) What is the least possible extra distance the ant travels because the box is in its way?

   (b) What is the greatest possible extra distance?

   (c) If the box is placed so that the face in its way is at right angles to its normal path, when would it be better for the ant to crawl round the box rather than over it?

6   Calculate the volume of the pyramid in Figure 27:6.

7   Calculate the volume of the triangular prism in Figure 27:10 (see question 14).

8   In Figure 27:6, what fraction of the volume of the pyramid is VAMX?

9   Calculate the volume of water in a pool 30 metres long and 10 metres wide, which is 4 metres deep at the deep end and 1 metre at the shallow end, the bottom sloping along the whole 30-metre length. (Give your answer in litres in standard form.)

10   (a) Figure 27:8 shows a cuboid. Copy the diagram carefully.

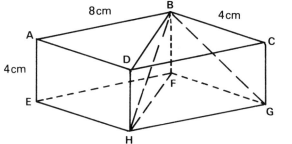

Fig. 27:8

   (b) Each of the following triangles is right-angled. Draw a sketch of each triangle, clearly showing its right angle as a true one.
   (i) △BCD   (ii) △HDB   (iii) △BHF   (iv) △BGH.

   (c) If BC = 4 cm, CD = 8 cm, and DH = 4 cm, use triangles (i) and (ii) in part (b) to calculate:
   (i) BD   (ii) BH (use BD^2 from part (i))   (iii) ∠BDC   (iv) ∠DBH.

11   (a) Copy Figure 27:9, then draw separate sketches of triangles EHG and AEG, showing clearly their right angles as true ones.

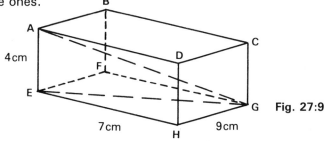

Fig. 27:9

161

(b) Calculate AG if EH = 7 cm, GH = 9 cm, and AE = 4 cm. (Hint: Find EG² but not EG.)

(c) Calculate ∠ AGE.

12 Calculate the longest diagonal of a 4 cm cube.

13 Can a 3.7 metre rod be put in a box 3 m long, 2 m wide, and 1 m deep?

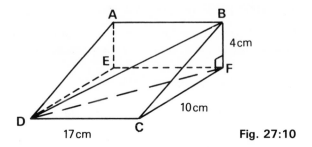

Fig. 27:10

14 (a) Copy the diagram of a wedge (Figure 27:10).

(b) Sketch △BCF, right-angled at F, and calculate BC.

(c) Sketch △FCD, right-angled at C, and calculate FD.

(d) Sketch △BFD, right-angled at F, and calculate BD. (Hint: Use FD² but do not find FD.)

(e) Calculate ∠ BCF and ∠ BDF. These are called the angles of greatest slope and of least slope.

15 On your copy of Figure 27:10, mark a point M, the midpoint of DC. Which of the following angles is the biggest and which is the smallest (or are they all the same size!)?
(a) ∠ BDF   (b) ∠ BMF   (c) ∠ BCF

16 In question 15, ∠ BCF is called 'the angle between the planes ABCD and EFCD'. Note that both BC and CF are at right angles to DC, the line of intersection of the two planes.

ABCD is the tailboard of a removal van, with AB = 2 metres and BC = 1 metre. AB is hinged to the van at a point 60 cm above the ground, and CD lies on the ground.

Calculate:
(a) the angle of greatest slope of the tailboard
(b) the angle of least slope of the tailboard.

17 Calculate the side of the largest cube that could be cut from a 10 cm-diameter sphere.

18 If the pyramid in question 1 is cut by a plane parallel to, and 2 cm from, its base, calculate the volume of the lower part (a 'frustum').

19 Consider the problem in question 5(c) if the face is not at right angles to the path.

28 Vectors: review; geometry

● You need to know . . .

A **vector** is a line with both length and direction. It is described by a column matrix, showing how far the end point of the vector is from the start point, measured horizontally and vertically. Positive and negative directions are the same as for graph axes. Figures 28:1 and 28:2 show two examples.

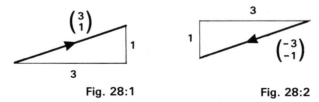

Fig. 28:1   Fig. 28:2

Position vectors always start at the origin, so the position vector $\begin{pmatrix} -4 \\ 2 \end{pmatrix}$ starts at (0, 0) and ends at (−4, 2).

Shift vectors describe translations (slidings). In Figure 28:3 the hatched square is translated to the shaded square by the vector $\begin{pmatrix} 3 \\ 1 \end{pmatrix}$. Each corner of the square moves 3 units to the right and 1 unit upwards.

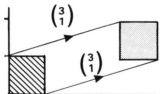

Fig. 28:3

Shift vectors can start at any point, and the same vector can be at several places on the same grid.

Vectors may be described as a matrix, $\begin{pmatrix} 3 \\ 1 \end{pmatrix}$, or by their end letters, $\overrightarrow{AB}$, or by a single letter distinguished with a wavy line underneath (or sometimes, in print, by being thicker). The same letter (or letters) can be used for parallel vectors, but different letters *must* be used for non-parallel vectors.

Figures 28:4 to 28:7 show some examples of parallel vectors.

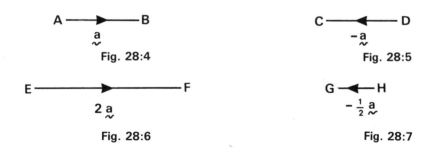

Fig. 28:4   Fig. 28:5

Fig. 28:6   Fig. 28:7

A **resultant vector** is the single vector that gives the same translation as all the others added together.

In Figure 28:8, $\overrightarrow{OA}$ is the resultant of $\underset{\sim}{a}$ and $\underset{\sim}{b}$ and $\underset{\sim}{c}$.

The resultant vector may be calculated by adding the matrices of the given set of vectors.

In Figure 28:8, $\overrightarrow{OA} = \underset{\sim}{a} + \underset{\sim}{b} + \underset{\sim}{c} = \begin{pmatrix} 4 \\ 0 \end{pmatrix} + \begin{pmatrix} -2 \\ -1 \end{pmatrix} + \begin{pmatrix} 0 \\ -3 \end{pmatrix} = \begin{pmatrix} 2 \\ -4 \end{pmatrix}$.

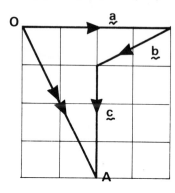

Fig. 28:8

The **magnitude of a vector** is its length. It is often written as $|\overrightarrow{OA}|$, and it is called the **modulus** of $\overrightarrow{OA}$.

In Figure 28:9,

$(|\overrightarrow{OA}|)^2 = 2^2 + 4^2$ (Pythagoras' theorem)

Hence $|\overrightarrow{OA}| = \sqrt{20} = 4.47$ to 3 s.f.

Fig. 28:9

Test yourself

1 If $\underset{\sim}{a} = \begin{pmatrix} 4 \\ 0 \end{pmatrix}$, $\underset{\sim}{b} = \begin{pmatrix} -2 \\ -1 \end{pmatrix}$, and $\underset{\sim}{c} = \begin{pmatrix} 0 \\ -3 \end{pmatrix}$, draw on squared paper the following vectors, starting each one from the end of the previous one. Remember the arrows!

$\underset{\sim}{a}$; $\underset{\sim}{b}$; $\underset{\sim}{c}$; $-\underset{\sim}{b}$; $\frac{1}{2}\underset{\sim}{a}$; $-\underset{\sim}{c}$; $2\underset{\sim}{a}$; $2\underset{\sim}{b}$; $-\frac{1}{2}\underset{\sim}{a}$; $\frac{1}{3}\underset{\sim}{c}$; $1\frac{1}{2}\underset{\sim}{a}$; $-2\underset{\sim}{b}$; $\underset{\sim}{c}$; $-4\underset{\sim}{a}$

*2 $\underset{\sim}{d} = \begin{pmatrix} 2 \\ 0 \end{pmatrix}$; $\underset{\sim}{e} = \begin{pmatrix} 0 \\ -2 \end{pmatrix}$; $\underset{\sim}{f} = \begin{pmatrix} 1 \\ 2 \end{pmatrix}$; $\underset{\sim}{g} = \begin{pmatrix} 3 \\ 2 \end{pmatrix}$; $\underset{\sim}{h} = \begin{pmatrix} -2 \\ 1 \end{pmatrix}$; $\underset{\sim}{i} = \begin{pmatrix} 1 \\ -2 \end{pmatrix}$

The resultant of $\underset{\sim}{d}$ and $\underset{\sim}{h}$ is $\begin{pmatrix} 2 \\ 0 \end{pmatrix} + \begin{pmatrix} -2 \\ 1 \end{pmatrix} = \begin{pmatrix} 0 \\ 1 \end{pmatrix}$.

Calculate the resultant of:
(a) $\underset{\sim}{d}$ and $\underset{\sim}{e}$ (b) $\underset{\sim}{e}$ and $\underset{\sim}{f}$ (c) $\underset{\sim}{e}$ and $\underset{\sim}{g}$ (d) $\underset{\sim}{e}$ and $\underset{\sim}{h}$ (e) $\underset{\sim}{d}$ and $\underset{\sim}{i}$
(f) $\underset{\sim}{d}$ and $\underset{\sim}{g}$ (g) $\underset{\sim}{f}$ and $\underset{\sim}{d}$ (h) $\underset{\sim}{i}$ and $\underset{\sim}{h}$ (i) $\underset{\sim}{g}$ and $\underset{\sim}{h}$ (j) $\underset{\sim}{i}$ and $\underset{\sim}{f}$.

*3 Figure 28:10 shows the resultant of vectors d̰ and h̰ (defined in question 2).

Draw on squared paper each pair of vectors given in parts (a) to (j) of question 2, and show their resultant. Check that your drawn answers agree with the ones you calculated.

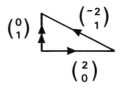

Fig. 28:10

*4 For the vectors given in question 2, calculate:
(a) |d̰| (b) |ḛ| (c) |f̰| (d) |g̰| (e) |h̰| (f) |ḭ|.

5 (a) Show by calculation and drawing that the resultant of vectors ḛ, 2h̰ and 2f̰ (as defined in question 2) is −2ḭ.

(b) Vector $\overrightarrow{AB}$ is described by the matrix $\begin{pmatrix} 3 \\ -5 \end{pmatrix}$. Sketch this vector, then calculate $|\overrightarrow{AB}|$ to 3 significant figures.

6 In Figure 28:11, state in terms of a̰ and b̰:

(a) $\overrightarrow{QP}$ (b) $\overrightarrow{SP}$ (c) $\overrightarrow{SR}$ (d) $\overrightarrow{RS}$
(e) $\overrightarrow{QR}$ (f) $\overrightarrow{RQ}$
(g) $\overrightarrow{PR}$ (the resultant of $\overrightarrow{PQ}$ and $\overrightarrow{PS}$).

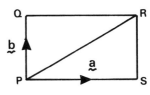

Fig. 28:11

7 In Figure 28:12, $\overrightarrow{SQ} = \overrightarrow{SP} + \overrightarrow{PQ}$ and $\overrightarrow{QS} = \overrightarrow{QP} + \overrightarrow{PS}$. Write $\overrightarrow{SQ}$ and $\overrightarrow{QS}$ in terms of a̰ and b̰.

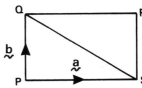

Fig. 28:12

8 In Figure 28:13, M is the midpoint of AC. $\overrightarrow{BA} = \underset{\sim}{x}$, $\overrightarrow{BC} = \underset{\sim}{y}$, and $\overrightarrow{AM} = \underset{\sim}{z}$.

Express in terms of x̰, y̰ and z̰:

(a) $\overrightarrow{AB}$ (b) $\overrightarrow{CB}$ (c) $\overrightarrow{AC}$ (d) $\overrightarrow{MA}$ (e) $\overrightarrow{CM}$
(f) $\overrightarrow{BM}$ (in 2 ways)   (g) $\overrightarrow{MB}$ (in 2 ways).

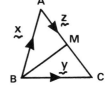

Fig. 28:13

9 In Figure 28:14, PQRS is a parallelogram. M is the midpoint of PS.

Express in terms of a̰ and b̰:

(a) $\overrightarrow{SP}$ (b) $\overrightarrow{SR}$ (c) $\overrightarrow{PM}$
(d) $\overrightarrow{QM}$ (e) $\overrightarrow{MR}$

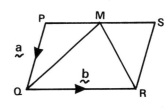

Fig. 28:14

10 KLMN is a square. D, E, F and G are the midpoints of KL, LM, MN and NK respectively. $\overrightarrow{GK} = \underset{\sim}{c}$ and $\overrightarrow{KD} = \underset{\sim}{d}$.

Express in terms of c̰ and d̰:

(a) $\overrightarrow{ML}$ (b) $\overrightarrow{LD}$ (c) $\overrightarrow{NF}$ (d) $\overrightarrow{GE}$ (e) $\overrightarrow{GD}$ (f) $\overrightarrow{GL}$ (g) $\overrightarrow{GM}$ (h) $\overrightarrow{GF}$.

11 State the missing vector:
    (a) $\overrightarrow{AB} + \overrightarrow{BC} = \dots$ (b) $\overrightarrow{AB} + \dots = \overrightarrow{AF}$.

Illustrate your answers with diagrams.

---

12 $\overrightarrow{AB}$ and $\overrightarrow{AC}$ are at an angle of 30°, and AB = 2AC. Sketch $\overrightarrow{AB}$ and $\overrightarrow{AC}$ and their resultant vector.

13 If $\overrightarrow{AB} = \overrightarrow{CD}$ then AB and CD are equal and parallel. Sketch $\overrightarrow{AB}$ and $\overrightarrow{BC}$ if $\overrightarrow{AB} = \overrightarrow{BC}$.

14 ABC is a straight line with AB : AC = 1 : 3. If $\overrightarrow{AB} = x$, state in terms of x:
    (a) $\overrightarrow{AC}$ (b) $\overrightarrow{BC}$

15 (a) c and d are two sides of a triangle. Explain why $c \neq d$.

    (b) If in part (a), $(h + k)c = (h - k + 1)d$, calculate h and k.

16 $\overrightarrow{AB}$ and $\overrightarrow{AC}$ are two vectors. M is the midpoint of BC. Express $\overrightarrow{BC}$ and $\overrightarrow{BM}$ in terms of $\overrightarrow{AB}$ and $\overrightarrow{AC}$, and hence show that $\overrightarrow{AM} = \frac{1}{2}(\overrightarrow{AB} + \overrightarrow{AC})$.

This is an important theorem about two vectors.

17 (a) If $\overrightarrow{XY} = h\overrightarrow{BC}$, what is true about $\overrightarrow{XY}$ and $\overrightarrow{BC}$?

    (b) X and Y are points on the sides AB and AC of $\triangle ABC$ such that $\dfrac{AX}{AB} = \dfrac{AY}{AC} = h$. It follows that AX = hAB and that $\overrightarrow{AX} = h\overrightarrow{AB}$.

    Show that $\overrightarrow{XY} = h\overrightarrow{BC}$ and hence that XY // BC and $\dfrac{XY}{BC} = h$.

18 Prove that when the midpoints of the sides of a parallelogram are joined in order they form another parallelogram.

Vectors, forces and velocities

Forces act on a body to try to make it move. Figure 28:15 shows some typical forces. Force is usually measured in newtons (N). Gravity makes a mass of 1 kg weigh 9.8 newtons.

Fig. 28:15

Vectors may be used to represent forces and speeds. The length of the vector represents the size of the force.

In Figure 28:16, a force of 2 N is pulling on the block, pulling it towards the left-hand corner of the page.

Fig. 28:16 Scale: 1 cm represents 1 N

In Figure 28:17 a second force, of 3 N, is also pulling on the block, tending to pull it towards the top right-hand corner of the page. As a result of both forces, it will actually move (if friction does not stop it) in a direction between the two forces.

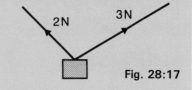

Fig. 28:17

Figure 28:18 shows how to find the strength and direction of the resulting force. It is called the **parallelogram of forces**.

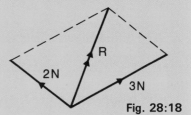

Fig. 28:18

The same result can be obtained by representing the forces in a triangle, as you saw in the 'Test yourself' exercise. Figure 28:19 illustrates this.

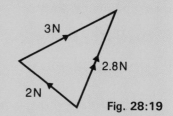

Fig. 28:19

Resultant speeds

On a very windy day you can see birds apparently flying sideways. The track (the actual path) of a bird, a plane or a ship is usually affected by two main forces, the engine (or the bird's wings) making it move along its axis of symmetry, and the wind or the sea-current trying to move it off its course. Figures 28:20 and 28:21 illustrate this effect. (We have exaggerated the wind and current force.) The ship (or plane's) rudder is used to help it stay on course. The on-board compass shows that the direction of travel (its track) is different to its course (its heading along the axis of symmetry).

Fig. 28:20

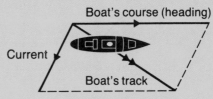

Fig. 28:21

Vectors can be used to represent the speed of the current/wind and the ship/plane, and the resultant track and speed found by drawing or (when you have done enough trigonometry) by calculation.

1 Find the resultant force and the angle it makes with the horizontal in each diagram in Figure 28:22.

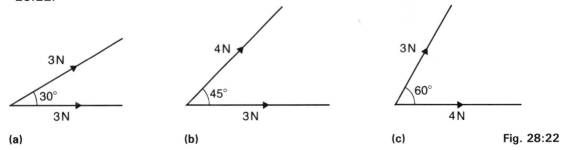

(a) (b) (c) **Fig. 28:22**

2 Find the resultant speed and its bearing for each diagram in Figure 28:23.

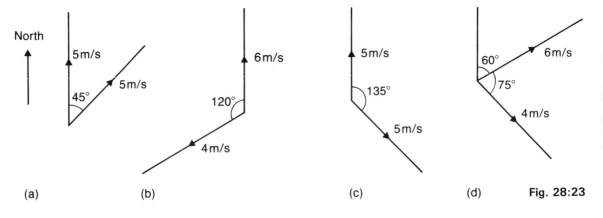

(a) (b) (c) (d) **Fig. 28:23**

*3 In each diagram in Figure 28:24, two forces are represented by vectors. By drawing, find the strength of the resulting force and its direction with the horizontal.

Scale: 1 cm represents 1 N

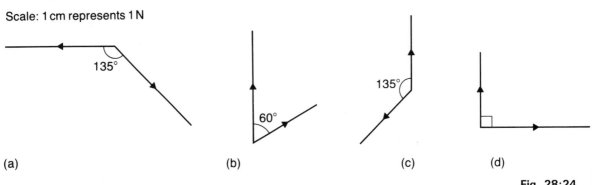

(a) (b) (c) (d)

Fig. 28:24

4 Judith, Katie and Jane are on an ice rink. Judith and Katie are each pulling Jane in different directions. Judith is pulling Jane west with a force of 200 N and Katie is pulling her south-east with a force of 150 N. In what direction does Jane move?

5 A pilot aims his plane due north at 100 m/s. A wind is blowing from the east at 30 m/s. What is the resulting bearing and speed of the plane?

6 A captain is heading on a bearing of 030 degrees at 15 knots. A current of 4 knots is running due north. What is the resulting speed and direction of the ship?

---

7 At 1130 Batwick airport lies 50 n.m. away on a bearing of 270° from a plane whose air-speed is 300 knots. A wind of 50 knots is blowing from bearing 000 degrees. In which direction should the pilot steer to land at Batwick, and what is her estimated time of arrival?

8 One point on a bridge is acted upon by three forces: a maximum design weight of 3000 N downwards; and two wires, one pulling upwards to the left at 35° to the vertical, and one upwards to the right at 25° to the vertical. The bridge is just prevented from moving in any direction. What force will be applied by each wire?

29 Statistical charts

● You need to know . . .

● Pictograms

Figure 29:1 is a pictogram. Each complete symbol represents 10 cars. The whole picture represents 25 cars.

 **Fig. 29:1**

● Line graphs

Figure 29:2 is a line graph. The points plotted with a cross are from correct data, but points on the lines joining the crosses may have no meaning, as in this line graph. It is then best to use a dashed line.

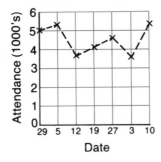

Fig. 29:2

● Bar charts or block graphs

Figure 29:3 is a bar chart, or block graph. It illustrates the data in the table, which shows the choices of 100 pupils in a survey at Upside School.

Life aim	Frequency
An interesting job	18
Happiness	20
Start a family	15
Plenty of money	25
Caring for people	10
Excitement	12

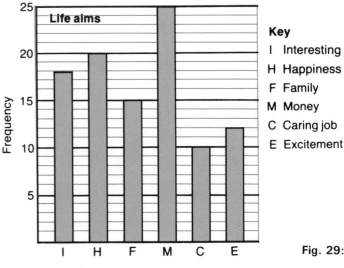

Key

I   Interesting job
H   Happiness
F   Family
M   Money
C   Caring job
E   Excitement

Fig. 29:3

Proportionate bar charts

Figure 29:4 shows the above data as a proportionate bar chart.

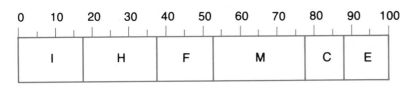

Key
I Interesting job
H Happiness
F Family
M Money
C Caring job
E Excitement

Fig. 29:4

Pie charts

Figure 29:5 shows the same data as a pie chart. As there were 100 pupils in the survey, 1 pupil is represented by 360° ÷ 100 = 3.6°, so the 18 pupil sector has an angle of 18 × 3.6° = 64.8° at its centre.

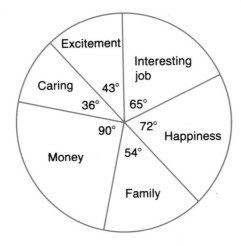

Fig. 29:5

Scattergrams

A scattergram compares two sets of data. From it we can see if the data is linked or 'correlated' in any way. The scattergram in Figure 29:6 shows a correlation between ability in maths and ability in music.

The random points in the scattergram in Figure 29:7 indicates that there is no correlation between height and ability to score runs in cricket.

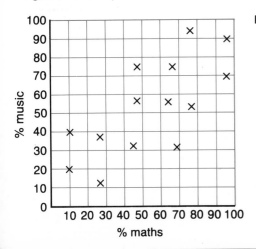

Fig. 29:6

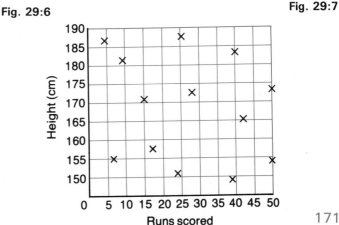

Fig. 29:7

171

● Growth and decay curves

These are graphs illustrating the way a measure increases or decreases. Figure 29:8 shows some examples. At any point on the curve the slope of a tangent to the curve gives the rate of growth or decay; see Figure 29:9.

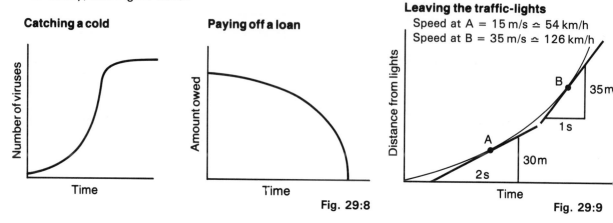

Catching a cold

Paying off a loan

Leaving the traffic-lights
Speed at A = 15 m/s ≃ 54 km/h
Speed at B = 35 m/s ≃ 126 km/h

Fig. 29:8

Fig. 29:9

● Histograms

These appear at first to be bar charts, and are often confused with them in other subjects, and even by some mathematicians! In a histogram the **area** of the bar represents the frequency, not the height. They are only used when the data is continuous and are intended to avoid giving a wrong impression when the bars are of unequal width. However, most people still look at the heights and reach the wrong conclusion! Figures 29:10 and 29:11 show a bar chart and a histogram representing the same data:

Age	Number of people seen
0–5	6
5–20	6
20–60	8
60–80	6

0–5 ⇒ up to but not including 5.

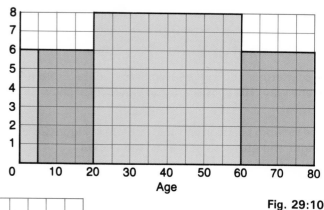

Fig. 29:10

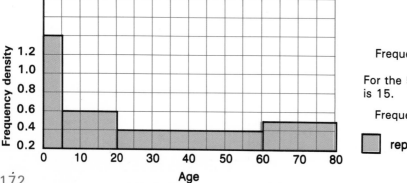

Frequency = Frequency density × class interval.
For the 5–20 class, the class interval is 15.

Frequency = 0.4 × 15 = 6.

☐ represents 1 person

Fig. 29:11

1 In the great gale of January 1990 the town of Wyke sustained the following injuries and damage:

110 trees blown down
90 houses damaged
20 people injured
60 cars damaged

Using suitable symbols to represent 10 trees, 10 houses, 10 people, and 10 cars, draw a pictogram to illustrate this data.

2 Look at Figure 29:12.

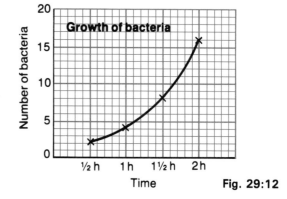

Fig. 29:12

(a) What does one square represent on
(i) the horizontal axis
(ii) the vertical axis?

(b) Are the bacteria steadily increasing, or increasing faster and faster as time goes on? Explain how you know.

(c) Copy the graph, then extend it to show how you think the bacteria will grow during the next hour.

(d) From your graph, how many bacteria might there be
(i) after $1\frac{1}{4}$ hours   (ii) after $1\frac{3}{4}$ hours?

3 Illustrate the hair colours in your class (e.g. fair, auburn, brown, black) with a proportionate bar chart.

4 Car insurers use accident statistics to help them decide the premiums to charge motorists. This table compares fatal accident statistics in the UK and West Germany.

	1936	1966	1976	1986
UK	6561	7985	6570	5382
W. Germany	*	16 868	14 820	8948

*Figures not available.

Copy the table, approximating the statistics (not the dates!) to the nearest 1000, then draw two line graphs on the same axes to compare the statistics for both countries. You should try to draw a smooth curve through your plotted points.

Write about the meaning of the statistics.

5 Figure 29:13 shows a graph to illustrate the number of people unemployed in the UK between 1979 and 1985.

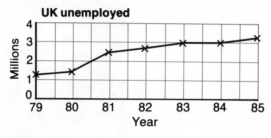

UK unemployed

Fig. 29:13

(a) About how many people were unemployed each January from 1979 to 1985?

(b) Do you think this graph makes the unemployment figures look 'not too bad' or 'dreadful'? Why?

(c) Redraw the graph choosing new scales so that the rise in people out of work looks much worse.

6 The charges of two estate agents are:

Pride & Co – 2% of the price of the house

First Service – 1% on the first £40 000
            3% on the remainder

Example   House price £50 000
          Pride & Co charge £50 000 × 2% = £1000
          First Service charge £40 000 × 1% = £400
                   plus £10 000 × 3% = £300
                   Total £700

(a) Copy and complete this table:

House price	Pride & Co	First Service
£50 000	£1000	£400 + £300 = £700
£60 000		
£70 000		
£80 000		
£90 000		
£100 000		

(b) Compare the charges of the two companies with a line graph.

(c) At what house price, if any, does Pride & Co charge less than First Services?

(d) If First Service charges include VAT at 17.5% but Pride and Co charges are 'VAT extra', who is the cheaper for a £90 000 house and for a £120 000 house, and by how much?

7 Sara has conducted a survey to find what filling pupils in her class would prefer in a baked potato. The table shows her data. Draw a pie chart to illustrate this. Show on your chart, or in a list at the side, the angles you use for each sector. Remember to label your graph clearly.

Choice	Number	Choice	Number
Butter	4	Pickle	7
Cheese	6	Onions	3
Baked beans	9	Sardines	1

8 A geography class is studying the climate of Calcutta.

Month	J	F	M	A	M	J	J	A	S	O	N	D
°C	19	22	28	30	31	29	28	27	26	25	22	21
mm rain	10	30	35	50	140	310	320	330	250	100	20	5

(a) Draw a scattergram to illustrate the given data. Figure 29:14 shows the start of the graph.

(b) Is there any truth in the statement that in Calcutta the hotter it gets the more it rains?

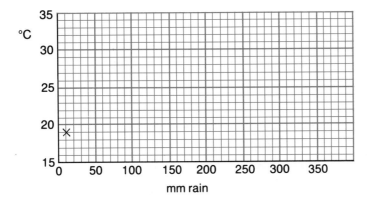

Fig. 29:14

9 Sixty cars are tested to see how far they will go on 10 litres of petrol. The findings are given in the table. Draw a histogram to illustrate the data. Use a horizontal scale of 1 cm to 10 km from 50 km to 180 km, and represent 3 cars with an area of 1 cm².

Distance in km	50 to 79	80 to 119	120 to 139	140 to 180
Number of cars	ЖHT ////	ЖHT ЖHT ЖHT ЖHT ////	ЖHT ЖHT ЖHT ///	ЖHT ЖHT ЖHT

10 The map shows the percentage increases in house prices in various parts of the UK between 1973 and 1987. Copy Figure 29:15 and draw a scattergram to find out if the increase in house prices was less the further the houses were from London.

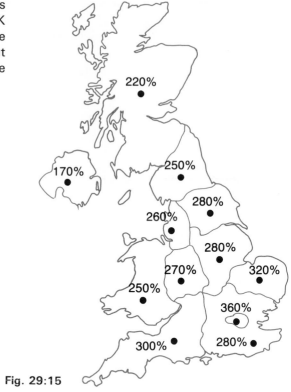

Fig. 29:15

11 (a) Using the data in Figure 29:16, draw a line graph to show the rate at which the cliff decayed between 1969 and September 1990.

How the sea crept up on 'Ons Huis'

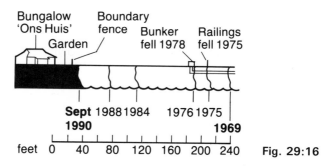

Fig. 29:16

(b) Describe how the rate of erosion changed over the years. Why do you think it was not constant?

(c) Draw a line on your graph to show how the same final cliff position could have been reached at a constant state of erosion. What is this average rate of erosion in feet per year?

(d) Estimate the date at which the bungalow would start to fall into the sea.

12 (a) Using the data in Figure 29:17, estimate the rate of change in the population of the developed and the developing regions in 1900 and in 1990.

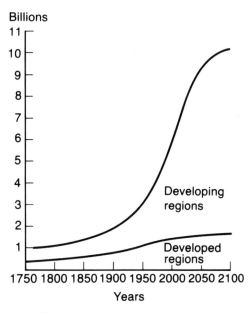

Fig. 29:17 World population growth from 1750 to 2100

(b) Draw a similar graph to show the total growth of world population between 1750 and 2100 (projected).

(c) What factors cause the wide difference in the rates of growth between the two regions? What could the developed regions do to try to prevent the projected catastrophic rate of growth in the developing regions? What are they doing?

13 Gareth says that a person's height is the same as the distance between the tips of the hands at widest stretch.

Investigate the truth of this statement. Illustrate your findings with a scattergraph.

14 Undertake a statistical survey of your own. Write a full report of your findings, including charts and graphs.

A   Chord and diameter

For discussion

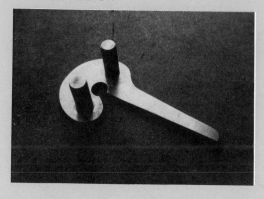
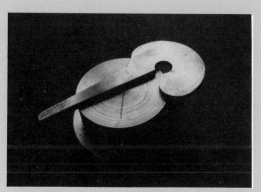

Fig. 30:1

Note: In all the diagrams in this chapter, point O is the centre of the circle.

1 (a) Construct Figure 30:2, using a circle of radius 20 mm and making AB = 30 mm.

    (b) Join A and B to the centre, O, then mark clearly *all* equal lines and angles.

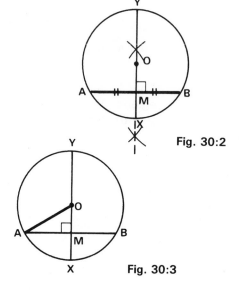

Fig. 30:2

*2 (a) Copy Figure 30:3, using radius about 2 cm.

    (b) If chord AB = 8 cm, write on AM the length it would be.

    (c) Copy and complete the following to calculate OM if the radius OA = 6 cm.

$$OA^2 = AM^2 + OM^2 \quad \text{(Pythagoras' theorem)}$$
$$36 = \ldots + OM^2$$
$$\therefore OM^2 = 36 - \ldots = \ldots$$
$$\therefore OM = \sqrt{20} \simeq \ldots \text{cm}$$

Fig. 30:3

*3 Using Pythagoras' theorem, as in question 2, and drawing a sketch for each question, calculate for Figure 30:3
  (a) OM if AB = 10 cm and OA = 7 cm
  (b) AM if OM = 3 cm and OA = 8 cm
  (c) OA if AB = 12 cm and OM = 6 cm

*4 State for Figure 30:3 the length of:
  (a) AB if AM = 7.6 cm
  (b) OA if OX = 4.9 cm
  (c) XY if OA = 10.8 cm.

5 By drawing a suitable small diagram (see Figure 30:3), then using Pythagoras' theorem (see question 2), calculate:

(a) the perpendicular distance of an 11 cm chord from the centre of a 7 cm radius circle.

(b) the length of a chord whose perpendicular distance from the centre of a 5.6 cm radius circle is 3 cm.

(c) the length of a chord whose perpendicular distance from the centre of an 8.1 cm radius circle is 2.9 cm.

6 Figure 30:4 represents a spherical goldfish-bowl.

(a) What shape is the surface of the water (AB)?

(b) Calculate the depth of the water at its deepest point if AB = 12 cm and the bowl has a radius of 10 cm. (Hint: First calculate the perpendicular distance of AB from O.)

(c) Water is added to the bowl until the water surface has a 12 cm diameter again. How deep is the water now?

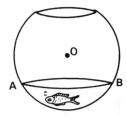

Fig. 30:4

7 Two parallel chords of lengths 6 cm and 8 cm are drawn in a 5 cm radius circle. Calculate the two possible distances between them.

8 Illustrate a method for finding the centre of a circle using two chords and their perpendicular bisectors.

9 Illustrate a method to find the circumcentre of a triangle using the perpendicular bisectors of two chords. Discuss the position of the circumcentre for acute-, right-, and obtuse-angled triangles.

B Angles at centre and circumference

In each of Figures 30:5, 30:6 and 30:7, the arc AB subtends ∠AOB at the centre O and subtends ∠ACB at the circumference.

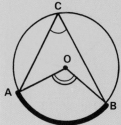

Fig. 30:5

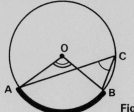

Fig. 30:6

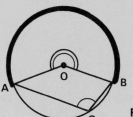

Fig. 30:7

∠AOB = 2∠ACB (Angles at centre and circumference)

Note that in Figure 30:7 it is the major (longer) arc which subtends the angles, and ∠AOB is reflex in this case.

Hints: (a) The pair of angles must start and finish with the same letters, e.g. ∠POQ = 2∠PXR could not be correct.

(b) Both angles must 'open out' the same way. This is especially important when the centre angle is reflex, as in Figure 30:7. This is illustrated in Figure 30:8.

 and but NOT

Fig. 30:8

For discussion

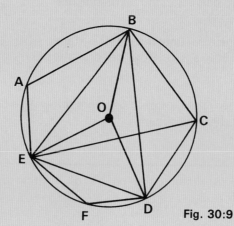

Fig. 30:9

1 Copy Figures 30:10 to 30:13, making them about the same size. Then calculate:
(a) ∠POQ   (b) ∠POQ reflex   (c) ∠AOC reflex   (d) ∠AOC   (e) ∠XZY
(f) ∠ZYO   (g) ∠MOK reflex   (h) ∠MNK.

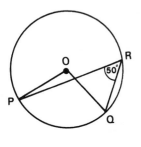

Fig. 30:10

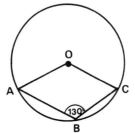

Fig. 30:11

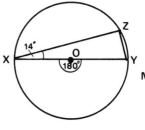

Fig. 30:12

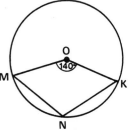

Fig. 30:13

2 Repeat question 1 for Figures 30:14 to 30:17.

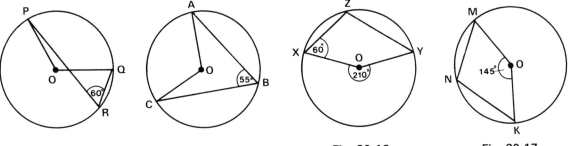

Fig. 30:14   Fig. 30:15   Fig. 30:16   Fig. 30:17

3 For Figures 30:18, 30:19 and 30:20 calculate:
  (a) ∠FDE   (b) ∠HIJ   (c) ∠RNQ   (d) ∠NPQ   (e) ∠PNQ
  (f) ∠NQP   (g) ∠MNR.

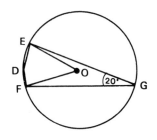

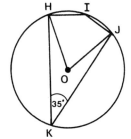

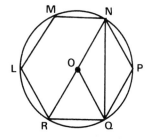

LMNPQR is a
regular hexagon

Fig. 30:18   Fig. 30:19   Fig. 30:20

---

4 On a clock face, the points representing 4 and 5 o'clock are joined by straight lines to the point representing 8 o'clock. Calculate the angle between the lines.

5 Calculate the angles of the triangle made by joining the clock face points 3, 8 and 12.

C   Angle in a semicircle

The angle in a semicircle is a right angle.

Fig. 30:21

1 In Figure 30:22, which two angles would be 90° if
(a) DF, (b) GE was a diameter?

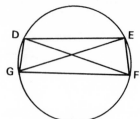

Fig. 30:22

2 Copy Figure 30:23, making it about twice as large,
(a) Name four angles that must be right angles.
(b) If ∠BAF = 47° calculate ∠ABF.
(c) If ∠FAC = 82° calculate ∠FOC.

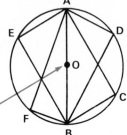

Fig. 30:23

AOB is a diameter.

3 (a) Copy Figure 30:24, then calculate the following
angles, giving reasons chosen from (Angle in a
semicircle), (Angles of an isosceles triangle),
(Alternate angles, CB//AD), and (Angle sum of a
triangle).
(i) ∠C (ii) ∠B (iii) ∠BAD
(iv) ∠D (v) ∠AOD

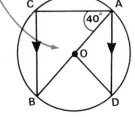

Fig. 30:24

(b) Explain why COD must be a straight line.

(c) Repeat (a) with ∠BAC = 35°.

4 Calculate the radius of the circumcircle of the triangle
in Figure 30:25.

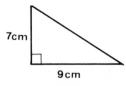

7cm

9cm   Fig. 30:25

5 In Figure 30:26, find six sets of four concyclic
points (i.e. points on the circumference of the
same circle); then draw a large copy of the
diagram and draw the circles.

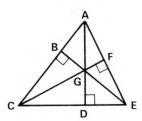

Fig. 30:26

31 Factorisation: $x^2 \pm bx + c$

Factorise the expressions in questions 1 to 6.

1 (a) $x^2 + 2x + 1$ (b) $x^2 + 3x + 2$ (c) $x^2 + 7x + 6$
   (d) $x^2 + 4x + 3$ (e) $x^2 + 8x + 12$ (f) $x^2 + 9x + 20$

2 (a) $x^2 - 2x + 1$ (b) $x^2 - 4x + 4$ (c) $x^2 - 3x + 2$
   (d) $x^2 - 6x + 8$ (e) $x^2 - 6x + 9$ (f) $x^2 - 11x + 10$

3 (a) $x^2 + 4x + 4$ (b) $x^2 - 16x + 15$ (c) $x^2 - 5x + 4$
   (d) $x^2 + 5x + 4$ (e) $x^2 + 7x + 12$ (f) $x^2 - 7x + 12$

4 (a) $x^2 + 20x + 51$ (b) $x^2 + 15x + 56$ (c) $x^2 - 16x + 48$
   (d) $x^2 - 10x + 21$ (e) $x^2 + 11x + 10$ (f) $x^2 - 12x + 36$

5 (a) $x^2 + 14xy + 48y^2$ (b) $x^2 - 10xy + 24y^2$ (c) $x^2 + 10xy + 21y^2$
   (d) $x^2 - 10xy + 16y^2$ (e) $x^2 - 4xy + 4y^2$ (f) $x^2 + 21xy + 68y^2$

6 (a) $a^2 - 9b^2$ (b) $p^2q^2 - 16$ (c) $x^4y^4 - 36$
   (d) $bcx - bcy + mx - my$ (e) $4ax + 6bx + 6ay + 9by$

A Angles in the same segment

A **chord** cuts a circle into two **segments**. In Figure 32:1, angles AXB and AYB are **angles in the same segment** (the segment cut off by chord AB). These angles are equal: $\angle$ AXB = $\angle$ AYB.

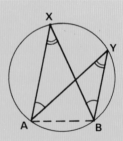

Fig. 32:1

If a chord was drawn from X to Y, then angles XAY and XBY would also be 'equal angles in the same segment', though of course it is a different segment to the first one.

Angles in the same segment must start and finish with the same letter, and the middle letter must be a point on the circumference.

For discussion

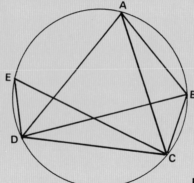

Fig. 32:2

1   In Figure 32:3, state which angle is an equal angle in the same segment as:
    (a) angle x (b) angle z.

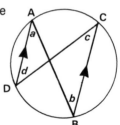

Fig. 32:3

2   In Figure 32:4, AD is parallel to CB. State why the following facts are true:
    (a) $a = c$ (b) $a = b$ (c) $b = c$ (d) $b = d$
    (e) $c = d$ (f) $a = d$.

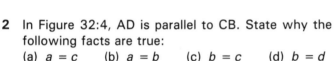

Fig. 32:4

*3 Copy Figure 32:5, where XY is parallel to UT.

(a) State the sizes of the seven angles *a* to *g*.

(b) Name two pairs of equal alternate angles (use capital letters).

(c) Name two pairs of equal vertically opposite angles (use small letters).

(d) Name four pairs of adjacent angles on a straight line (use small letters).

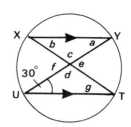

Fig. 32:5

4 In Figure 32:6 name an angle equal to each of the following angles, giving the reason.

(a) *a*   (b) *b*   (c) *c*   (d) *e*   (e) *i*   (f) *j*.

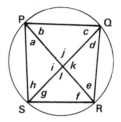

Fig. 32:6

5 Copy Figure 32:7. State with reasons the size of:

(a) ∠ABC   (b) ∠A   (c) ∠D.

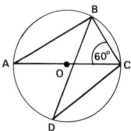

Fig. 32:7

6 In Figure 32:8, XD = XC. State the reason why:

(a) *c* = *d*

(b) *d* = *a*

(c) *a* = *c* (not 'equal alternate angles', as the lines are not known to be parallel)

(d) AB must be parallel to DC.

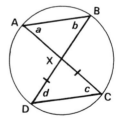

Fig. 32:8

7 In Figure 32:9:

(a) If ∠ABC = 90° what is AC?

(b) If X is the centre of the circle then name two angles half the size of ∠BXC.

8 Copy Figure 32:9. If ∠ABD = 50° and ∠ADC = 80° prove that triangle ADC is isosceles.

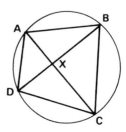

Fig. 32:9

185

9 In Figure 32:10 state:
(a) the size of ∠ACT
(b) the size of ∠ABC
(c) c + e in degrees
(d) c + a in degrees
(e) the reasons why a = e
(f) the reasons why a = d
(g) the reasons why d = e.

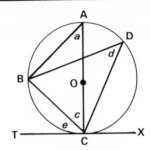

Fig. 32:10

10 ABCD is a cyclic quadrilateral (its corners lie on a circle). Diagonals AC and BD meet at X, and AX = AB. Prove that DX = DC.

B   Cyclic quadrilaterals

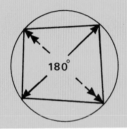

Fig. 32:11

A cyclic quadrilateral has its four corners on the circumference of a circle.

The opposite angles of a cyclic quadrilateral add up to 180° (they are 'supplementary').

1 In Figure 32:12, state the sizes of angles a and b.

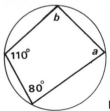

Fig. 32:12

2 In Figure 32:13, AB is parallel to DC. Angles b and c are interior angles between parallel lines. They add up to 180°. State with the reason the size of:
(a) angle d   (b) angle b.

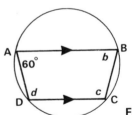

Fig. 32:13

3 Referring to Figure 32:14, copy and complete:

$$a = 2c \text{ (angles at centre and circumference)}$$
$$b = \ldots \text{ (angles at centre and circumference)}$$
$$a + b = \ldots° \text{ (angles round a point)}$$
$$\therefore 2c + 2d = 360° \ (a = 2c \text{ and } b = 2d)$$
$$\therefore \quad c + d = \ldots° \text{ (dividing by 2)}$$

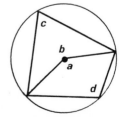

Fig. 32:14

*4 In Figure 32:15:
  (a) AOCB is *not* a cyclic quadrilateral. Why not?
  (b) If reflex angle AOC = 200°, what is the size of angle ABC?

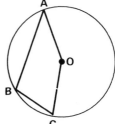

Fig. 32:15

*5 Try to draw the following polygons so that each corner lies on the circumference of a circle (draw the circles first).
  (a) An obtuse-angled triangle   (b) An isosceles triangle   (c) An equilateral triangle
  (d) A square   (e) A rectangle   (f) A parallelogram   (g) A rhombus
  (h) A kite   (i) An isosceles trapezium   (j) A non-isosceles (scalene) trapezium.

6 Write down the five cyclic quadrilaterals in Figure 30:9 (see Exercise 30B, 'For discussion').

7 Both pairs of opposite angles of a certain cyclic quadrilateral are equal. What special kinds of quadrilateral could it be?

8 In Figure 32:16, calculate, with reasons:
  (a) *g* and *e* if *f* = 100°
  (b) *g* and *e* if *f* = 120°
  (c) *g* and *e* if *f* = 75°.

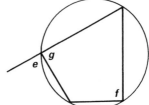

Fig. 32:16

You should have found that *e* = *f* for any value of *f*. This is stated as:

The exterior angle of a cyclic quadrilateral is equal to the opposite interior angle.

9 Copy Figure 32:17, where AB = AC and ADE is a straight line. Prove that ABCD is a cyclic quadrilateral.

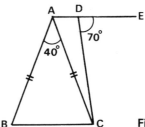

Fig. 32:17

10 In Figure 32:18, ABC is a straight line. Prove that ∠AOX = 2∠CBX.

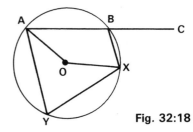

Fig. 32:18

187

11 For Figure 32:19:
    (a) Calculate, giving reasons, angles *f* and *b*.
    (b) Why must DA be parallel to CB?
    (c) Show that DA is always parallel to CB for any value of ∠ DAE (say *x*°).

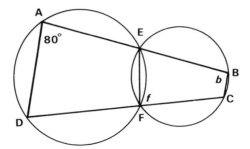

Fig. 32:19

---

12 Show that quadrilateral ABCD, with angles in the ratio A : B : C : D = 3 : 4 : 6 : 5, is a cyclic quadrilateral.

13 AB is the diameter of a circle. C and D are points on the circumference such that ∠ CAB = 30° and DB bisects ∠ ABC. Prove that CA bisects ∠ DAB.

14 The side RS of cyclic quadrilateral PQRS is produced (made longer in the direction RS) to a point T. If PR = PQ prove that PS is the bisector of angle TSQ.

As $(x - 2)(2x + 1) \to 2x^2 - 3x - 2$, it follows that $2x^2 - 3x - 2 \to (x - 2)(2x + 1)$.

By no means all quadratic expressions factorise into two brackets, but an examiner will not ask you to factorise one that will not.

There is no 'golden rule' which will give you the correct answer first time, but the following will help:

(a) If the last sign is $+$, then both brackets have the sign of the middle term.

    Examples $x^2 + 10x + 21 \to (x + 3)(x + 7)$
                Check: $+7x + 3x \to 10x$
                        $+3 \times +7 \to +21$

                $x^2 - 10x + 21 \to (x - 3)(x - 7)$
                Check: $-7x - 3x \to -10x$
                        $-3 \times -7 \to +21$

(b) If the last sign is $-$, then one bracket is $+$ and the other is $-$, and you must be very careful to get the correct sign with each number. For example, $(2x + 1)(x - 2)$ gives $2x^2 - 3x - 2$, whilst $(2x - 1)(x + 2)$ gives $2x^2 + 3x - 2$.

    Examples $x^2 + 4x - 12 \to (x + 6)(x - 2)$
                Check: $-2x + 6x \to +4x$
                        $+6 \times -2 \to -12$

                $x^2 - 4x - 12 \to (x - 6)(x + 2)$
                Check: $+2x - 6x \to -4x$
                        $-6 \times +2 \to -12$

(c) If there are a lot of factors to choose from, start with the pair closest together and work upwards, e.g. for 12 try 3×4, then 2×6, then 1×12.

Where the coefficient of the first term is not prime, then there is a choice for the start of each bracket. Once again you just have to try possibilities until you hit on the right one. You will find that you get cleverer at deciding the most likely possibilities.

Example $6x^2 + 11x - 10$ could start $(3x \quad)(2x \quad)$ or $(x \quad)(6x \quad)$.
              By trial we find that $6x^2 + 11x - 10 \to (3x - 2)(2x + 5)$.

If the constant term (the number on the end) is prime, it is better to put this in first, then work out the start of the bracket.

Example   Factorise $12x^2 - 17x - 5$.

              $12x^2$ could come from $3x \times 4x$, or $2x \times 6x$, or $1x \times 12x$.
              But 5 must come from 1×5.
              So start with $(\quad 1)(\quad 5)$ and then try the possibilities to give $12x^2$.

              The answer is $(3x - 5)(4x + 1)$.

Factorise:

1 (a) $x^2 + x - 2$ (b) $x^2 - 3x - 4$ (c) $x^2 + x - 6$ (d) $x^2 - 5x - 6$

(e) $x^2 + x - 12$.

2 (a) $x^2 - 4x - 12$ (b) $x^2 - 8x - 20$ (c) $x^2 + 3x - 18$ (d) $x^2 - 7x - 18$

(e) $x^2 - 5x - 36$.

3 (a) $x^2 + 13x + 36$ (b) $x^2 + 9x - 36$ (c) $x^2 + 5x - 36$ (d) $x^2 + 16x - 36$

(e) $x^2 - 15x + 36$.

4 Example $2x^2 - 5x - 3 \rightarrow (2x + 1)(x - 3)$

            Check: $-6x + 1x \rightarrow -5x$

                  $+1 \times -3 \rightarrow -3$

(a) $2x^2 + 3x + 1$ (b) $2x^2 - 3x + 1$ (c) $2x^2 - x - 3$ (d) $2x^2 + x - 3$.

*5 (a) $2x^2 - 9x + 4$ (b) $2x^2 - 7x + 3$ (c) $3x^2 - 2x - 16$ (d) $3x^2 + 2x - 8$.

6 (a) $2x^2 - 5x + 2$ (b) $3x^2 + 7x + 2$ (c) $2x^2 - x - 1$ (d) $x^2 + 2x - 8$.

7 (a) $3x^2 + 2x - 16$ (b) $2x^2 - 3x - 35$ (c) $3x^2 - 7x - 6$ (d) $3x^2 - 2x - 16$.

8 (a) $2x^2 - 21x - 36$ (b) $2x^2 + 7x - 30$ (c) $x^2 + 17x + 30$

(d) $2x^2 - x - 36$.

9 (a) $2x^2 - 7x - 30$ (b) $2x^2 - 17x + 30$ (c) $3x^2 - 71x - 24$

(d) $2x^2 + 11x - 30$.

10 (a) $4x^2 + 3x - 1$ (b) $4x^2 + 4x + 1$ (c) $6x^2 + 13x + 6$ (d) $6x^2 - 7x - 24$.

11 (a) $6x^2 - 11x + 4$ (b) $6x^2 + 11x + 4$ (c) $6x^2 - 5x - 4$ (d) $6x^2 + 5x - 4$.

12 Not all quadratic expressions will factorise. For example, $x^2 + 2x + 12$.

Factorise the following where possible.

(a) $x^2 - x - 6$ (b) $x^2 - 5x + 6$ (c) $x^2 - 3x + 6$ (d) $2x^2 + 7x - 35$

(e) $2x^2 + 7x - 6$ (f) $3x^2 - x - 2$ (g) $3x^2 + 11x + 6$ (h) $3x^2 - 3x + 8$

(i) $x^2 + 5x - 11$ (j) $3x^2 - 9x - 7$ (k) $4x^2 + 5x + 1$ (l) $6x^2 + 13x + 6$

(m) $3x^2 + 13x + 12$ (n) $6x^2 - 23x - 4$ (o) $8x^2 + 14x + 3$

(p) $8x^2 - 2x - 15$.

13 Always check for common factors before factorising by quadratic brackets.

Example $8x^2 + 4x - 12 \rightarrow 4(2x^2 + x - 3) \rightarrow 4(2x + 3)(x - 1)$

Factorise:

(a) $3x^2 + 12x + 12$ (b) $2x^2 + 14x + 24$ (c) $3x^2 - 15x + 12$

(d) $9x^2 + 6x - 3$ (e) $4x^2 - 10x + 4$ (f) $12x^2 - 8x - 64$.

14 Factorise:

(a) $9a^2 - 6ab + b^2$ (b) $35 - 12x + x^2$ (c) $35 - 2x - x^2$

(d) $3x^2 + 5xy - 2y^2$ (e) $8x^2 - 18x + 9$ (f) $25x^2 - 30xy + 9y^2$

(g) $x^2 + x + \frac{1}{4}$ (h) $x^2 + x - \frac{3}{4}$ (i) $24 - 2x - x^2$.

15 Is it possible to program a computer to factorise?

Wildlife in peril

Poachers and the modern materialistic society are decimating the wildlife of Africa. People want ivory for ornaments, or for a hedge against inflation; rhino horn for dagger handles, or powdered for medicine; zebra skins for drums and mats; antelope antlers and ostrich eggs for souvenirs; giraffe tails for fly-whisks; cheetah pelts for coats; even gorilla hands for ash-trays.

In 1971, Uganda's Rwenzori National Park had 3000 elephants, 18 000 buffaloes, and 10 500 hippos. Ten years later Idi Amin's army had reduced the numbers to 160 elephants, 4000 buffaloes, and 2900 hippos.

In 1982, 40 000 elephants were killed in Africa, the ivory selling at £17 a pound (a tusk can weigh as much as 100 pounds). Britain alone imported £400 000-worth of tusks, as well as 111 863 items of carved ivory.

Between 1973 and 1983, black rhinos were reduced by 80% to about 10 000, Kenya's reduction being from 16 000 to 1000. North Yemen alone imported 20 tons of horn for traditional daggers, representing 8000 dead rhinos. A rhino's horn could bring an African peasant £300, perhaps thirty times his annual income; yet when powdered for medicine it would fetch £450 an ounce.

It is not only poaching that threatens the wildlife. Parkland is in increasing demand for farming; in 1983 Kenya's population of 17 million was growing at 4% per annum.

Unless every African country establishes heavily policed reserves, like Nairobi's 44 sq mile National Park, where 10 000 animals live in safety, it is only a matter of time before many African animals will only be found in zoos.

Use the information opposite and your calculator to answer the following questions.

1 What is meant by 'a hedge against inflation'?

2 What does 'decimating' mean?

3 Percentage reduction $= \dfrac{\text{reduction}}{\text{original number}} \times 100\%$.

What was the percentage reduction in Rwenzori Park between 1971 and 1981 of:
(a) elephants   (b) buffaloes   (c) hippos?

4 About how much was paid for the ivory from the elephants killed in 1982? (Give the answer in millions of pounds.)

5 About how many tusks did Britain import in 1982?

6 About how many rhinos lived in Africa in 1973?

7 What was the percentage reduction in Kenya's rhino population between 1973 and 1983?

8 What is the average weight of one rhino's horn in pounds? (2240 pounds = 1 ton).

9 Percentage profit $= \dfrac{\text{profit}}{\text{original cost}} \times 100\%$.

What is the percentage profit on a ton of powdered rhino horn?
(16 ounces = 1 pound; 2240 pounds = 1 ton)

10 If Kenya's population continued to grow at the 1983 rate, what would it have been in 1986 (after 3 years of increase)?

11 What is the area of Nairobi's National Park in:
(a) square kilometres   (b) hectares?
(Take 5 miles = 8 kilometres. One hectare = $10\,000\,\text{m}^2$.)

12 How many square metres does each animal in the National Park have, on average?

$$o = a \times \tan \theta \qquad o = h \times \sin \theta \qquad a = h \times \cos \theta$$

$$\frac{o}{a} = \tan \theta \qquad \frac{o}{h} = \sin \theta \qquad \frac{a}{h} = \cos \theta$$

One ancient **t**eacher of **h**istory **s**wore **at** his **c**lass!

Finding sides

$x = 5 \times \tan 54°$
$\simeq 6.88$

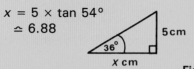

5 cm

36°

x cm

Fig. 34:1

$x = 5 \times \sin 40°$
$\simeq 3.21$

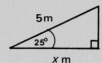

5 cm   40°

x cm   Fig. 34:2

$x = 5 \times \cos 25°$
or $x = 5 \times \sin 65°$
$\simeq 4.53$

5 m

25°

x m   Fig. 34:3

Sample key sequence: 5 ⨯ 54 TAN =

We can find a formula for the hypotenuse by making h the subject of either the sine or the cosine formula.

$o = h \times \sin \theta$

$$h \xrightarrow{\ \times \sin \theta\ } h \times \sin \theta$$
$$\downarrow$$
$$\frac{o}{\sin \theta} \xleftarrow{\ \div \sin \theta\ } o$$

Hence $h = \dfrac{o}{\sin \theta}$ and similarly $h = \dfrac{a}{\cos \theta}$.

Alternatively, h may be found using Pythagoras' theorem once o and a are known.

Finding angles

$\frac{7}{6} = \tan \theta$
$\theta \simeq 49.4°$

7 cm

θ

6 cm   Fig. 34:4

$\frac{7}{9} = \sin \theta$
$\theta = 51.1°$

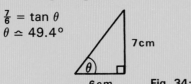

9 cm   θ

7 cm   Fig. 34:5

$\frac{7}{9} = \cos \theta$
or $\frac{7}{9} = \sin \alpha \rightarrow \alpha \simeq 51.1°$
$\theta \simeq 38.9°$

9 cm   α

θ   7 cm   Fig. 34:6

Sample key sequence: 7 ÷ 6 = ARCTAN

Note: ARCTAN may be INV TAN or TAN⁻¹

Instead of using decimal divisions of degrees, we sometimes divide them into minutes (symbol ′) and seconds (symbol ″).
1° = 60′ = 360″.

Your calculator probably has a key to enter angles in this form, marked ⟦DMS⟧ or ⟦°′″⟧. To enter 15° 45′, key 15 ⟦DMS⟧ 45 ⟦DMS⟧.

If you do not have such a key, enter 15° 45′ by 15 ⟦+⟧ 45 ⟦÷⟧ 60 ⟦=⟧. You cannot do this in the middle of a calculation, so do it first and, if necessary, save it in the memory to recall when needed.

In all questions, give sides correct to 3 significant figures and angles to the nearest 0.1°.

1 Find the value of *x* or *θ* for each triangle in Figure 34:7.

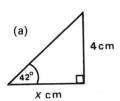 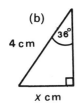 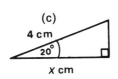 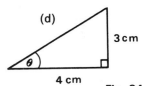

(a) 4 cm 42° *x* cm

(b) 36° 4 cm *x* cm

(c) 4 cm 20° *x* cm

(d) 3 cm *θ* 4 cm

Fig. 34:7

2 Find the value of *x* or *θ* for each triangle in Figure 34:8.

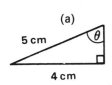 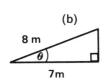 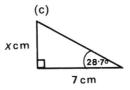

(a) 5 cm *θ* 4 cm

(b) 8 m *θ* 7 m

(c) *x* cm 28.7° 7 cm

(d) *θ* 7 cm 5 cm

Fig. 34:8

3 Find the value of *x* or *θ* for each triangle in Figure 34:9.

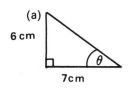 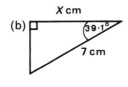 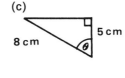 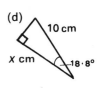

(a) 6 cm *θ* 7 cm

(b) *X* cm 39.1° 7 cm

(c) 8 cm 5 cm *θ*

(d) 10 cm *x* cm 18.8°

Fig. 34:9

4 Find the value of *x* or *θ* for each triangle in Figure 34:10.

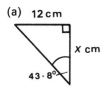 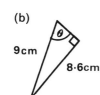 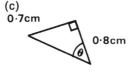 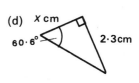

(a) 12 cm *x* cm 43.8°

(b) *θ* 9 cm 8.6 cm

(c) 0.7 cm 0.8 cm *θ*

(d) *x* cm 60.6° 2.3 cm

Fig. 34:10

*5 Sketch (not accurately) a triangle for each of the following. Give answers correct to 3 s.f. or 0.1°.

(a) △ABC, ∠B = 90°; ∠A = 63.2°; AB = 4 cm.
Calculate BC.

(b) △HIG, ∠G = 90°; HG = 4.5 cm; GI = 2 cm.
Calculate ∠H.

(c) △JKL, ∠L = 90°; ∠J = 32.2°; JK = 11 cm.
Calculate JL.

(d) △MNO, ∠M = 90°; ∠N = 32.6°; NO = 4.1 m.
Calculate MO.

(e) △PQR, ∠Q = 90°; PQ = 5 cm; PR = 7 cm.
Calculate ∠P.

(f) △VWX, ∠W = 90°; WX = 6 mm, ∠V = 18°.
Calculate VW.

*6 Use the angle sum of a triangle, Pythagoras' theorem, or trigonometry, to find the remaining sides and angles in the triangles for question 5.

7 Copy each diagram in Figure 34:11, then calculate all sides, correct to 3 s.f., and all angles, correct to 0.1°.

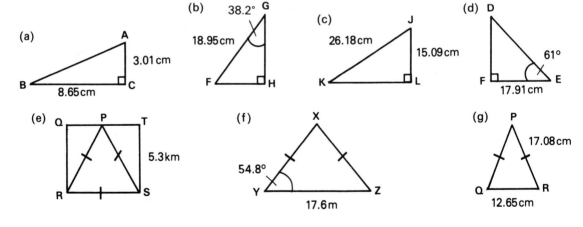

PRS is equilateral.
QTSR is a rectangle.
Write the angles on your
copy of the diagram.

How are you going to
make a right-angled
triangle in this isosceles
triangle?

Fig. 34:11

The sine rule

When a triangle is not right-angled, the trigonometric ratios cease to be true. However, it is possible to obtain a rule, called the **sine rule**, that can be used when the triangle is not right-angled. You must know one side and the angle opposite it, together with another side or angle.

In Figure 34:12, △ABC is not right-angled, but △APC and △CPB are. From these triangles:

$$CP = a \times \sin B \text{ and also } CP = b \times \sin A.$$

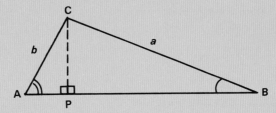

Fig. 34:12

Therefore $a \times \sin B = b \times \sin A$. This is the **sine rule**, usually written:

$$\frac{a}{\sin A} = \frac{b}{\sin B} \quad \text{or} \quad \frac{\sin A}{a} = \frac{\sin B}{b}$$

$$\text{to find a side} \qquad \text{to find an angle}$$

Always start the rule with the side, or the sine of the angle, that you are trying to find.

You can only use the sine rule if you know a side and the angle opposite to it.

Example   In Figure 34:13,

$$\frac{x}{\sin 27°} = \frac{12 \text{ cm}}{\sin 48°}$$

$$x = \frac{12 \text{ cm}}{\sin 48°} \times \sin 27°$$

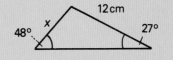

Fig. 34:13

Key: 12 ÷ 48 sin × 27 sin =

Answer: $x = 7.33$ cm correct to 3 s.f.

Example   In Figure 34:14,

$$\frac{\sin \theta}{3.6 \text{ cm}} = \frac{\sin 37°}{3.9 \text{ cm}}$$

$$\sin \theta = \frac{\sin 37°}{3.9 \text{ cm}} \times 3.6 \text{ cm}$$

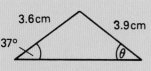

Fig. 34:14

Key: 37 sin ÷ 3.9 × 3.6 = ARCSIN

Answer: $\theta = 33.7°$ to the nearest 0.1°.

8 (a) In Figure 34:15, find:
   (i) *x*   (ii) *θ*   (iii) *y*.

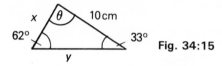

Fig. 34:15

   (b) In Figure 34:16, find:
   (i) *θ*   (ii) *α*   (iii) *x*.

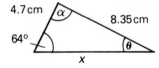

Fig. 34:16

   (c) In Figure 34:17, find:
   (i) *x*   (ii) *θ*   (iii) *y*.

Fig. 34:17

9 Find all the sides and angles in:
   (a) △ABC where ∠B = 40°9′, BC = 18.5 m, and AC = 12.6 m
   (b) △DEF where ∠E = 46°18′, ∠F = 63°13′, and EF = 11.4 cm
   (c) △GHI where ∠G = 78°41′, GI = 4.32 cm, and HI = 9.05 cm.

10 Using Pythagoras' theorem find:
   (a) $\sin \theta$ if $\cos \theta = \frac{3}{5}$ (b) $\tan \theta$ if $\sin \theta = \frac{5}{13}$.

11 The sine of an obtuse angle, $\theta°$, is the same as the sine of $(180 - \theta)°$. For example, $\sin 150° = \sin 30° = 0.5$. Check this on your calculator, then find the acute angle whose sine is the same as:
   (a) $\sin 100°$ (b) $\sin 116.8°$ (c) $\sin 152°12′$.

12 In △ABC, ∠A = 48.3°, ∠C = 27.6°, and AC = 15.6 cm. Calculate:
   (a) ∠B   (b) BC   (c) AB.

13 Draw a graph of $y = \sin \theta$ and a graph of $y = \cos \theta$ using θ as the horizontal axis with θ at 10° intervals from 0° to 360°. You may be able to draw this curve using a computer, and your science department can probably produce one on an oscilloscope.

14 Investigate the relationships between the sines of angles from 0° to 360°. Repeat for tangent and cosine. How does Figure 34:18 help?

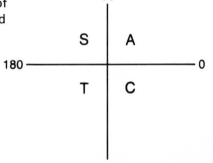

Fig. 34:18

A   Solution by factorisation

For discussion

▷ Find x if:
(a) $3x = 0$ (b) $xy = 0$ when $y = 5$ (c) $xy = 0$ when $y \neq 0$.

▷ What can you say about x and y if $xy = 0$?

▷ Find x if:
(a) $4x = 0$ (b) $x - 4 = 0$ (c) $x + 8 = 0$ (d) $3x + 15 = 0$
(e) $2x - 3 = 0$ (f) $6x + 3 = 0$ (g) $4x + 12 = 0$ (h) $2x - 5 = 0$
(i) $3x - 2 = 0$.

If two factors multiply to give zero, one or both of them must be zero.

Example   If $x(x - 4) = 0$, then either $x = 0$ or $x - 4 = 0$.
Hence $x(x - 4) = 0$ when $x = 0$ and when $x = 4$.

Example   If $(x - 2)(x + 4) = 0$, then either $x - 2 = 0$ or $x + 4 = 0$.
Hence $(x - 2)(x + 4) = 0$ when $x = 2$ and when $x = -4$.

Example   If $(2x - 7)(4x + 2) = 0$, then either $2x - 7 = 0$ or $4x + 2 = 0$.
If $2x - 7 = 0$ then $2x = 7$, so $x = 3\frac{1}{2}$ is one solution.
If $4x + 2 = 0$ then $4x = -2$, so $x = -\frac{1}{2}$ is the other solution.

Find all possible solutions to the equations in questions 1 to 10.

1   (a) $(x - 2)(x - 3) = 0$ (b) $(x + 6)(x - 2) = 0$ (c) $(x - 4)(x + 5) = 0$.

2   (a) $(x - 2)^2 = 0$ (b) $(x + 4)^2 = 0$ (c) $(2x - 6)(x - 5) = 0$.

3   (a) $(x - 3)(2x - 3) = 0$ (b) $(x + 4)(2x + 3) = 0$ (c) $(4x - 2)(x + 3) = 0$.

4   (a) $(2x + 9)(x - 7) = 0$ (b) $(3x - 1)(x + 2) = 0$ (c) $(2x - 3)^2 = 0$

5   Example   Solve $x^2 - 3x + 2 = 0$.

$x^2 - 3x + 2 = 0 \rightarrow (x - 2)(x - 1) = 0$
$\therefore x = 2$ and $x = 1$ are the solutions.

Example   Solve $x^2 - 4x = 0$.

Quadratics with no constant term are easy to factorise by taking out the common factor. Make a special point of remembering this.

$x^2 - 4x = 0 \rightarrow x(x - 4) = 0$
$\therefore x = 0$ and $x = 4$ are solutions.

Example   Find the roots of $2x^2 + 3x - 9 = 0$.

The **roots** of an equation are the values of x that make it true.

$2x^2 + 3x - 9 = 0 \rightarrow (2x - 3)(x + 3) = 0$
The roots are $x = 1\frac{1}{2}$ and $x = -3$.

Solve:
(a) $x^2 - 4x + 4 = 0$ (b) $x^2 - 2x + 1 = 0$ (c) $a^2 - 6a + 9 = 0$.

6   (a) $n^2 - 7n + 10 = 0$ (b) $2w^2 + w - 3 = 0$ (c) $2t^2 - t - 3 = 0$.

7   (a) $2x^2 - 5x + 3 = 0$ (b) $a^2 - 4 = 0$ (c) $x^2 - 49 = 0$.

8   (a) $f^2 + 7f = 0$ (b) $2e^2 - 5e = 0$ (c) $2d^2 + 7d = 0$.

*9   (a) $x^2 - 5x + 4 = 0$ (b) $s^2 - 11s + 28 = 0$ (c) $h^2 - 8h + 15 = 0$.

*10   (a) $2t^2 - 7t - 15 = 0$ (b) $2x^2 - 3x - 5 = 0$ (c) $2k^2 + k - 6 = 0$.

11   Rearrange the following equation terms to make equations that equal zero, then find their solutions.
(a) $x^2 = 25$ (b) $h^2 - 4h = 32$ (c) $w^2 - w = 90$ (d) $x^2 - 22 = -9x$
(e) $m^2 + 6 = 7m$ (f) $7x^2 = 3x$.

12   **Example**   The length of a rectangle is 5 cm more than its breadth. If its area is 24 cm², find its dimensions.

Let its breadth be x cm.
Then its length is $x + 5$ cm.
Area of rectangle = length × breadth
so $x(x + 5) = 24 \rightarrow x^2 + 5x = 24$
$\rightarrow x^2 + 5x - 24 = 0 \rightarrow (x - 3)(x + 8) = 0$
$\therefore x = 3$ or $x = -8$.

24 cm²	x cm

$(x + 5)$ cm

A dimension cannot be -8, so the only solution is $x = 3$, making the breadth 3 cm and the length 8 cm.

(a)   A room is 8 metres longer than it is wide, and its area is 20 m². Use a similar method to the example to find its dimensions.

(b)   A square of paper is reduced by 5 cm in one direction and by 1 cm in the other direction, leaving a rectangle of area 60 cm². How long was a side of the original square? (Start by letting this be x cm.)

(c)   The square of a number added to ten times itself equals 39. What could the number be?

(d)   Ten times the square of a fraction is nine more than forty-three times the fraction. What could the fraction be? (Start by letting it be f.)

13 Find the equation whose solutions are:
   (a) 2 and 4   (b) −2 and 2   (c) −3 and 5   (d) −2 and −4
   (e) −4 and 0   (f) $\frac{1}{2}$ and $-\frac{2}{3}$.

14 State the coordinates of the crossing points on the x- and y-axes for the parabolic graphs whose equations are given.

Remember that $y = ax^2 + bx + c$ must cross the y-axis at $y = c$.

   (a) $y = x^2 - 2x - 3$ (b) $y = x^2 - 3x - 4$ (c) $y = x^2 - 9$
   (d) $y = x^2 + 4x + 4$ (e) $y = 2x^2 - 5x + 3$ (f) $y = x^2 + 6x + 9$.

15 Use your answers to question 14 to sketch the parabolas.

16 (a) Find the side of a square whose area doubles when its length is increased by 6 cm and its breadth is increased by 4 cm.

   (b) The ages of two children are 4 years and 8 years. In how many years' time will the product of their ages be 165?

   (c) The sum of the first n natural numbers is $\frac{1}{2}n(n + 1)$.
   What is n if the sum is 210?

B   Harder equations

Many quadratic equations will not factorise; the following two methods may then be used. Your teacher will explain them fully.

Method 1   Completing the square

Example   Solve $x^2 + 5x - 1 = 0$.

$$x^2 + 5x - 1 = 0 \rightarrow \left(x + \frac{5}{2}\right)^2 - \frac{25}{4} - 1 = 0$$

$$\left[\text{Note: } \left(x + \frac{5}{2}\right)\left(x + \frac{5}{2}\right) = x^2 + 5x + \frac{25}{4}\right]$$

$$\rightarrow \left(x + \frac{5}{2}\right)^2 - \frac{29}{4} = 0$$

$$\rightarrow \left(x + \frac{5}{2}\right)^2 = \frac{29}{4} = 7.25$$

$$\rightarrow x + 2.5 = \sqrt{7.25}$$
$$\rightarrow x + 2.5 \simeq \pm 2.69$$

So $x \simeq -2.5 + 2.69 = \underline{0.19}$

or $x \simeq -2.5 - 2.69 = \underline{-5.19}$

Plus or minus 2.69

Example Solve $3x^2 - 2x - 2 = 0$.

$$3x^2 - 2x - 2 = 0 \xrightarrow{\div \text{ all by } 3} x^2 - \tfrac{2}{3}x - \tfrac{2}{3} = 0$$

$$\rightarrow (x - \tfrac{1}{3})^2 - \tfrac{1}{9} - \tfrac{2}{3} = 0$$

$$\rightarrow (x - \tfrac{1}{3})^2 - \tfrac{7}{9} = 0$$

$$\rightarrow (x - \tfrac{1}{3})^2 = \tfrac{7}{9} = 0.\dot{7}$$

$$\rightarrow x - 0.\dot{3} = \sqrt{0.\dot{7}}$$

$$\rightarrow x - 0.\dot{3} \simeq \pm 0.882$$

Either $x \simeq 0.\dot{3} + 0.882 \simeq \underline{1.22}$

or $x \simeq 0.\dot{3} - 0.882 \simeq \underline{-0.55}$

We divide by 3 to reduce the coefficient of x^2 to unity.

Method 2   The quadratic equation formula

The formula is obtained by applying the completion of the square method to the general quadratic equation $ax^2 + bx + c = 0$. Your teacher will illustrate this.

$$x = \frac{-b \pm \sqrt{b^2 - 4ac}}{2a}$$

Learn: x equals minus b plus or minus the square root of b squared minus four ac, **all** divided by two a.

Example Solve $x^2 + 5x - 1 = 0$.

$$a = 1 \qquad b = 5 \qquad c = -1$$

$$x = \frac{-5 \pm \sqrt{25 + 4}}{2} = \frac{-5 \pm \sqrt{29}}{2}$$

$$x \simeq \frac{-5 \pm 5.385}{2}$$

Solutions are $x \simeq 0.19$ and $x \simeq -5.19$

Example Solve $3x^2 - 2x - 2 = 0$.

$$a = 3 \qquad b = -2 \qquad c = -2$$

$$x = \frac{+2 \pm \sqrt{4 + 24}}{6} = \frac{2 \pm \sqrt{28}}{6}$$

$$x \simeq \frac{2 \pm 5.29}{6}$$

Solutions are $x \simeq 1.22$ and $x \simeq -0.55$

Solve the following equations, either by completing the square, or by using the formula, or both. Your teacher will tell you which to do.

1 (a) $x^2 + 4x - 1 = 0$ (b) $x^2 - 2x - 5 = 0$ (c) $x^2 + 5x + 3 = 0$.

2 (a) $x^2 - 7x - 12 = 0$ (b) $x^2 + 8x + 9 = 0$ (c) $x^2 + x - 3 = 0$.

3 (a) $2x^2 + 2x - 1 = 0$ (b) $2x^2 - 4x + 1 = 0$ (c) $3x^2 + 5x - 3 = 0$.

*4 (a) $x^2 - 3x - 3 = 0$ (b) $2x^2 + 4x + 1 = 0$ (c) $3x^2 + x - 1 = 0$.

5 Rearrange the following equations to make them equal zero. Do not solve the equations.
(a) $2x^2 - 4x = 1$ (b) $3x^2 = 4x - 1$ (c) $2x^2 - 2 = x$ (d) $3 - 4x = 2x^2$
(e) $3x - 3 = x^2$ (f) $x^2 + 4 = 4x$.

6 Solve the following equations.
(a) $2x(x + 4) = 1$ (b) $x^2 = 5(1 - x)$ (c) $3(x^2 - 1) = 4x$.

---

7 Example   Solve $\dfrac{x^2}{2} - x - \dfrac{3}{4} = 0$

First remove the fractions by multiplying every term by 4, which is the common denominator.

As $4 \times \dfrac{x^2}{2} \rightarrow 2x^2$, and $4 \times \dfrac{3}{4} \rightarrow 3$, then the equation becomes:

$2x^2 - 4x - 3 = 0$.
This can now be solved as before.

Write each of the following as an equation without fractions. Do not solve the equations.

(a) $\dfrac{x^2}{3} + x + \dfrac{7}{9} = 0$ (b) $2x^2 - \dfrac{3x}{4} + \dfrac{1}{2} = 0$ (c) $\dfrac{3x^2 - 2x}{5} + 1 = 0$

(d) $x^2 - \dfrac{2x + 1}{3} = 0$ (e) $\dfrac{x(3x - 2)}{4} + \dfrac{1}{3} = \dfrac{1}{4}$ (f) $\dfrac{(2x + 1)(x - 1)}{2} = \dfrac{3x}{4}$.

8 $ax^2 + bx + c = 0$ is solved by $x = \dfrac{-b \pm \sqrt{(b^2 - 4ac)}}{2a}$

(a) Investigate what will happen if $b^2 < 4ac$. Illustrate your answer with a graph of $y = x^2 + x + 1$, being used to try to solve the equation $x^2 + x + 1 = 0$.

(b) Investigate what will happen if $b^2 = 4ac$. Illustrate your answer with a graph of $y = x^2 + 2x + 1$, being used to solve $x^2 + 2x + 1 = 0$.

(c) State which of the equations in the answers to questions 5 and 7 have:
    A solutions   **B** no solutions   **C** equal roots.

9 The solutions of the equation $ax^2 + bx + c = 0$ are called its 'roots'. These roots are usually referred to as α (alpha) and β (beta).

$$\alpha + \beta = -\dfrac{b}{a} \quad \text{and} \quad \alpha\beta = \dfrac{c}{a}$$

These two facts can be used to check solutions to a quadratic equation. Use them to check your answers to questions 2 and 3.

10 Write a computer program which will solve a quadratic equation, or inform you that there are no solutions.

● You need to know . . .

A matrix is a table of numbers.

The corners of a shape on a grid can be represented by a matrix as follows:

Coordinates	Position vectors	Matrix			

Coordinates   Position vectors   Matrix   *y*-axis

A: (1, 1) $\overrightarrow{OA} = \begin{pmatrix} 1 \\ 1 \end{pmatrix}$

$$\begin{array}{c} \quad A \quad B \quad C \\ x \begin{pmatrix} 1 & 1 & 3 \\ 1 & 2 & 1 \end{pmatrix} \\ y \end{array}$$

B: (1, 2) $\overrightarrow{OB} = \begin{pmatrix} 1 \\ 2 \end{pmatrix}$

C: (3, 1) $\overrightarrow{OC} = \begin{pmatrix} 3 \\ 1 \end{pmatrix}$

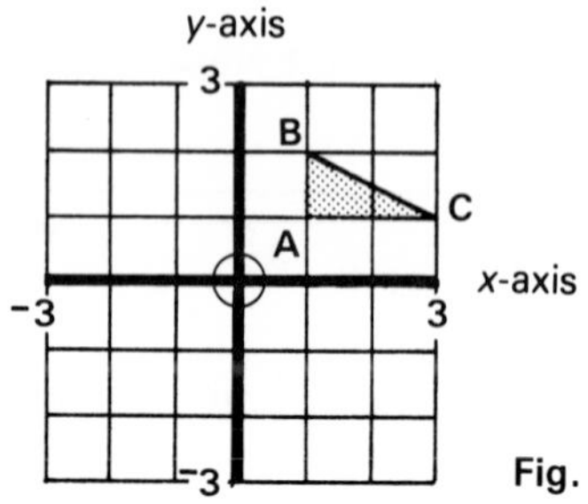

Fig. 36:1

By changing the matrix we can transform the shape.
First, though, you will have to master the multiplication of matrices.

● Multiplication of matrices

Constant times matrix

Example $3\begin{pmatrix} 2 & -1 \\ 0 & 3 \end{pmatrix} = \begin{pmatrix} 6 & -3 \\ 0 & 9 \end{pmatrix}$

Matrix times matrix

Example $\begin{pmatrix} 2 & 3 \\ 2 & 5 \end{pmatrix}\begin{pmatrix} 4 & 2 \\ 1 & 5 \end{pmatrix} = \begin{pmatrix} 11 & 19 \\ 13 & 29 \end{pmatrix}$

Step 1: $(2 \quad 3)\begin{pmatrix} 4 \\ 1 \end{pmatrix} \rightarrow 8 + 3 = 11$

Step 2: $(2 \quad 3)\begin{pmatrix} 2 \\ 5 \end{pmatrix} \rightarrow 4 + 15 = 19$

Step 3: $(2 \quad 5)\begin{pmatrix} 4 \\ 1 \end{pmatrix} \rightarrow 8 + 5 = 13$

Step 4: $(2 \quad 5)\begin{pmatrix} 2 \\ 5 \end{pmatrix} \rightarrow 4 + 25 = 29$

Be especially careful when negative (minus) numbers are involved. Check the following example carefully:

$$\begin{pmatrix} 2 & -1 \\ -3 & 1 \end{pmatrix}\begin{pmatrix} -1 & -2 \\ 1 & 4 \end{pmatrix} = \begin{pmatrix} -3 & -8 \\ 4 & 10 \end{pmatrix}$$

Most matrices give different answers when multiplied together, depending on which one is at the front (we say multiplication of matrices is 'not commutative').

For example,
$$\begin{pmatrix} 1 & 0 \\ 1 & 2 \end{pmatrix}\begin{pmatrix} 2 & 1 \\ 0 & 0 \end{pmatrix} = \begin{pmatrix} 2 & 1 \\ 2 & 1 \end{pmatrix}$$

but
$$\begin{pmatrix} 2 & 1 \\ 0 & 0 \end{pmatrix}\begin{pmatrix} 1 & 0 \\ 1 & 2 \end{pmatrix} = \begin{pmatrix} 3 & 2 \\ 0 & 0 \end{pmatrix}$$

The computer program "MATRIX2" (see the Teachers' Resource Book for Book 3, page 114) can be used to practise matrix multiplication. You could develop the program so that it gives matrices for the operator to multiply, then have the computer check the answer.

Test yourself

$$A = (4 \quad 2) \qquad B = (1 \quad 3) \qquad C = \begin{pmatrix} 1 & 2 \\ 3 & 1 \end{pmatrix} \qquad D = \begin{pmatrix} 3 & 4 \\ 1 & 0 \end{pmatrix}$$

$$E = \begin{pmatrix} 2 & 4 \\ 3 & 1 \end{pmatrix} \qquad F = \begin{pmatrix} 5 & 1 \\ 1 & 5 \end{pmatrix}$$

1 Calculate:

(a) AC $\left(\text{that is, } (4 \quad 2)\begin{pmatrix} 1 & 2 \\ 3 & 1 \end{pmatrix}\right)$ (b) AD   (c) AF   (d) BE

2 Calculate:
   (a) CD   (b) DC   (c) CE   (d) EC   (e) DF   (f) FD   (g) CF   (h) FC

3 Multiply out the following matrices:

(a) $(1 \quad 3)\begin{pmatrix} 2 \\ 4 \end{pmatrix}$ (b) $(2 \quad 1)\begin{pmatrix} 1 & 2 \\ 2 & 3 \end{pmatrix}$ (c) $\begin{pmatrix} 1 & 0 \\ 0 & 1 \end{pmatrix}\begin{pmatrix} 2 \\ 3 \end{pmatrix}$

(d) $\begin{pmatrix} 1 & -1 \\ 0 & 0 \end{pmatrix}\begin{pmatrix} 1 & -1 & 0 \\ 1 & 2 & -1 \end{pmatrix}$ (e) $\begin{pmatrix} -1 & 0 \\ 0 & -1 \end{pmatrix}\begin{pmatrix} -1 & 1 & 0 \\ 1 & -1 & -2 \end{pmatrix}$

4 $A = \begin{pmatrix} 1 & -1 \\ 0 & 1 \end{pmatrix} \qquad B = \begin{pmatrix} 1 & 1 & 0 \\ 2 & 0 & 1 \end{pmatrix}$

(a) Find the product AB.
(b) Briefly explain why you cannot find the product BA.

Transforming using matrices

Example Using the matrix method to define the triangle, we can find the coordinates of triangle ABC after a rotation of 270° about (0, 0) by multiplying by the matrix $\begin{pmatrix} 0 & 1 \\ -1 & 0 \end{pmatrix}$:

$$\begin{pmatrix} 0 & 1 \\ -1 & 0 \end{pmatrix} \begin{matrix} A & B & C \\ \begin{pmatrix} 1 & 1 & 3 \\ 1 & 2 & 1 \end{pmatrix} \end{matrix} = \begin{matrix} A' & B' & C' \\ \begin{pmatrix} 1 & 2 & 1 \\ -1 & -1 & -3 \end{pmatrix} \end{matrix}$$

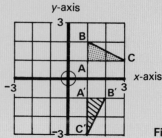

Fig. 36:2

1 Draw eight pairs of axes from −4 to 4 each. On each grid plot the quadrilateral whose vertices are at (1, 1), (4, 1), (4, 2) and (2, 2).

Plot the result of multiplying the matrix of the quadrilateral by each of the eight matrices $\begin{pmatrix} a & 0 \\ 0 & b \end{pmatrix}$, $\begin{pmatrix} 0 & a \\ b & 0 \end{pmatrix}$ where $a, b \in \{1, -1\}$. For example, if $a = -1$ and $b = 1$ the matrices are

$\begin{pmatrix} -1 & 0 \\ 0 & 1 \end{pmatrix}$ and $\begin{pmatrix} 0 & -1 \\ 1 & 0 \end{pmatrix}$. Describe each transformation fully.

∈ means 'are members of the set!'

2 On axes from −6 to 6, plot the octagon with vertices, in order, at (0, 0), (6, 0), (6, −4), (4, −4), (4, −3), (5, −3), (5, −1) and (1, −1). Plot, all on the same grid, the transformations caused by each of the matrices in question 1.

3 Investigate the effect of multiplying $\begin{pmatrix} 0 & 1 & 0 \\ 0 & 0 & 1 \end{pmatrix}$ by any 2 by 2 matrix, e.g. $\begin{pmatrix} 3 & 4 \\ 5 & 6 \end{pmatrix}$.

4 Investigate the effect of multiplication by the following on the triangle represented by $\begin{pmatrix} 0 & 1 & 0 \\ 0 & 0 & 1 \end{pmatrix}$.

(a) $\begin{pmatrix} 1 & 0 \\ -1 & 1 \end{pmatrix}$ (b) $\begin{pmatrix} 1 & 0 \\ -2 & 1 \end{pmatrix}$ (c) $\begin{pmatrix} 1 & 3 \\ 0 & 1 \end{pmatrix}$ (d) $\begin{pmatrix} 1 & -1 \\ 0 & 1 \end{pmatrix}$ (e) $\begin{pmatrix} 1 & 2 \\ 0 & 1 \end{pmatrix}$

(f) $\begin{pmatrix} 1 & -2 \\ 0 & 1 \end{pmatrix}$ (g) $\begin{pmatrix} -2 & 0 \\ 0 & -2 \end{pmatrix}$ (h) $\begin{pmatrix} 2 & 0 \\ 0 & 1 \end{pmatrix}$ (i) $\begin{pmatrix} 1 & 0 \\ 0 & 2 \end{pmatrix}$.

5 (a) On the axes from −4 to 6, plot the quadrilateral whose coordinate matrix is $\begin{pmatrix} 0 & 2 & 2 & 1 \\ 0 & 0 & 1 & 1 \end{pmatrix}$
Repeat this on three more grids.

(b) Calculate $\begin{pmatrix} 2 & 0 \\ 0 & 2 \end{pmatrix} \begin{pmatrix} 0 & 2 & 2 & 1 \\ 0 & 0 & 1 & 1 \end{pmatrix}$ and plot the quadrilateral given by your answer on one of your grids.

(c) On your other three grids plot the transformation given by:

(i) $\begin{pmatrix} 3 & 0 \\ 0 & 3 \end{pmatrix}$ (ii) $\begin{pmatrix} -1 & 0 \\ 0 & -1 \end{pmatrix}$ (iii) $\begin{pmatrix} -2 & 0 \\ 0 & -2 \end{pmatrix}$.

6 On four grids, each from -3 to 6, plot the triangle with vertices at (3, 0), (6, 0) and (6, 6).
Plot the transformations caused by:

(a) $\begin{pmatrix} \frac{1}{2} & 0 \\ 0 & \frac{1}{2} \end{pmatrix}$ (b) $\begin{pmatrix} \frac{1}{3} & 0 \\ 0 & \frac{1}{3} \end{pmatrix}$ (c) $\begin{pmatrix} -\frac{1}{2} & 0 \\ 0 & -\frac{1}{2} \end{pmatrix}$ (d) $\begin{pmatrix} -\frac{1}{3} & 0 \\ 0 & -\frac{1}{3} \end{pmatrix}$.

7 Question 5(b) shows *an enlargement, scale factor 2, centre (0, 0)*.
Question 6(c) shows *a negative enlargement, scale factor $-\frac{1}{2}$, centre (0, 0)*.

Label these two diagrams as given in italics above, then label the other diagrams in a similar way.

8 On six grids, *x* from -2 to 4, *y* from -3 to 1, plot the square with vertices at (0, 0), (1, 0), (1, 1) and (0, 1). (This is usually called the **unit square**.)

Investigate the transformation caused by:

(a) $\begin{pmatrix} 1 & 2 \\ 0 & 1 \end{pmatrix}$ (b) $\begin{pmatrix} 1 & 0 \\ -3 & 1 \end{pmatrix}$ (c) $\begin{pmatrix} 1 & -2 \\ 0 & 1 \end{pmatrix}$ (d) $\begin{pmatrix} 1 & 3 \\ 0 & 1 \end{pmatrix}$ (e) $\begin{pmatrix} 1 & 0 \\ -2 & 1 \end{pmatrix}$

(f) $\begin{pmatrix} 1 & -1 \\ 0 & 1 \end{pmatrix}$.

Under each of your diagrams write a description of the transformation.

Example (a) Shearing, invariant line $y = 0$, such that $(1, 1) \rightarrow (3, 1)$

9 On six grids, each from 0 to 6, plot the square $\begin{pmatrix} 0 & 2 & 2 & 0 \\ 0 & 0 & 2 & 2 \end{pmatrix}$.

Investigate the effect on this square of:

(a) $\begin{pmatrix} 2 & 0 \\ 0 & 1 \end{pmatrix}$ (b) $\begin{pmatrix} 3 & 0 \\ 0 & 1 \end{pmatrix}$ (c) $\begin{pmatrix} 1 & 0 \\ 0 & 2 \end{pmatrix}$ (d) $\begin{pmatrix} 1 & 0 \\ 0 & 3 \end{pmatrix}$ (e) $\begin{pmatrix} 2 & 0 \\ 0 & 3 \end{pmatrix}$ (f) $\begin{pmatrix} 3 & 0 \\ 0 & 2 \end{pmatrix}$.

Under each diagram write a description of the transformation.

Examples (a) One-way stretch from $x = 0$, stretch factor 2
(e) Two-way stretch from $x = 0$, stretch factor 2, and from $y = 0$, stretch factor 3

10 Investigate the effects of other 2 by 2 matrices on the square in question 9.

11 Investigate the effect of two matrix multiplications, using the special matrices in question 1.

Example $\begin{pmatrix} 0 & -1 \\ 1 & 0 \end{pmatrix} \begin{pmatrix} 1 & 0 \\ 0 & 1 \end{pmatrix} \begin{pmatrix} 0 & 2 & 1 \\ 0 & 0 & 2 \end{pmatrix} = \begin{pmatrix} 0 & -1 \\ 1 & 0 \end{pmatrix} \begin{pmatrix} 0 & -2 & -1 \\ 0 & 0 & 2 \end{pmatrix}$

$= \begin{pmatrix} 0 & 0 & -2 \\ 0 & -2 & -1 \end{pmatrix}$

Papers

Paper 1

1 A cube is painted on all faces, then cut into 27 identical smaller cubes. How many of the smaller cubes are painted on:
(a) three faces   (b) two faces   (c) one face   (d) no face?

2 Julia travels 9 miles in 45 minutes. How far would she travel in 3 hours at the same average speed?

3 Joy spends three-quarters of her money and then has 15p left. How much did she have to start with?

4 (a) 3 h 16 min + 48 min   (b) 6 h − 3 h 27 min.

5 What should be the next two numbers in the following sequences?
(a) 3, 5, 8, 12, 17   (b) 5, 9, 17, 33, 65   (c) 0, 3, 8, 15, 24.

6 Figure P1:1 is a travel graph showing a journey made by a cycling club.

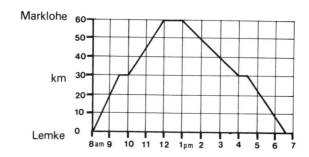

Fig. P1:1

(a) When did they take the first break?
(b) How long was the break at Marklohe?
(c) What was the average speed from Lemke to Marklohe?
(d) How long did they spend resting altogether?
(e) How far did they cycle altogether?

7 Using axes from −2 to 5 each, draw the triangle with coordinates A (2, 2), B (3, 5), C (4, 2). Using (4, 5) as the centre of enlargement, enlarge the triangle by a scale factor of 2. Write down the coordinates of A′, B′ and C′.

*8 Sketch a compass showing the eight cardinal points N, E, S, W, NE, SE, SW and NW.

*9 How many degrees, turning clockwise, are there between:
(a) E and W   (b) SE and W   (c) NW and SE   (d) NE and SE   (e) E and NE?

10 Between 1243 and 1423 a train covers 80 miles. What is its average speed?

11 Find two consecutive numbers such that one-third of the smaller is greater by 3 than one-quarter of the larger.

Paper 2

1 State the coordinates of the crossing points of:
   (a) $x = 4$ and $y = 2$ (b) $y = 2$ and $x = 6$ (c) $y = 2$ and $y = x$.

2 On one pair of axes, from -4 to 4 each, draw the lines of the equations $y = 3$, $y = -x$ and $y = 2x + 1$.

3 (a) Using axes from -4 to 6 each, draw the quadrilateral with coordinates A (1, 1), B (1, 3), C (3, 3) and D (4, 1). Write down the name given to this type of quadrilateral.

   (b) Reflect the figure in the line $y = 0$. Write down the coordinates of A′, B′, C′ and D′.

   (c) Using (2, 2) as the centre of enlargement, enlarge the quadrilateral ABCD by a scale factor of 2. Write down the coordinates of A″, B″, C″ and D″.

4 Solve to find the number n:
   (a) $3n = 12$ (b) $4n = -12$ (c) $3n - 5 = 4$ (d) $n + 8 = 4$.

5 If twelve tickets cost £2.52, how many could you buy for £4?

6 A lawn 25 m by 15 m is surrounded by a concrete path 2 m wide. What is the area of the path? (A diagram may help you.)

*7 Write in 12-hour-clock time:
   (a) 1500   (b) 0842   (c) 1426.

*8 (a) 3 min 48 s + 51 s + 2 min 6 s   (b) 3 min 21 s − 1 min 51 s.

9 Alan, Bill and Colin went fishing. Alan caught 5 more fish than Colin, and Bill caught 4 fewer than Alan and Colin together. If in all they caught 58 fish, how many did they each catch?

10 Solve simultaneously $2x + y = 3$ and $x + 2y = 0$.

11 (a) Construct the grid shown in Figure P2:1.
   (b) On your grid draw the set of cubes shown in Figure P2:2.
   (c) How many cubes are needed to build Figure P2:2?

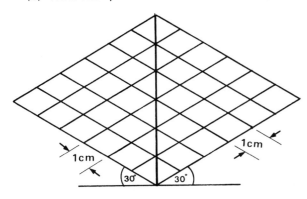

Fig. P2:1

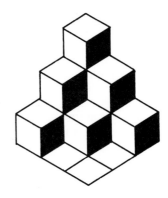

Fig. P2:2

Paper 3

1 Express as a percentage:
(a) $\frac{1}{2}$ (b) $\frac{3}{4}$ (c) $\frac{2}{3}$.

2 Express as a decimal fraction:
(a) 25% (b) 62.5%.

3 A firm which employed 32 workers increased its workforce by 25%. How many workers does it now employ?

4 After completing his training Adrian's salary rose by 15% to £7360. What was his salary during his training?

5 Remove the brackets and simplify:
(a) $4(2a - 3) + 6a - 4$ (b) $-(2a + 4) + 3(2a - 5)$.

6 A family size survey of form 4DB produced the following results:

Size (X)	Tally	Frequency (f)	$X \times f$
2	///	3	6
3	̶L̶H̶T̶ //	7	21
4	̶L̶H̶T̶ ̶L̶H̶T̶ ///		
5	////		
6	//		
7	/		
	Grand totals		

Copy and complete the table. Use the table to help you work out:
(a) the median family size
(b) the modal family size
(c) the mean family size.

*7 Solve:
(a) $3(a - 2) = a + 2$ (b) $2(3b - 2) = 2(2b - 5)$ (c) $3(2c + 2) = 2(2c + 4)$.

*8 What is the equation of the straight line joining (0, 2) to (−5, 2)?

9 Solve simultaneously: $2x + 3y = 17$ and $x + 2y = 10$.

10 Using axes from −2 to 6 each, draw the lines with equations $y = 2x - 1$ and $y = -x + 5$. Use your graph to solve simultaneously the equations $y - 2x = -1$ and $x + y = 5$.

11 Find a number such that when 8 is added to it the result is twice as much as when 4 is subtracted from it.

Paper 4

1 Find the mean of 36, 42, 37, 41, 35, 40, 36, 37, 40 and 39.

2 Use your answer to question 1 to write down the mean of 236, 242, 237, 241, 235, 240, 236, 237, 240 and 239.

3 When throwing rings at a target Alison obtains the following scores:

Score	0	1	2	3	4	5
Number of rings with this score	15	20	16	15	24	10

Find:
(a) the modal score   (b) the median score   (c) the mean score.

4 Remove the brackets then simplify:
(a) $2(b - 3) + 4(b - 5)$ (b) $3(b + 3) + 2(b - 4)$ (c) $-2(3 + b) + 2(b - 4)$.

5 (a) 3 h 16 min + 48 min + 2 h 38 min   (b) 6 h 24 min − 3 h 37 min.

*6 Solve simultaneously:
(a) $x + y = 2$
    $3x - y = 14$ (Add)
(b) $x + 3y = 11$ (Multiply top equation by 3,
    $3x + 2y = 12$ then subtract).

*7 Using axes from −4 to 6 each, draw the rectangle with coordinates A (−2, −2), B (−2, 2), C (4, 2) and D (4, −2). Using the origin as the centre of enlargement:

(a) enlarge the figure ABCD by a scale factor of 1.5. Write down the coordinates of A′, B′, C′ and D′.

(b) enlarge the figure ABCD by a scale factor of 0.5. Write down the coordinates of A″, B″, C″ and D″.

8 Solve to find h:
(a) $3(2h - 4) = 3h - 6$ (b) $2(h + 3) = h + 9$.

9 Solve simultaneously: $2x - y = 8$ and $3x + 2y = 5$.

10 Each of the n teams in a league are to play each of the others once. State, in terms of n, the number of matches required.

Paper 5

1 Using compasses, construct a triangle with sides 6 cm, 6 cm and 7 cm.

Now use compasses to bisect each angle and so find the centre of the incircle. Draw this incircle, and measure its radius.

2 Draw two triangles which satisfy the conditions:
AB = 6 cm, BC = 4 cm, ∠A = 35°. (Use a protractor for the angle.)

In each triangle measure the size of angle C.

3 Discuss which design, Figure P5:1 or Figure P5:2, would produce a stronger gate.

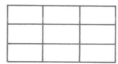 Fig. P5:1
 Fig. P5:2

4 Find the value of f if:
(a) $5(f - 3) = 15$ (b) $5(f - 3) + 2(2f - 5) = 11$.

5 Mark sells a computer game for £8. If he made a loss of 20%, how much had the game cost him?

6 The ages of a family of four are 47 years 6 months, 50 years 7 months, 23 years 2 months and 21 years 5 months. What is the mean age of the family?

7 The mean average age of 15 girls was 14 years 7 months. When one girl was away, the average fell to 14 years 6 months. How old was the absent girl?

*8 Find the approximate mean age for the members of Radford Football Club.

Age	14–18	19–23	24–26	29–33	34–38
Frequency	15	9	12	6	6

*9 How many chickens and how many cows are there in a farmyard if the total number of heads is 64 and the total number of feet is 158?

10 Alexa sells a stamp for £56. The number of pounds that she paid for it is the same as the percentage profit made when she sold it. What did she pay for it?

11 On a journey of 143 miles a train covered the first 60 miles at 50 m.p.h. and the next 40 miles at 30 m.p.h. At what rate was the remainder of the journey covered if the average speed for the whole journey was 40 m.p.h.? (You should use a calculator.)

Paper 6

1 Write the following numbers approximated to 3 significant figures.
   (a) 3042   (b) 42.38   (c) 1.234   (d) 3004   (e) 20.48   (f) 8.999.

2 Write in 12-hour-clock time (including a.m. or p.m.):
   (a) 0500   (b) 0842   (c) 2105.

3 Change to seconds:
   (a) 3 min 16 s   (b) 7 min 48 s.

4 Find the value of x if:
   (a) $13x + 5(x + 4) - 9 = 4(2x + 8) - 1$
   (b) $6(3x + 5) = 2(x - 5) + 4(2x + 6)$.

5 A bag contains 4 black, 1 white, and 3 grey counters. State as the simplest possible fraction
   the probability of picking, if each picked counter is immediately replaced:
   (a) a black   (b) a white   (c) a black then a white   (d) two blacks
   (e) a black and a grey in either order.

*6 Using the British Airways information given below, calculate the cost of booking in March a
   one-way flight departing on Saturday August 1st, for two adults and one 18-month old infant
   going on a fortnight's holiday.

Fares:	Super Apex (return)	Economy (one-way)	Standby (one-way)
April 1–May 31 and Oct 1–Oct 31	£329 (Mon–Thu) £369 (Fri–Sun)	£233 (Mon–Thu) £248 (Fri–Sun)	£170 (available for travel from July 1)
June 1–Sept 30	£349 (Mon–Thu) £389 (Fri–Sun)	£267 (Mon–Thu) £282 (Fri–Sun)	
Child discount:	Infants under 2 years 90%; 2–11 years 33.3%		Infants 90%
Conditions:	Must be booked at least 21 days before travel. Min stay 7 days, max stay 6 months.	—	Must travel within 3 months of purchase. Seat confirmed at airport. No standbys on eastbound flights after Sept 30.

*7 The price of a television in six different shops was £326, £304, £335, £317, £310 and £318.
   (a) What was the mean price?
   (b) How much cheaper than the mean price was the cheapest?
   (c) How much more expensive than the mean price was the most expensive?
   (d) What was the difference between the cheapest and the most expensive?

8 Solve simultaneously: $2x + 3y = 1$ and $4x + 2y = 6$.

9 By substituting $y = x$ into the equation $2y + 3x = 15$, find a pair of values for x and y that
   satisfies (makes true) both equations. Illustrate your answer with a graph.

Paper 7

1 Using a calculator, and giving your answer correct to 3 s.f., simplify $\dfrac{375 \times 0.148}{16.35}$.

2 (a) 3 min 48 s + 51 s + 2 min 6 s   (b) 3 min 21 s − 1 min 43 s.

3 (a) Increase 48 by 25%   (b) Decrease 48 by $12\frac{1}{2}$%.

4 Copy Figure P7:1 as neatly as you can. Make the sides of the large triangle about 60 mm.

Fig. P7:1

5 The marks scored by pupils in class 4DB in their last test were:

Marks	0	1	2	3	4	5	6	7	8	9	10
No. of pupils	0	2	0	2	1	3	4	8	3	3	4

Find:
(a) how many pupils there are in 4DB   (b) the modal mark
(c) the mean mark   (d) the median mark.

*6 Rewrite the following formulae so that *r* becomes the subject.
(a) $p = r - 4$ (b) $p = r + d$ (c) $m = t + r$ (d) $V = 4r$ (e) $k = pr - d$
(f) $d = try$.

*7 When two dice are thrown at the same time and their scores added, what is the probability of scoring:
(a) 2   (b) 7   (c) 11   (d) 1?

8 A trader buys a box of 24 tins of tomatoes for £9.60. She sells the tomatoes at 60p per tin. What is her percentage profit?

9 (a) Find the external angle of a regular pentagon.

(b) Use your answer to (a) to find:
(i) the interior angle of a regular pentagon
(ii) the sum of the interior angles of a regular pentagon.

10 Construct a triangle with sides 6 cm, 6 cm and 7 cm. Bisect each side to find the centre of the circumcircle. Draw the circle and measure its radius.

Paper 8

1 Use Pythagoras' theorem to calculate side x, correct to 3 significant figures, in each triangle in Figure P8:1.

(a)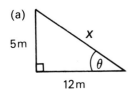

5m · 12m · x · θ

(b)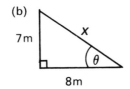

7m · 8m · x · θ

(c)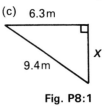

6.3m · 9.4m · x

Fig. P8:1

2 Use the [TAN] key on your calculator to find x, correct to 3 significant figures, in Figure P8:2.

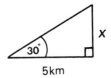

30° · 5km · x · **Fig. P8:2**

3 Use the tangent ratio $\left(\dfrac{o}{a} = \tan\theta\right)$ to calculate the two angles marked θ in Figure P8:1. Give the answers to the nearest tenth of a degree.

4 Find the values of x and y that make the following pairs of equations true.

(a) $2x + 4y = 16$
   $2x + 2y = 12$ SUBTRACT

(b) $3x + 2y = 13$
   $2x - 2y = 2$ ADD

*5 Write as a 24-hour-clock time:
(a) 6:30 a.m.   (b) 5:15 p.m.
(c) ten minutes to eight in the morning
(d) a quarter past nine in the evening

6 Rearrange to make p the subject:
(a) $m = c - p$ (b) $b = cp$ (c) $g = pc + t$.

7 (a) Draw a travel graph to show the following journeys. Use 2 mm graph paper, with scales: 0 to 60 km, 1 cm represents 10 km; 8 a.m. to 7 p.m., 1 cm represents 1 h.

Some cyclists left Epworth at 8 a.m. and cycled at an average speed of 20 km/h for $1\frac{1}{2}$ hours. They then stopped for 30 min before cycling for another 2 hours to a town 60 km from Epworth. An hour later they set off for Epworth, averaging 15 km/h until they reached the half-way point, where they stopped for half an hour. They completed the journey at an average speed of 10 km/h.

Show also a second group of cyclists who left Epworth an hour later, joining the first group at 11 a.m. without a break.

(b) (i) What was the average speed of the second group up to the time they joined the others?
(ii) What was the average speed for the whole journey for each group, correct to the nearest km/h?

215

P

Paper 9

1. Use a calculator to find:

   (a) $\dfrac{628 \times 17}{6.8}$ (b) $\dfrac{648 \times 31.4}{726 \times 11.3}$ correct to 2 decimal places.

2. If $H = \dfrac{PLAN}{33\,000}$, calculate H when $P = 66$, $L = 5$, $A = 5$ and $N = 40$.

3. The cost of buying some books valued at £2.35 each, and of having them delivered, was £42.31. The delivery charge was £2.36. How many books were bought?

4. The sill of a window is 4.8 metres above the ground. What is the length of the shortest ladder that can just reach the sill if the base of the ladder has to be at least 2 metres from the wall?

5. Use tangents to find θ and x in Figure P9:1.

   (a) 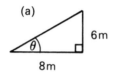   (b)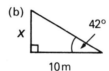

   Fig. P9:1

6. Express correct to 3 significant figures:
   (a) 2.324   (b) 0.038 76.

*7. Copy Figure P9:2, using a radius of 3 cm for the complete circle.

Fig. P9:2

8. Using a calculator, find correct to 3 significant figures:

   (a) $\dfrac{40.28 \times 27.64}{3.64}$ (b) $\dfrac{39.374 \times 16.8^2}{4.9^3}$.

9. Make a the subject of:
   (a) $P = 2a + 2b$ (b) $b = 2a - r$ (c) $V = ab(p - r)$.

10. Find the values of a in question 9 if $b = 2$, $p = 8$, $r = 3$ and $V = 19.6$.

Paper 10

1　A bag contains 4 red, 2 white and 6 blue counters. State, as the simplest possible fraction, the probability of picking, if the counter is immediately replaced:
(a) a red　(b) a blue　(c) a red then a white　(d) two whites.

2　Write as a 24-hour-clock time:
(a) 6:30 a.m.　(b) 5:15 p.m.

3　Give the number of hours and minutes between:
(a) 7:14 a.m. and 8:06 a.m.　(b) 7:42 a.m. and 11:37 a.m.　(c) midday and 4.32 p.m.

4　Find the value of y if:
(a) $4(2y - 1) = 20$　(b) $9(y + 1) - 6 = 2(y + 12)$.

5　Working to an accuracy of 3 significant figures, calculate:
(a) $\dfrac{4.26 \times 3.18}{1.4}$　(b) $\dfrac{1}{6.4 \times 18.6}$.

*6　Use Pythagoras' theorem to calculate side h in Figure P10:1.

12 m

h

7 m

Fig. P10:1

7　The average age of the eleven players in a hockey team is 19 years 7 months. If the oldest player is 22 years 11 months, what is the average age of the rest of the team?

8　In how many different ways (that is, so that at least one man has at least one different person by his side) can four men:
(a) sit on a park bench　(b) sit round a table?

9　The volume of a cone is found by using the formula $V = \frac{1}{3}\pi r^2 h$.

Using the calculator value of π, find the value of:
(a) V to 4 s.f., if $r = 8$ cm and $h = 14$ cm
(b) h to 2 s.f., if $V = 222.4$ cm and $r = 5$ cm
(c) r to 1 s.f., if $V = 302.7$ cm and $h = 5.9$ cm.

Paper 11

1 State the coordinates of the crossing point of:
  (a) $x = -1$ and $y = 0$ (b) $y = x$ and $x = 5$
  (c) $y = 2$ and $y = x$ (d) $y = x + 1$ and $x = 2$.

2 Complete the coordinates $(2, \ )$, $(0, \ )$ and $(-4, \ )$ to lie on the line:
  (a) $y = x$ (b) $y = 3x$ (c) $y = -2x$.

3 Two sides of a right-angled triangle are 12 cm and 16 cm. Use Pythagoras' theorem to calculate the length of the hypotenuse.

4 Calculate the size of each lettered angle in Figure P11:1.

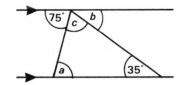 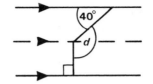 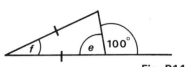

Fig. P11:1

5 If $v = u + at$:
  (a) rewrite the formula to make u the subject
  (b) calculate u when $v = 16$, $a = 3.5$ and $t = 4$.

*6 Use a ruler and compasses, but not a protractor, in this question.

  (a) Construct $\triangle ABC$ where $\angle A = 90°$, AB = 4.5 cm and AC = 6 cm. Measure BC.

  (b) Construct $\triangle DEF$ where $\angle D = 90°$, $\angle E = 60°$ and DE = 4 cm. Measure EF.

*7 Evaluate, without using a calculator and showing all necessary working:
  (a) $3.8 + 0.048 + 24$ (b) $194 - 0.37$ (c) $6.2 - 0.56$ (d) $(0.2)^2$
  (e) $\sqrt{0.16}$ (f) $1.6188 \div 0.38$.

8 The scale of a map is 5 cm to 1 km. What distance is represented by:
  (a) 1 cm   (b) 4.2 cm?

9 Draw a circle of radius 45 mm. Divide it accurately into twelve equal sectors.

10 A ship sails 20 km due south and then 14 km due west. Calculate how far it then is from its starting point, correct to 3 s.f., and its bearing from this point, correct to one-tenth of a degree, both as a three-figure and as a cardinal bearing.

Paper 12

1 Write as a decimal fraction:
(a) 7.3×10^{-2}
(b) the fraction displayed on a calculator as 6.04   −04.

2 Write in standard form ($A \times 10^x$ where $1 \leqslant A < 10$ and x is integral):
(a) 0.35   (b) 0.0035   (c) 706.

3 Calculate, writing your answer in standard form:
(a) $3.7 \times 10^4 \times 500$ (multiplication may be done in any order)
(b) $7.8 \times 3 \times 2000$
(c) $12.8 \times 100 + 4.2 \times 10^3$ (multiplication must be done before addition)

4 Find the value of the letter in each of the following equations.
(a) $3 + a = 5$ (b) $4 + b = 2$ (c) $2c + 2 = 0$
(d) $4d - 8 = 12 + 2d$ (e) $7 + e = -e - 9$.

5 Remove the brackets and simplify:
(a) $6a + (2a + 3d)$ (b) $7a - (5b - 3a)$ (c) $7a - (4a + 3b)$.

6 Showing all working, calculate:
(a) 76×80 (b) 9.3×0.54 (c) $10.2 \div 0.2$.

*7 A bag contains 5 red, 2 white and 3 blue counters. State the probability of picking, if the first counter picked is replaced:
(a) a red   (b) a red then a white   (c) a white then a blue.

*8 (a) In Figure P12:1, find the third angle, and use this angle and the tangent ratio to calculate side x correct to 3 significant figures.

(b) Why is it easier to use the third angle rather than the 48° one?

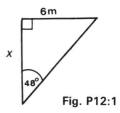

Fig. P12:1

9 Solve simultaneously: $3x + 2y = 12$ and $x + y = 3$.

10 Design a diagram to show the six possible ways that Alan (A) and Bob (B) could each choose a dancing partner from Clare (C), Dawn (D) and Eve (E) if Alan always asks a girl to dance before Bob plucks up the courage.

Use your diagram to find the probability that:
(a) Alan asks Eve to dance
(b) Alan does not ask Eve to dance
(c) Bob asks Eve to dance
(d) Dawn dances with one of the two lads
(e) Dawn does not dance with one of the two lads
(f) Clare dances with one of them, but Eve does not.

P

Paper 13

1. Write as a decimal fraction:
   (a) $\frac{1}{2}$ (b) $\frac{1}{4}$ (c) $\frac{3}{4}$ (d) $\frac{1}{10}$ (e) $\frac{1}{100}$.

2. Write the fractions in question 1 as percentages.

3. A bag contains 4 green (G), 1 red (R) and 3 yellow (Y) balls. State as a simplified fraction the probability of picking, if each picked ball is replaced:
   (a) GR (green then red)   (b) RR   (c) GRY   (d) RGG.

4. Suggest the next term in the sequence:
   (a) 1, 2, 4, 7, 11   (b) 3, 6, 12, 36   (c) 2, −4, 8.

5. Construct an isosceles trapezium with parallel sides of 5 cm and 3 cm and the perpendicular distance between them 3 cm. Draw the diagonals. Measure and write on the figure the length of a diagonal.

6. Solve:
   (a) $1 + 2(a - 3) = 3$ (b) $2(3 + 2b) - 4(3b - 2) = 2$.

7. Mary Lamb invests £500 in a building society account paying interest at 13.5%. How much interest will they pay her at the end of the year?

*8. Write in standard form:
   (a) 600   (b) 72.4   (c) 0.046   (d) 0.000 032

*9. What is the longest straight-line race-track that can be laid out in a rectangular field 80 metres long and 60 metres wide?

10. A ship sails 9 miles north then 17 miles west then 9 miles north again. Calculate how far and on what bearing it then is from its starting position.

11. In Figure P13:1, O is the centre of the circle. Calculate:
    (a) the perpendicular distance from O to AB
    (b) the length of the chord CD.

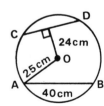

Fig. P13:1

Paper 14

1 Calculate the angle θ in both triangles in Figure P14:1.

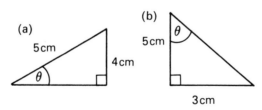

Fig. P14:1

2 Simplify:
(a) $(37.2 \div 6) - (0.34 \times 6)$ (b) $(3.5 \times 8) + (1.33 \times 6)$.

3 Find the highest common factor of:
(a) 32 and 48 (b) 24, 42 and 51.

4 How many 7p stamps can be bought for £3.99?

5 A rectangular carpet is 7 m long and 4 m wide. Calculate:
(a) the area of the carpet (b) the cost of the carpet if 1 m² costs £7.20.

6 A car travels on a motorway at a constant speed of 120 km/h. How far does it travel in:
(a) 2 hours (b) half an hour (c) 20 minutes?

7 Solve:
(a) $27 + 3x = 5x + 15$ (b) $5x + 4 = 2x + 10$.

*8 Simplify:
(a) $\frac{3}{4} - \frac{2}{3}$ (b) $\frac{3}{4} + \frac{2}{3}$ (c) $\frac{3}{4} \times \frac{2}{3}$ (d) $\frac{3}{4} \div \frac{2}{3}$.

9 Giving the answer in standard form, find:
(a) $8 \times 10^4 \times 3.6 \times 10^2$ (b) $(7.45 \times 10^{-2}) + (3.6 \times 10^{-1})$.

10 Solve:
(a) $2(4a + 3) - 4a = 2(a - 1) + 14$ (b) $7(b - 2) = 3(3b + 4)$.

11 Solve simultaneously: $2a - 3b = 14$ and $3a - 2b = 16$.

12. A fishing boat leaves Falmouth and sails 24 miles south then 7 miles east. Use a sketch of the journey to help you calculate:
(a) how far the boat is from Falmouth
(b) the bearing of the boat from Falmouth
(c) the bearing of Falmouth from the boat.
(Scale drawing answers will not be accepted.)

221

P

Paper 15

1 Multiply:
(a) $(x + 3)(x + 2)$ (b) $(x - 4)(x - 2)$.

2 Solve simultaneously: $2x + y = 4$ and $3x + 2y = 5$.

3 Give the number of hours and minutes between:
(a) 7:14 a.m. and 1:20 p.m.   (b) 7:14 a.m. and 9:06 p.m.
(c) 9:38 p.m. and 1:27 a.m.

4 $83.5 + 5.248 + 27$

5 Oranges on Mike's market stall are priced at 7 for 24p. On Mary's they are 42p a dozen. Showing clear working, find who is selling the cheaper oranges.

*6 Accurately construct Figure P15:1, making the large circle of radius 5 cm.

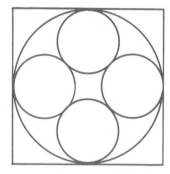

Fig. P15:1

*7 Write down the next term in the sequence:
(a) 3, 7, 11   (b) 2, −2, −6   (c) 1, 3, 6, 10.

8 A cable-railway is 4400 m long and ascends an average slope of 35°. What height does it rise to, to the nearest metre?

9 The scale of a map is 1 : 50 000.
(a) Find the distance in km represented by 30 cm on the map.
(b) Find the true area in km² of a lake of area 2 cm² on the map.

10 A pond of radius 12 m is to be surrounded by a lawn 4 m wide. Taking $\pi = 3.142$, and using a calculator, find the area of the lawn.

Paper 16

1 (a) Subtract 3.96 from 8.007. (b) Add two hundredths to 125.699.

2 (a) $2\frac{1}{4} + 1\frac{1}{3}$ (b) $2\frac{1}{4} - 1\frac{1}{3}$ (c) $2\frac{1}{4} \times 1\frac{1}{3}$ (d) $2\frac{1}{4} \div 1\frac{1}{3}$.

3 **Example** $48 = 2 \times 2 \times 2 \times 2 \times 3$

Write as a product of prime factors:
(a) 12 (b) 16 (c) 28 (d) 36 (e) 60.

4 Find the highest common factor (HCF) of:
(a) 16 and 24 (b) 28 and 35 (c) 27 and 30.

5 Find the lowest common multiple (LCM) of:
(a) 4 and 6 (b) 8 and 12 (c) 9 and 15.

6 Draw axes: x from -3 to 3, 1 cm to 1 unit; y from -5 to 6, 1 cm to 1 unit. Plot the graph of $y = x^2 - 4$. Write down the values of x where the curve crosses the x-axis.

*7 Write as a denary number:
(a) 1.6×10^4 (b) 9.6×10^{-2}.

*8 Write in standard form, as in question 7:
(a) 136 (b) 0.0097.

9 Simplify:
(a) $(5\frac{1}{3} \div 1\frac{3}{5}) + (1\frac{2}{3} \times \frac{7}{10})$ (b) $4\frac{2}{5} \div (\frac{1}{3} + \frac{2}{5})$.

10 Solve simultaneously by substitution: $y = 2x + 8$ and $2y + x = 1$.

11 Giving your answer in standard form, simplify:
(a) $4.3 \times 10^{-2} \times 2 \times 10^4$ (b) $6.7 \times 10^2 + 3.4 \times 10^{-2}$.

Paper 17

1 Factorise:
   (a) $2a + 8$ (b) $b^2 - 4$ (c) $c^2 - 4c$.

2 (a) $2\frac{2}{3} + 3\frac{2}{5}$ (b) $3\frac{1}{4} - 2\frac{2}{3}$ (c) $5\frac{3}{5} \times 3\frac{4}{7}$ (d) $3\frac{3}{4} \div 2\frac{1}{3}$.

3 Calculate the lengths x, correct to 2 s.f., in Figure P17:1.

(a)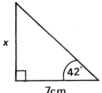

(b)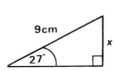

(c)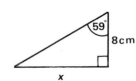

Fig. P17:1

4 A bag contains 5 red, 2 white, and 3 blue counters. State the probability of picking, if the first counter is not replaced before the second one is picked:
   (a) red then white   (b) red then red.

5 In question 4, which of the two events is the more likely?

6 Expand:
   (a) $(a + 2)(a - 3)$ (b) $(a - 4)(a - 2)$ (c) $(2a - 3)(a - 3)$.

7 The average age of a form of 20 pupils is 14 years 9 months. Find the total of their ages in years.

*8 A car mileage meter reads 56 716 when the tank is filled. It reads 56 909 when it is next filled, the tank then taking 25 litres of petrol. What is the average fuel consumption in miles per litre, correct to the nearest whole number?

*9 Posts cost £8 each and six-foot fencing panels cost £15 each.

   (a) How many posts and panels are needed to fence 32 feet of garden? (The posts are 4 inches (a third of a foot) square.)

   (b) What is the cost of fencing the garden?

10 Solve simultaneously $y = x$ and $y = 2x - 4$ by a graphical method, using axes x from 0 to 4 and y from -4 to 4.

11 Two boats set sail from a harbour at 0600. *Kingfisher* sails on a bearing of 030° at a speed of 10 knots and *Pearlfisher* sails on a bearing of 120° at a speed of 12 knots. (A knot is one nautical mile per hour.)
   Find:
   (a) how far the boats have sailed in three hours
   (b) how far apart the boats are.

Paper 18

1 Write as a product of prime factors:
   (a) 12   (b) 15   (c) 38   (d) 48.

2 State the highest common factor of:
   (a) 12 and 16   (b) 32 and 68   (c) 24, 16 and 56.

3 State the lowest common multiple of:
   (a) 12, 16 and 30   (b) 15, 18 and 30.

4 Simplify:
   (a) $8\frac{1}{4} - 5\frac{2}{5}$ (b) $1\frac{5}{6} \times 1\frac{1}{8}$.

5 Express correct to 1 significant figure:
   (a) 7284   (b) 3.7265   (c) 0.026 17.

6 Repeat question 5, but correct to 2 significant figures.

7 Repeat question 5, but correct to 3 significant figures.

8 A girl cycles 20 km in an hour and a boy cycles 5 m in a second. Who goes the faster, and by how many km/h?

*9 Using the 'difference of two squares' method, evaluate:
   (a) $69^2 - 31^2$ (b) $58^2 - 38^2$ (c) $72^2 - 28^2$ (d) $83^2 - 78^2$.

*10 Find the value of the letter if:
   (a) $\dfrac{x}{5} = 10$ (b) $4 - a = 1$ (c) $1 - y = 4$ (d) $2k - 3 = 9$.

11 Expand:
   (a) $(2x - 4)(3x + 2)$ (b) $(x - 4)(3x - 2)$.

12 Find the size of angles x and y in Figure P18:1.

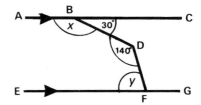

Fig. P18:1

13 For the four integers $n, n + 1, n + 2$ and $n + 3$, say which of the following are (a) always true, (b) sometimes true, (c) never true.

   A: Two are even   B: Two are multiples of 3   C: One is a multiple of 4
   D: Their sum is exactly divisible by 4   E: Their product is exactly divisible by 120
   F: The sum of two of them is half their total sum
   G: The product of two of them equals the product of the other two.

Paper 19

1 Express:
(a) 16 out of 40 as a percentage (b) 250 g as a percentage of 1 kg.

2 Jethro buys an antique chair for £400 and sells it at a gain of 45%. What is his selling price?

3 In a year Polly grows from 1.50 m to 1.55 m. What is the percentage change in her height? (Work in centimetres.)

4 Simplify: $4a^3 - 3ac + 8ac - 2a^2 + 14$.

5 Using a calculator, and taking π as 3.142, calculate C, A and V, correct to 2 decimal places, if:

(a) $C = 2\pi R$ and $R = 3.6$ (b) $A = \pi r^2$ and $r = 2.7$ (c) $V = \dfrac{4\pi r^3}{3}$ and $r = 6.2$.

6 Find the size of each angle in Figure P19:1.

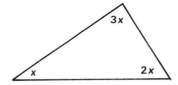 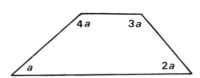

Fig. P19:1

*7 Copy Figure P19:2, making the large square of side 2.5 cm. Then fill in further squares to give it rotational symmetry of order 4.

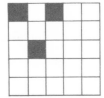

Fig. P19:2

8 How many complete turns does a car wheel of diameter 24 inches make in a mile? (12 inches = 1 foot; 3 feet = 1 yard; 1760 yards = 1 mile. Take $\pi = 3.14$.)

9 An object travelling initially at a velocity of u m/s and accelerating at a m/s^2, will travel s metres in t seconds, where $s = ut + \frac{1}{2}at^2$, assuming that there is no resistance to the motion.

Find the distance travelled by an object in 3 seconds if it is travelling initially at 80 m/s, and is accelerating at 32 m/s^2.

10 Find the simultaneous solution of $y = 2x - 4$ and $y = x - 1$ by drawing a graph on axes: x from 0 to 4, y from -4 to 4.

Paper 20

1 The price of a £20 radio rises by 18%. Find the new price.

2 Factorise:
(a) $4a - 8$ (b) $a^2 - 9$ (c) $3c^3 + 2c^2 + c$.

3 Showing all working, calculate:
(a) 2.35×1.32 (b) $0.56 \div 0.7$.

4 Copy and complete the table for the graph of $y = x^2 - 3x - 4$, then draw the parabola, using 1 cm to 1 unit on both axes.

x	-2	-1	0	1	2	3	4	5
x^2		1	0		4		16	25
$-3x$		3	0		-6		-12	-15
-4		-4	-4		-4		-4	-4
y		0	-4		-6		0	6

*5 Calculate:
(a) $\frac{1}{3} - \frac{1}{4}$ (b) $2\frac{1}{2} + 5\frac{1}{3}$ (c) $6 - 3\frac{7}{8}$.

*6 A ship sails 5 nautical miles east, then 12 nautical miles north. Calculate how far it then is from its starting point.

7 Calculate:
(a) $1\frac{7}{8} \times 3\frac{1}{5} \div \frac{4}{9}$ (b) $3\frac{1}{3} \times 2\frac{1}{4} - 1\frac{1}{2}$.

8 Solve simultaneously: $3x + 6y = 12$ and $2x + 5y = 11$.

9 Find the original cost of an item priced £24 in a '20% off' sale.

10 Three prizes together cost £48. The second is worth £7 more than the third and £10 less than the first. What is each prize?

11 Figure P20:1 shows the path of a windscreen wiper. What area of glass is swept clear by the blade? (Use $\pi = \frac{22}{7}$.)

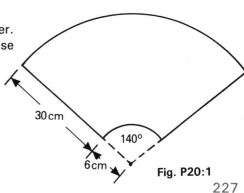

30 cm

140°

6 cm

Fig. P20:1

Paper 21

1 Showing all working, simplify:
(a) $3.8 + 0.048 + 24$ (b) $194 - 0.37$ (c) $6.2 - 0.57$ (d) 0.2×0.2
(e) $9.684 \div 12$ (f) 147.5×11.2.

2 A television originally costing £280 is reduced in a sale by 15%. What is the new price?

3 In Figure P21:1, the two triangles are similar, as they have the same angles. Side AC corresponds (is in the same position relative to the angles) to side DE, so the sides of the two triangles are in the ratio 4:12.

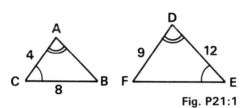 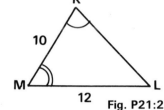

Fig. P21:1   Fig. P21:2

(a) Write the ratio 4:12 in its simplest form.

(b) Calculate the length of: (i) FE   (ii) AB.

(c) Calculate the unknown sides in Figure P21:2.

*4 For Figure P21:3, taking $\pi = \frac{22}{7}$;
(a) calculate the length of the arc
(b) find the area of the sector.

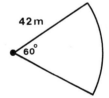

Fig. P21:3

*5 In Figure P21:4, AB = 10 cm, BC = 24 cm and AD = 6 cm.
Calculate:
(a) the length of DB
(b) the length of CD
(c) the area of triangle ABC.

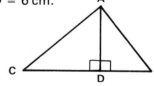

Fig. P21:4

6 Make r the subject of:
(a) $r - p = 9$ (b) $p = rt$ (c) $c = 2\pi r$.

7 Remembering to cancel as much as possible, simplify:
(a) $1\frac{1}{2} \times 1\frac{1}{3} \times 1\frac{1}{4}$ (b) $1\frac{1}{2} \times 1\frac{1}{3} \times 1\frac{1}{4} \times 1\frac{1}{5}$ (c) $1\frac{1}{2} \times 1\frac{1}{3} \times 1\frac{1}{4} \times 1\frac{1}{5} \times 1\frac{1}{6}$.

8 On axes x from -4 to 4 and y from 0 to 9, plot the graphs of $3x + 2y = 9$ and $y - 3x = 9$, and hence solve these two equations simultaneously.

Also shade on your graph the region $\{(x, y); 3x + 2y \geq 9; y - 3x \leq 9; x \leq 0\}$.

Paper 22

1 Find for a regular octagon:
   (a) the size of one exterior angle
   (b) the size of one interior angle
   (c) the sum of the interior angles.

2 Find the interior angle sum of a polygon with 39 sides.

3 The population of a town was 400 000 in 1989 and 464 000 in 1990. What was the percentage increase?

4 Solve simultaneously: $5x - 2y = 13$ and $3x + y = 21$.

5 Express correct to 1 significant figure:
   (a) 43 527   (b) 5.007 34   (c) 0.038 37.

6 Write the numbers in question 5 correct to 2 significant figures.

7 Simplify:
   (a) $a^4 \times a^2$ (b) $4a^2 \times 3a^3$ (c) $a^6 \div a^4$ (d) $33a^4 \div 3a^3$.

*8 (a) $V = a^3$. Find V when $a = 3$.

   (b) $A = \frac{1}{2}bh$. Find A when $b = 16$ and $h = 3.6$.

   (c) Where have you met the formulae in (a) and (b) before?

9 Using the ratio of the sides of similar triangles, calculate the unknown sides in Figure P22:1.

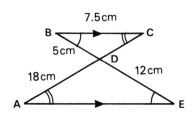 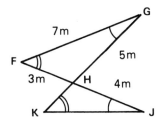

Fig. P22:1

10 A circular saw of diameter 40 cm is driven at 1500 revolutions per minute. What is the speed of the cutting edge in metres per second, correct to the nearest whole number? (Take $\pi = 3.142$. You may use a calculator.)

11 Using two sets of axes, from −5 to 5 each, show the following regions.
   (a) $\{(x, y): -3 \leqslant x < 1; 2 < y < 4\}$
   (b) $\{(x, y): x + 1 \geqslant y > 1; x \leqslant 3\}$.

Paper 23

Note: These solids should be made in preparation for working Exercise 27A.

Use 1 cm-squared paper to copy the nets in Figure P23:1, marking them clearly with letters as shown. Each square drawn here represents a 1 cm square on your nets. Cut out the nets and make the solids. You (or your teacher) should keep them carefully for use when you work Exercise 27A.

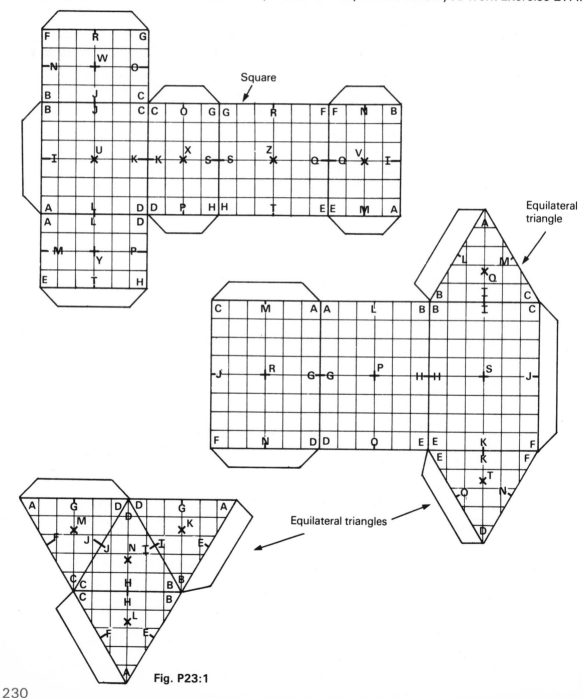

Fig. P23:1

Paper 24

1. Calculate the values of x, y, θ, α and z in Figure P24:1.

2. Factorise:
   (a) $3x + 30$ (b) $4x^2 - 1$ (c) $4c^3 + 6c^2$.

3. Write down the value of h if $\dfrac{25}{30} = \dfrac{5}{h}$.

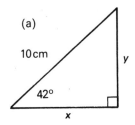

(a)

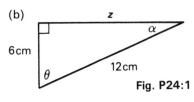

(b)

Fig. P24:1

4. Write 12 cm^2 in m^2. (It is *not* 0.12 m^2.)

5. A typist types 24 pages, each containing an average of 270 words, in one hour. How many words could she type:
   (a) in 1 hour   (b) in 6 hours   (c) in 1 minute?

*6. Write the next term in the sequence:
   (a) $-3, 6, -12$ (b) $2, 3, 5, 9, 17$ (c) $-\frac{1}{2}, \frac{1}{4}, -\frac{1}{8}$.

*7. If $a = 2$, $b = -3$, and $c = 4$, find the value of
   (a) abc (b) $c^2 - b$ (c) $2c^2$ (d) a^3.

*8. Find the value of the letter if:
   (a) $9 - a = 6$ (b) $a - 9 = 6$ (c) $6a = 9$ (d) $9a = 6$ (e) $\dfrac{a}{9} = 6$.

9. Given that $a = \frac{1}{3}$ and $b = -2$, evaluate:
   (a) $6a - 2b$ (b) $9a^2 - 2b^2$.

10. Find the simultaneous solution of $y = x - 3$ and $2y = x - 1$ by a graphical method. Use axes x from 0 to 7 and y from -3 to 3.

11. Make a the subject of:
    (a) $s = ut + \frac{1}{2}at^2$ (b) $h = \dfrac{24b}{a + b}$.

12. For $\triangle ABC$ in Figure P24:2, calculate:
    (a) its area   (b) the length BC
    (c) the perpendicular distance of A from BC
    (d) $\angle ABC$ and $\angle ACB$ correct to the nearest $0.1°$.

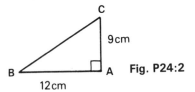

Fig. P24:2

13. Work out

$$(7.028 \times \sqrt{5.3}) - \frac{300\pi - \sin 25°}{\sqrt[3]{30} + 1} + \frac{3 + 10^3}{16.9 \times 0.18}$$

correct to 3 s.f. (You may use a calculator!)

Paper 25

1 Divide £35 in the ratio $2:3$.

2 (a) Increase 36 in the ratio $4:3$.   (b) Decrease 24 in the ratio $5:16$.

3 Factorise $x^2 + 7x + 10$.

4 Simplify:
(a) $(x - 4)(x - 2)$ (b) $(x + 2)(3x - 4)$.

5 (a) Copy and complete the table, then draw the graph of $y = x^2 + 2x - 4$.
Use scales: x, 2 cm to 1 unit: y, 1 cm to 1 unit.

x	-5	-4	-3	-2	-1	0	1	2
x^2	25		9	4			1	
$+2x$	-10		-6	-4			2	
-4	-4		-4	-4			-4	
y	11		-1	-4			-1	

(b) State the values of x that make $x^2 + 2x - 4 = 0$, giving your answers correct to one place of decimals.

*6 Simplify:
(a) $\frac{3}{4} + \frac{2}{3} - \frac{1}{2}$ (b) $5\frac{4}{5} - 3\frac{1}{10}$ (c) $3\frac{1}{3} - 1\frac{3}{4}$ (d) $\frac{2}{3} \div \frac{5}{6}$ (e) $1\frac{1}{2} \div 1\frac{7}{8}$.

7 Evaluate: $\frac{5}{6}(2\frac{7}{8} + 1\frac{1}{2}) \div 2\frac{3}{16}$.

8 Write $3\,\text{cm}^2$ in m^2.

9 A map is made to the scale $1:25\,000$.

(a) How many metres are represented by: (i) 1 cm   (ii) 2.3 cm?

(b) What distance on the map would represent 500 metres?

10 Write without indices:
(a) 4^3 (b) $8^{\frac{2}{3}}$.

11 A pendulum swings through an arc of $12°$. If the tip of the pendulum is 21 cm from the point of suspension, how long is the arc it makes? (Take $\pi = 3\frac{1}{7}$).

12 In question 11, through what area does the pendulum sweep?

13 Draw a picture to show how a pole should be held to cast the longest possible shadow at about ten o'clock one sunny morning.

Paper 26

1 (a) Increase 35 cm in the ratio 6:5.
   (b) Decrease £48 in the ratio 5:6.

2 In Figure P26:1, calculate:
   (a) BC (use ∠A)   (b) CD   (c) BD.

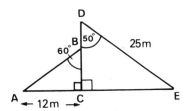

Fig. P26:1

3 Figure P26:2 shows two similar triangles.
   Triangle ABC has an area of 9 cm². Calculate:
   (a) the area of triangle DEF
   (b) the length of the altitude from A to CB.

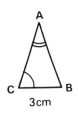 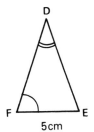

Fig. P26:2

4 Factorise:
   (a) $2x^2 + 4x$ (b) $4a^2 - 25$ (difference of two squares)   (c) $2ab + 4a^2 + 6ab^2$.

5 (a) Write 2 m² in cm².   (b) Write 200 cm² in m².

*6 An examination is timed to take $1\frac{3}{4}$ hours. At what 24-hour-clock time should it finish if it starts
    at: (a) 9 a.m.   (b) 9:40 a.m.   (c) 2:12 p.m.?

*7 How many days are there from 18 March to 12 June inclusive?

*8 Use a calculator to find $\dfrac{130 \times 24.6}{17 \times 93}$ correct to 3 s.f.

9 Write without indices:
   (a) 5^{-1} (b) 2^{-3} (c) $16^{\frac{3}{4}}$ (d) $27^{\frac{2}{3}}$.

10 Use a calculator to find a, correct to 3 s.f., if $a^3 = \dfrac{3}{0.071\,36}$.

11 Given that $x = \dfrac{1+z}{z}$ express z in terms of x. (Note: You cannot use the flow-diagram method,
    as the subject letter appears twice in the formula.)

12 Solve: (a) $3(x - 2) - 2(3x - 3) + 1 = 0$ (b) $\dfrac{x}{3} + \dfrac{x}{2} = \dfrac{5}{6}$.

13 Mary is eight years older than Nicola. In five years' time she will be twice as old as Nicola is
    then. How old are they now?

Paper 27

1 A solid cylinder has a diameter of 14 cm and is 11 cm high. Find:
(a) the area of one end   (b) the curved surface area.
(Take $\pi = \frac{22}{7}$.)

2 The outside measurements of a box without a lid are: length 32 cm, breadth 27 cm, depth 10 cm. If it is made from 1 cm thick plastic find the inside volume.

3 Figure P27:1 shows the path of a boat which sails 8 km from port A to a point B on the bearing of 220°. Calculate the distances BC and AC (called its 'northing' and 'easting' from A).

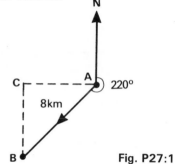

Fig. P27:1

4 Find for 56, 14 and 28:
(a) their HCF   (b) their LCM.

*5 Draw and label two pairs of axes from −5 to 5 each. On one set of axes mark the points (−3, 1) and (−3, 4). On the other set mark the points (2, 3) and (−4, 3). State the equations of the straight lines that join your pairs of points.

*6 Using a pencil, compasses and a ruler, draw Figure P27:2, giving the circle a radius of 3 cm.

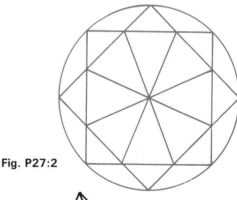

Fig. P27:2

7 Expand:
(a) $(2x - 4)(x - 2)$ (b) $2(3a + 4)(2a - 2)$.

8 Calculate angles x and y in Figure P27:3.

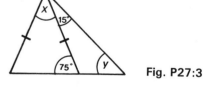

Fig. P27:3

9 A pipe has an internal radius of 8 cm and an external radius of 12 cm. It is 14 m long. Calculate the weight of the pipe in kg, correct to 3 s.f., if the metal from which it is made has a density of 7.5 g/cm³. (Take $\pi = \frac{22}{7}$.)

10 Draw four pairs of axes, each from −2 to 4. Find the equation of the straight line which passes through:
(a) (−1, −1) and (1, 3)   (b) (1, 1) and (2, 3)   (c) (1, 1) and (4, −2)
(d) (−2, 3) and (0, −1).

11 Solve graphically the simultaneous equations $y = x - 1$ and $y = 3x - 8$.

Paper 28

1 Find the volume of a cylinder of height 42 cm and radius 8 cm, taking $\pi = \frac{22}{7}$.

2 What is the difference in volume between a 4 cm cube and 4 cm³?

3 In Figure P28:1, calculate:
   (a) BD   (b) ∠DBC
   (c) DC (Use your answers to parts (a) and (b).)
   (d) the area of the triangle.

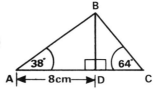

Fig. P28:1

4 Francesca needs an average of 50 marks over seven tests to gain a pass certificate. So far she has scored 32, 70, 41, 61, and 58. How many marks must she score in the last two tests if she is to just reach her target?

5 In marking an examination a teacher accepts that $\dfrac{15}{20} + \dfrac{29}{30} = \dfrac{44}{50}$. How can this be?

*6 A pyramid has a base 300 m square and a height of 150 m. Find its volume.

*7 Find the area of Figure P28:2, taking π as $\frac{22}{7}$.

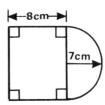

Fig. P28:2

8 How many revolutions does a cycle wheel of diameter 30 inches make in one mile? (36 inches = 1 yard; 1760 yards = 1 mile; take $\pi = 3\frac{1}{7}$.)

9 In Figure P28:3, TAM and TBN are tangents to the circle. Find the sizes of the lettered angles.

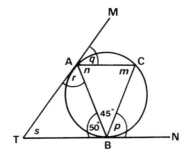

Fig. P28:3

10 State the equation of the line joining:
   (a) $(-3, 3)$ to $(-3, -3)$ (b) $(-3, 3)$ to $(3, -3)$
   (c) $(0, 4)$ to $(4, 0)$ (d) $(0, -2)$ to $(2, 4)$

11

No. of questions wrong	0	1	2	3	4	5	6	7
No. of pupils (frequency)	5	7	11	15	14	10	3	1

(a) Find: (i) the mean   (ii) the median   (iii) the mode.
(b) Draw up a cumulative frequency table, then draw the cumulative frequency diagram.

Paper 29

1 Refer to Figure P29:1.

(a) Write as a column matrix:
   (i) $\overrightarrow{AB}$ (ii) $\overrightarrow{BC}$ (iii) $\overrightarrow{AB} + \overrightarrow{BC}$.

(b) Calculate $|\overrightarrow{AB}|$ (that is the modulus, or magnitude, of $\overrightarrow{AB}$) correct to 2 decimal places.

(c) State $|\overrightarrow{AC}|$ correct to 2 decimal places.

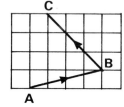

Fig. P29:1

2 Figure P29:2 shows a house extension.
(a) Find the area of the end wall, ABCD.
(b) Find the volume of the extension.

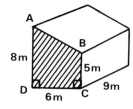

Fig. P29:2

3 (a) Write $3\,m^2$ in cm^2.   (b) Write $1\,cm^2$ in m^2.

4 Find the value of n if:

(a) $2n = 3$ (b) $3n - 1 = 8$ (c) $\dfrac{4}{n} = 2$ (d) $\dfrac{6}{n} + 1 = 7$.

*5 Construct a trapezium with parallel sides of 4 cm and 3 cm, with the perpendicular distance between them being 2 cm. Then calculate its area.

*6 Taking $\pi = \frac{22}{7}$, find the total surface area of a cylinder 8 cm high with a radius of 10.5 cm.

7 State, as simply as possible, the equation solved by the x coordinates of the crossing points of $y = x^2 - x$ and $y = \frac{1}{2}x + 3$.

8 Find the values of x and y in Figure P29:3.

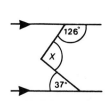

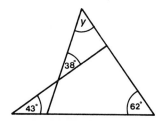

Fig. P29:3

9 Solve:
   (a) $3(a - 1) + 4(2a - 1) = 26$ (b) $5(b - 4) + 28 = 3(b - 2)$.

10 Two ships set sail from the same port at 1000 hours. One sails NE at a speed of 12 knots and the other SE at 16 knots. Calculate how far apart they are at noon. (1 knot is 1 nautical mile per hour.)

11 Calculate the total compound interest on £280 invested at 8% for 4 years.

12 A cylindrical drum 24 cm high and of internal diameter 12 cm is half full of water.

   (a) Calculate: (i) the capacity of the drum   (ii) the volume of the water.

   (b) What is the volume of a sphere of radius 6 cm?

   (c) If such a sphere is placed in the drum, show that the sphere and the water take up a total volume of about 2260 cm³, then calculate how far up the drum the water now reaches, assuming the sphere to be completely immersed in the water.

   (Take $\pi = 3.142$. Give answers correct to 3 s.f.)

Paper 30

1 Calculate the sizes of the lettered angles in Figure P30:1. O is the centre of the circle.

 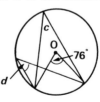

2 Solve:
   (a) $x^2 - x - 6 = 0$ by factorisation
   (b) $2x^2 + 3x + 1 = 0$ by using the quadratic equation formula.

Fig. P30:1

3 How many sides has a regular polygon if its exterior angles are each:
   (a) 36°   (b) 20°   (c) $22\frac{1}{2}$°?

4 Sarai earns £75 and spends $\frac{3}{5}$ of it. How much has she left?

5 How many boxes of ten 30 cm square carpet tiles should be bought to carpet a rectangular area 9 metres long and 6 metres wide?

*6 In Figure P30:2, state the size of:
   (a) ∠ABC   (b) ∠ACB   (c) ∠BAC
   (d) ∠ADC   (e) ∠BDC   (f) ∠ABD
   (g) ∠CBD   (h) ∠CAD.

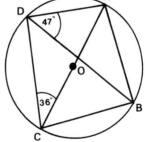

Fig. P30:2

O is the centre

237

7 The price of a ticket rises from £6.25 to £7.25. What is the percentage increase?

8 In its first 8 matches a hockey team averaged 3.25 goals per match. After 12 matches the average was 3.5 goals per match. How many goals were scored in the last four matches?

9 In Figure P30:3, use the sine rule to help you find:
(a) ∠A   (b) ∠C   (c) AB.

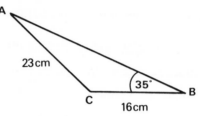

Fig. P30:3

10 A box holds 1000 cm³ of powder and has a width of 11 cm. Calculate the width of a box, mathematically similar in shape, but holding 27 000 cm³ of powder. (Note that the answer is not 287 cm! Remember the connection between lengths' ratio and volumes' ratio.)

11 Andrew's salary is £10 000. His tax-free allowance is £2 800. He is taxed on the remainder at 30%. He also pays 6% of his gross salary to a superannuation (pension) fund, and National Insurance of 8% on the first £1500 of his gross salary and 5% on the remainder. What is his monthly net income?

Information for aural tests

Focus: Then and now

People

	Then*	Now
Population (millions)	47.5	57.2
Percentage of population over 64	8.6	15.6
Life expectancy at birth:		
male	60	72
female	65	78
Births outside marriage per 1000 live births	45	266
Divorces (GB)	7,038	164,105
Crimes per 100,000 population (GB)	741	7,526
Prison population (daily average, GB)	12,629	55,178

Spending

	Then	Now
Purchasing power	4p	£1
Prices:		
pint of milk	1.5p	30p
dozen eggs	9p	£1.20
loaf of bread	1.5p	65p
tea (125g)	3p	53p
Private cars (millions GB)	1.9	19.2
Owner occupation, percentage of population (England & Wales)	32	68

Work and education

	Then	Now
Male manual workers in manufacturing: average wage per week	£3.55	£229.87
average hours worked per week	47.8	43.4
Strikes - working days lost (millions)	1.3	4.1
Number of university students	63,420	383,644

*The 'then' column represents 1938, the last normal year before the war.

Fig. 11:1

SECOND CLASS FARES FROM LONDON

	Ordinary Single	Senior Citizen Single	Economy Fare Single Day Sailing	Economy Fare Single Night Sailing	European Saver (5-day Return)	Family Fare Single
Aachen	£53.70	£29.70	—	—	£59.70	£92.20
Berlin	£86.60	—	—	—	—	—
Bremen	£71	£49.10	£58.30	£60	£75.60	£125.40
Dortmund	£61	£46.10	£55.40	£51.80	£70.70	£109.30
Frankfurt	£66.90	£50.40	£59.70	£56.20	£77.80	£121.20
Hamburg	£72.40	£53.20	£59.20	£65.40	£82.60	£132.80
Hannover	£67.20	£49.70	£55.50	£59.10	£76.70	£122.30
Köln	£55	£42	£50.80	£47.20	£62	£97.30
Mainz	£64.50	£48.80	£57.80	£54.30	£75.60	£116.50
München	£86.40	£70.70	£74.30	£63.90	£101.50	£160

Fig. 11:2

PRICES OF ADMISSION

Front Circle £6.00
Back Circle £5.00
Stalls £4.40

CHILDREN HALF PRICE

Fig. 11:3

BEDS · BEDS · BEDS 30% OFF

Fig. 11:4

CALLS VIA THE OPERATOR

Charge Band	Outgoing Operator Calls 3 mins (min charge) £	5 mins £	10 mins £	Each add'l min £	Incoming Operator Calls billed in UK Collect (Reverse Charge) BT Chargecard, UK Dir. 3 mins (min charge) £	5 mins £	10 mins £	Each add'l min £
1	3.59	5.98	11.96	1.20	2.76	4.60	9.20	0.92
2	3.59	5.98	11.96	1.20	3.11	5.18	10.35	1.04
3	4.49	7.48	14.95	1.50	3.97	6.61	13.23	1.32
4	4.49	7.48	14.95	1.50	4.11	6.84	13.69	1.37
5	4.66	7.76	15.52	1.55	4.31	7.19	14.38	1.44
6	6.21	10.35	20.70	2.07	6.21	10.35	20.70	2.07
7	6.21	10.35	20.70	2.07	6.21	10.35	20.70	2.07
8	6.38	10.64	21.27	2.13	6.21	10.35	20.70	2.07
9	7.94	13.23	26.45	2.65	6.73	11.21	22.43	2.24
10	7.94	13.23	26.45	2.65	6.73	11.21	22.43	2.24
11	8.11	13.51	27.03	2.70	6.73	11.21	22.43	2.24
12	8.11	13.51	27.03	2.70	6.73	11.21	22.43	2.24
13	8.11	13.51	27.03	2.70	6.73	11.21	22.43	2.24

Fig. 11:5

BBC1

6.45 **OPEN UNIVERSITY.**
8.00 **NEWS.**
8.15 **OPEN UNIVERSITY.**
8.40 **PLAYDAYS.**
9.00 **NEWS.**
9.15 **MORNING WORSHIP.**
Introduced by Mike Wooldridge.
10.00 **A VOUS LA FRANCE!** With
Carolle Rousseau. (R)
10.25 **ESPANA VIVA.** With Yolanda
Varquez. (R)
10.50 **STEP UP TO WORDPOWER.**
With Chris Searle. (R)
11.15 **A WAY WITH NUMBERS.**
11.40 **BAZAAR.** Nerys Hughes passes
on some hints for saving money
around the home.
12.05pm **SEE HEAR!**
12.30 **COUNTRY FILE.** The needs of
local communities in national
parks, with a report from the
Brecon Beacons. Introduced by
John Craven. Followed by **THE
WEEK'S WEATHER.**
1.00 **NEWS.** Followed by **ON THE
RECORD** with Jonathan
Dimbleby.
2.00 **EASTENDERS.*** (R)
3.00 **SNOOKER.** The final of the
Benson and Hedges Masters, from
Wembley Conference Centre.
5.05 **THE CLOTHES SHOW.**
5.30 **ANTIQUES ROADSHOW.** From
Ayr, Scotland, Highly collectable
items include a 1930s coffee set,
an electric clock and a spinet.*
6.15 **NEWS AND WEATHER.***
6.40 **SONGS OF PRAISE.** Coming,
like today's *Antiques Roadshow*,
from Ayr.*
7.15 **SNOOKER.** Introduced by Tony
Gubba, with commentaries by Ted
Lowe.*
8.05 **LOVEJOY.** *One Born Every
Minute.* Lovejoy (Ian McShane)
hosts his own *Antiques Roadshow*
from a motorcycle with sidecar.*
9.00 **NEWS AND WEATHER.**
9.30 **THAT'S LIFE!** Esther Rantzen is
still searching for someone to join
her gang. More misprints from
Scott Sherrin and Doc Cox.
10.10 **MASTERMIND.** Featuring
Antarctic exploration, Barbara
Pym, Henry VII and Erwin
Rommel.
10.40 **EVERYMAN.** *Forty Million
Hostages.* Democracy — and the
lack of it — in Myanmar
(formerly Burma).
11.25 **SNOOKER.** Down to the final
black, with commentaries and last
thoughts on this year's Masters.
12.25 **NEWS.**
12.35 **WEATHER.** *To 12.40am.*

Fig. I2:1

FARES

Standard Single Fares

VEHICLES AND THEIR PASSENGERS	E TARIFF £	D TARIFF £	C TARIFF £	B TARIFF £
Cars, Minibuses and Campers				
Up to 4.00m (13′1″) in length/ Motorcycle combinations	20.00	30.00	39.50	48.00
Up to 4.50m (14′9″) in length	20.00	35.00	47.50	57.00
Up to 5.50m (18′) in length	20.00	40.00	56.50	67.00
Over 5.50m: per extra metre or part thereof	10.00	10.00	11.00	12.00
Caravans and Trailers				
Up to 4.00m (13′1″) in length	19.00	24.00	26.00	28.00
Up to 5.50m (18′) in length	19.00	36.00	38.00	40.00
Over 5.50m: per extra metre or part thereof	10.00	10.00	10.00	10.00
Motorcycles, Scooters and Mopeds	11.00	11.00	12.00	13.00
Each Adult	11.50	11.50	11.50	11.50
Each Child (4 but under 14 yrs)	6.00	6.00	6.00	6.00

Fig. I2:2

Use this "Ready Reckoner" to decide which plan is right for you

	PLAN A	PLAN B	PLAN C	PLAN D	PLAN E
Minimum Cover You Get	£10,000	£20,000	£35,000	£50,000	£65,000
Double Cover if Death Accidental	£20,000	£40,000	£70,000	£100,000	£130,000
Age (nearest)	Amount you pay monthly				
20–30	£5.00	£6.00	£7.35	£10.50	£13.65
31–35	£5.00	£6.20	£9.10	£13.00	£16.90
36–40	£5.40	£8.40	£12.95	£18.50	£24.05
41–45	£6.00	£12.00	£19.25	£27.50	—
46–50	£9.30	£18.60	£30.80	—	—
51–55	£14.70	£29.40	—	—	—

Fig. I2:3

Fig. I2:4

April

Mon	1	8	15	22	29
Tue	2	9	16	23	30
Wed	3	10	17	24	
Th	4	11	18	25	
Fri	5	12	19	26	
Sat	6	13	20	27	
Sun	7	14	21	28	

Fig. I2:5

	Inflation		Interest rates		GNP/GDP growth		Industrial prod'n		Unemployment	
	annual charge, %		3 mth money mkt, %		annual change, %		annual change, %		rate, %	
	latest	year ago	latest	year ago	latest	year ago	latest	year ago	latest	year ago
UK	9.3	7.7	14.00	15.31	0.9	1.8	−2.8	−0.3	6.5	5.7
Australia	6.0	8.0	11.85	15.87	−0.7	5.8	−1.7	3.7	8.1	5.9
Belgium	3.5	3.6	10.00	10.75	4.0	4.5	4.1	4.7	8.2	7.8
Canada	5.0	5.1	10.69	12.13	0.5	2.8	−5.0	0.1	9.3	7.7
France	3.4	3.6	10.13	11.26	3.0	3.9	−0.8	2.3	9.0	9.2
Germany	2.9	2.7	9.22	8.30	5.5	2.9	5.6	5.1	6.6	7.7
Italy	6.4	6.5	12.50	12.88	1.9	3.3	−3.4	2.9	9.9	11.1
Japan	4.2	3.4	8.38	5.68	5.4	4.7	6.3	3.2	2.1	2.1
Netherlands	2.6	1.3	9.26	8.93	4.1	2.9	2.6	2.8	7.0	8.1
Spain	6.7	7.3	15.12	15.98	4.9	5.0	−3.8	4.7	15.8	16.4
Sweden	11.4	6.5	12.79	12.70	2.1	2.3	−3.9	0.4	2.0	1.3
USA	6.1	4.7	7.00	8.38	0.3	1.8	−1.4	1.1	6.2	5.3
OECD	7.4	5.7	—	—	3.5	4.5	2.4	2.9	6.2	6.1

Fig. I3:1

BIGGER SAVINGS

165.70-13 Budget	£16.50
165.70-13 Dunlop	£19.50
165.70-13 Goodyear GPS	£22.60
175.70-13 Budget	£17.50
175.70-13 Goodyear GPS	£24.50
175.70-13 Firestone	£21.80
175.70-13 Budget (HR)	£20.95
185.70-13 Budget	£19.80
185.70-13 Goodyear GPS	£26.50
185.70-13 Firestone Dayton	£21.50
185.70-13 Budget HR	£22.50
185.70-14 Budget	£20.50
185.70-14 Budget (HR)	£23.50
185.70-14 Goodyear GPS	£27.50
185.70-14 Firestone Dayton	£21.95
185.60-13 Budget (HR)	£25.00
185.60-13 Continental	£28.10
185.60-13 Pirelli P6	£37.90
185.60-14 Firestone	£27.90
185.60-14 Goodyear NCT 2	£37.50
185.60-14 Pirelli P6	£36.50
195.60-14 Firestone	£31.00
195.60-14 Pirelli P6	£39.90
195.60-14 Pirelli P600 VR	£44.99
195.60-14 Goodyear NCT 2	£42.50

Fig. I3:2

Caravan, Baggage and Boat Trailers	Single
Overall length of vehicle not exceeding	
2.50m (8'2")	£8.80
4.00m (13'1")	£12.70
5.50m (18'0")	£16.60
each extra 1.00m (3'3") or part in excess of 5.50m	£3.00

Fig. I3:3

CHARGES		First Class		Second Class	
Car + driver		Single	Return	Single	Return
(Basic charge for all journeys)		£	£	£	£
Fridays, Saturdays & 19–23 Dec incl.		99	180	88	155
All Other Dates		80	140	70	120
Accompanying Passengers					
Adult	each*	35	67	26	49
Child (5 to 15 years)	each*	22	43	17	32

Fig. I3:4

RADIO 1

(MW 1053/1089kHz, 285/275m; FM 97.7-99.6)
5.00am Jenny Costello. **7.00** Bruno and Liz. **9.30** Dave Lee Travis. **12.30** Pick of the Pops. **3.00** Phillip Schofield. **5.00** The Complete UK Top 40. **7.00** Anne Nightingale. **9.00** Andy Kershaw. **11.00** John Peel.

RADIO 2

(FM 88-90.2)
4.00am David Allan. **6.00** Graham Knight. **7.30** Don Maclean. **9.05** Richard Baker. **11.00** Desmond Carrington. **2.00pm** Benny Green. **3.00** Alan Dell. **4.00** Palm Court Time. **4.30** Sing Something Simple. **5.00** Charlie Chester. **7.00** Moira's Music. Moira Anderson introduces a selection accompanied by the City of Glasgow Philharmonic Orchestra, conducted by Iain Sutherland. **8.00** Victor Silvester Orchestra. **8.30** Sunday Half Hour. **9.00** Alan Keith. **10.00** The Radio 2 Arts Programme. **12.05** Encore. **1.00** Andrew Lane.

Fig. I3:5

241

INTERNATIONAL CALLS

Charge Band	Charge Rate	Timings of Charge Rate	1 min £	5 mins £	10 mins £
1	Cheap	Mon-Fri 8pm-8am All Weekend	0.35	1.72	3.39
	Standard	Mon-Fri 8am-8pm	0.46	2.13	4.25
2	Cheap	Mon-Fri 8pm-8am All Weekend	0.51	2.33	4.60
	Standard	Mon-Fri 8am-8pm	0.61	2.83	5.62
3	Cheap	Mon-Fri 8pm-8am All Weekend	0.61	2.99	5.92
	Standard	Mon-Fri 8am-8pm	0.71	3.49	6.98
4	Cheap	Mon-Fri 8pm-8am All Weekend	0.61	2.99	5.92
	Standard	Mon-Fri 8am-3pm and 5pm-8pm	0.71	3.49	6.98
	Peak	Mon-Fri 3pm-5pm	0.81	3.85	7.69

Fig. 14:1

Surface mail to all countries Letters and Postcards

Not over		Not over		Not over		Not over	
20g	26p	250g	£1.26	500g	£2.36	1750g	£7.31
60g	46p	300g	£1.47	750g	£3.53	2000g	£8.45
100g	63p	350g	£1.73	1000g	£4.60		
150g	84p	400g	£1.94	1250g	£5.58		
200g	£1.05	450g	£2.15	1500g	£6.56		

Fig. 14:2

HOLIDAY & TRAVEL INSURANCE

Premiums payable per person

Period of cover	Persons 16 years and over	Persons under *16 years
4 days	£7.00	£4.00
10 days	£11.50	£5.75
18 days	£14.85	£6.00
31 days	£16.20	£7.00
Each additional week or part thereof over 31 days up to 26 weeks in all	£1.50	£0.60

*Children under 4 years covered FREE

Fig. 14:3

This chart shows the distances in miles between six towns

	Belfast	Cork	Downpatrick	Dublin	Larne
Cork	252				
Downpatrick	22	245			
Dublin	101	160	94		
Larne	21	274	43	122	
Londonderry	74	272	96	145	72

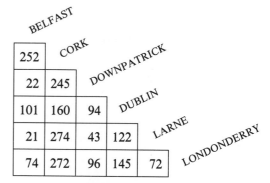

Fig. 14:4

Paddington	*d*	06 40	07 00	07 25	08 00	08 05	08 35
Slough	*d*	06 54	07 14	07 39	—	07 49	08 49
Reading E	*d*	07 08	07 28	07 53	08 24	08 30	09 03
Didcot	*d*	07 19	07 40	08 04	—	—	09 14
Swindon	*a*	07 40	08 01	08 25	—	08 58	09 35
Chippenham	*a*	07 53	—	08 38	—	—	09 48
Bath Spa	*a*	08 07	—	08 50	—	09 22	10 00
Bristol Parkway	*a*	—	08 25	—	09 10	—	—
Bristol Temple Meads	*a*	08 25	—	09 07	—	09 37	10 17

Fig. 14:5

Glossary

A

Acre An area of 4840 square *yards* or about 0.4 *hectares*.

Acute An angle between 0° and 90°.

Adjacent Next to each other, as angles *a* and *d* in Figure G1. They add up to 180°.

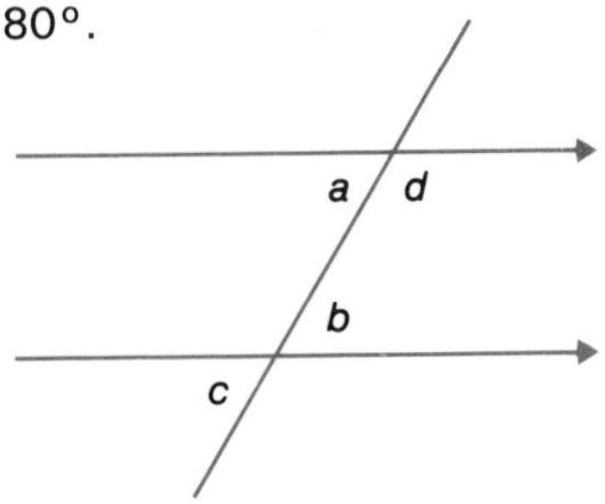

Fig. G1

Allied Joined together, as angles *b* and *d* in Figure G1. They add up to 180°.

Allowances Tax allowances are amounts you may earn free of income tax.

Alternate On opposite sides. In Figure G1, angles *a* and *b* are equal alternate ('Z') angles.

Altitude Height. A triangle has three altitudes, depending which side is taken as the base line.

Amount For *compound interest*, the *principal* plus interest.

Ante Before.

Apex The top point, especially of a triangle or pyramid.

Appreciate To increase in value.

Approximate About the same as, represented by the symbol $\approx$ or $\simeq$.

Are (say 'air') A metric unit of the same area as a square 10 m by 10 m.

Ascending Rising in *magnitude*, e.g. 1, 3, 6, 10.

Associative An *operation* which is unaffected by brackets when three or more terms are combined, e.g. addition is associative as $3 + (4 + 5) = (3 + 4) + 5$, but subtraction is not as $(3 - (4 - 5)) \neq (3 - 4) - 5$.

Average An attempt to represent a whole range of data, as in 'Julian is of average height for his age'. In mathematics, one of the three statistical measures *mean, mode*, or *median*.

Axis (pl. axes) A line about which a body rotates. In mathematics we call the numbered lines on a graph the *x*- and *y*-axes. See also *symmetry*.

B

Bar chart A chart showing *frequency* by the height of columns.

Bar-line graph Like a *bar chart* but using lines rather than bars.

Basic hours The hours at work for which you receive the *basic wage*.

Basic wage	The wage you agree to work for, usually given 'per hour'.
Biased	Not being fairly balanced, affecting the *impartial* outcome of a *trial*.
Billion	A thousand million.
Binary	Base 2, using only the digits 0 and 1, with column headings in powers of 2. Computer and calculator arithmetic is done in base 2.
Bisect	To divide into two equal parts.
Block graph	A *bar chart* with the bar divided up to look like bricks piled up on each other.
BODMAS	An aid to remembering the order of operations: work out what is in Brackets first, then Of (times), Divide and Multiply, then Add and Subtract.
Bonus	An extra payment made to an employee.

C

Cancelling	To cross out, as in cancelling fractions to make them simpler, e.g. $\dfrac{^2\cancel{4}}{_3\cancel{6}} = \dfrac{2}{3}$.
Capacity	The amount of space inside a container.
Cardinal point	One of the directions north, south, east and west.
Chain	The imperial measurement of 22 *yards* (just over 20 *metres*).
Change of subject	To change a formula, e.g. from $F = 1.8C + 32$ to $C = \dfrac{F - 32}{1.8}$.
Chord	A straight line joining two points on the circumference of a circle.
Circumcircle	The circle passing through all the *vertices* of a polygon.
Class	In data handling, a group of items between two limits.
Coefficient	The *constant* that multiplies a letter term, e.g. the 3 in $3x^2$.
Collinear	In the same straight line.
Column matrix	A *matrix* with only one column of figures, e.g. the *vector* $\begin{pmatrix} 2 \\ 3 \end{pmatrix}$.
Commission	Pay that depends on the value of a salesperson's sales.
Common fraction	A fraction less than a whole, written like $\frac{3}{4}$.
Community charge	Payment made by every person who can vote, to pay for local council services. Generally called 'the poll tax'. (Widely disliked and at the time of writing likely to be discontinued.)
Commutative	An *operation* which is unaffected by the order in which it is worked out, e.g. addition is commutative as $2 + 3 = 3 + 2$, but a subtraction is not as $2 - 3 \neq 3 - 2$.

Complement	One of two parts that make up a whole. Complementary angles add up to 90°.
Compound	Made up of a number of parts, as in compound interest, where each new interest is based on the original amount plus all previous interest.
Concave	Curving or pointing inwards; a concave polygon has at least one *vertex* pointing inwards (sometimes called a re-entrant polygon).
Concurrent	Meeting at the same point.
Cone	A *pyramid* with a circular base.
Congruent	Exactly the same, in size and shape. See *Similar*.
Conjecture	A guess or a forecast without proof.
Consecutive	Following on with no gaps, like 3, 4, 5, 6.
Constant	Not changing. In algebra, the number term.
Construct	To draw accurately; traditionally using only a straight edge and a pair of compasses.
Convert/conversion	To change. A conversion graph helps you change between two amounts, e.g. from miles per hour to kilometres per hour.
Convex	Curving or pointing outwards; the opposite of *concave*.
Coordinates	The two numbers which fix the position of a point on a grid, in the order (how far *horizontally*, how far *vertically*).
Corresponding	In the same kind of position. In Figure G1, angles *a* and *c* are equal corresponding (sliding) angles.
Credit	A bank credit is money paid into an account. Credit also means time to pay, as in a *credit card*.
Credit card	'Plastic money'. A card allowing you to pay for goods or services at a later date, or over a long time (paying quite a lot extra for the interest!).
Cross-section	The *plane* surface made by cutting a solid.
Cubic	In the shape of a cube. In algebra a cubic expression involves power 3, e.g. $2a^3 - 7a + 1$.
Cuboid	A solid with six rectangular faces, like a plank of wood.
Cumulative frequency curve	A statistical graph which shows how the data grows in frequency from start to finish.
Cyclic quadrilateral	A quadrilateral with all its *vertices* on the circumference of a circle.

D

Data	Facts from which other facts may be found.
Debit	A bank debit is money paid out of an account.
Decade	Ten years.

Decagon	A ten-sided *polygon*.
Decimal places	The number of figures to the right of the *decimal point*.
Decimal point	Placed between units and tenths, to divide whole numbers from fractions.
Deduce	To reach a conclusion by reasoning.
Deduction	Something taken away. Something worked out by considering all the facts.
Denary	Based on ten, our usual number system.
Denominator	The bottom number in a *common fraction*, telling you into how many pieces the whole was divided.
Density	The heaviness of an object, measured in grams per cubic centimetre. The density of water is 1.
Deposit	To pay an amount into a bank or savings account. A part payment to a seller, who then cannot sell it to anyone else unless you do not pay in full within the agreed time, when you will lose your deposit.
Depreciation	Loss of value.
Diagonal	A straight line joining two *vertices* of a *convex polygon*.
Diameter	The *chord* of a circle that passes through the centre.
Die	The correct singular of dice.
Difference	The result of subtracting a smaller number from a larger.
Digit	One of the figures 0, 1, 2, 3, 4, 5, 6, 7, 8, 9.
Digit sum	The result of repeatedly adding the digits of a number until the result is a single digit. The digit sum of 49 is 4.
Direct debit	Permission to your bank to *debit* your account at the request of named people or firms.
Direct proportion	Two amounts are in direct proportion when they change at the same rate, e.g. if one doubles the other doubles, if one is halved the other is halved. See also *inverse proportion*.
Directed number	A number that has a sign to indicate whether it is above or below zero. (See *positive* and *negative*.)
Discount	The amount taken off a price.
Discrete	Able to be measured exactly by counting, e.g. the number of pages in a book. All other measurements are continuous and can only be given to a certain degree of accuracy.
Dividend	The number being divided, e.g. the 8 in 8 ÷ 4. The share in a company's profit paid to its shareholders.
Divisor	The number you are dividing by, e.g. the 4 in 8 ÷ 4.
Domain	The set of numbers on which *operations* are performed. See *range*.

Double time — Overtime paid at twice the *basic wage*.

E

Empirical — Found by experiment or past experience.

Equilateral — Equal sided.

Equivalent — Having the same value, e.g. $\frac{3}{6} = \frac{1}{2} = 0.5 = 50\%$.

Estimate — To give an *approximate* value.

Evaluate — Find the value of.

Event — Something which happens, e.g. in probability an event may be the selection of a card. See also *outcome, trial, independent* and *exclusive*.

Exchange rate — The amount of currency you can buy using another currency, e.g. £1 buys $1.80.

Exclusive — Exclusive *outcomes* of *events* are those where only one outcome can happen in any one *trial*. See also *independent*.

Expand — In algebra, to remove brackets, e.g. $5(x + 6)$ expands to $5x + 30$.

Express — To write in a certain way, e.g. express 5 cm in metres.

Expression — A collection of terms with no equals sign, e.g. $4x - 2y^2 + 3z$.

Exterior angle — The angle between a *produced* side of a polygon and the *adjacent* side. The exterior angle sum of all polygons is 360°.

F

Face — One side of a *polyhedron*.

Factorise — To split a number or an algebraic expression into *factors*. e.g. 12 factorises to 3×4 or 2×6 or $2 \times 2 \times 3$, and $3x - 9$ factorises to $3(x - 3)$.

Factor — An *integer* or algebraic term which multiplies another integer or term to make the original number or term. See *factorise* and *highest common factor*.

Fibonacci sequence — A *sequence* where each new term is made by adding the previous two terms, often starting 1, 1, 2, 3, 5.

Foot (pl. feet, abbrev. ft) — An imperial length of 30.48 cm.

Formula (pl. formulae) — A recipe to make something, e.g. the formula for the area of a rectangle is 'multiply the base by the height. Formulae in mathematics often use letters, e.g. $A = bh$.

Formulate — To express in a clear or definite form.

Frequency — The number of times something occurs.

Frustum — The part of a pyramid or cone contained between the base and a plane parallel to it.

| **Function** | An algebraic 'event', e.g. a function of x such that any value of x becomes x^2, which may be written $f(x): x \rightarrow x^2$. Then $f(2) = 4$. |

G

Gallon	An imperial measure of liquid volume, about 4.55 litres.
Generalise	To cover all situations; e.g. the general equation for a straight line graph is $y = mx + c$.
Googol	1×10^{100}, or 1 followed by 100 zeros.
Gradient	The slope of a line defined in mathematics as the tangent of the angle made with the horizontal. See under $y = mx + c$.
Gram (abbrev. g)	A metric weight, about the same as two drawing pins.
Grid reference	See *Six-figure reference*.
Gross	Without any *deduction*. Also 144 items.

H

Hatch	To mark an area with many sloping lines.
Hectare	100 *ares*.
Hecto	A hundred.
Heptagon	A seven sided *polygon*.
Hexadecimal	Base sixteen, using the digits 0 to 9 and A to F (for ten to fifteen). Computers may be programmed using hexadecimal ('machine') code, which much speeds up the execution of a program.
Hexagon	A six-sided *polygon*.
Highest common factor (abbrev. HCF)	The highest number which is a *factor* of each number in a set of numbers.
Hire purchase (abbrev. HP)	Payment for an article by *instalments*. Largely replaced by *credit cards*.
Histogram	A *bar chart* where the area of the bars represents the *frequency*.
Horizontal	Across the page. Remember it by 'horizon'.
Hourly rate	The *basic wage* paid per hour.
Hypotenuse	The longest side of a right-angled triangle. It is always opposite the right-angle.

I

Image	The result of the *transformation* of an object.
Impartial	Free from *bias*.
Improper fraction	A fraction, more than a whole one, where the *numerator* is more than the *denominator*.

Inch	An imperial measure of length, equal to 2.54 cm. There are 12 inches in a *foot*.
Incircle	A largest circle which fits inside a polygon.
Inclusive	Including both ends.
Independent	Not relying on anything else. Independent outcomes of *events* can all happen in one *trial*, with no outcome changing the probability of the others. See also *non-independent*.
Index	The raised figure used in a power, e.g. the 2 in 5^2 (meaning multiply two fives together) and the -2 in 10^{-2} (which is another way of writing $\frac{1}{10}^2$ or $\frac{1}{100}$).
Income tax	Money taken from pay to finance government spending.
Increment	An increase.
Inequality	An expression showing that two things are not equal. Symbols: $-5 > -7$, meaning -5 is more than -7; $x \geqslant 8$, meaning the value of x is 8 or more; $3 < 6$, meaning 3 is less than 6; $x \leqslant 4$, meaning x is not more than 4.
Infinite	Without end.
Inflation	In finance, the decrease in the value of money, e.g. a loaf costing 12p in 1970 cost 70p in 1990.
Instalment	One of a series of payments.
Integer	A whole number, like 4 and -4. Zero is usually taken to be an even integer.
Intercept	Part of a line between two crossing points.
Interior angle	The angle between two *adjacent* sides of a polygon. The interior angle sum of an *n*-sided polygon is $(n - 2) \times 180°$.
Intersection	The crossing point.
Inverse	Opposite or upside down. The inverse of addition is subtraction. The inverse of $\frac{5}{6}$ is $\frac{6}{5}$.
Inverse proportion	One amount increasing at the same rate as another decreases, e.g. double the speed, half the time.
Invoice	A bill, setting out the payment required.
Irrational	Unable to be written as an exact fraction. All *square roots* of *prime numbers* are irrational, as is π.
Irregular	Not *regular*.
Isosceles	With two equal sides. (*Iso* – 'equal', *sceles* – 'legs').

K

Kilo	A thousand. Kilo is sometimes taken as short for kilogram (1000 grams).

| **Kite** | A *quadrilateral* with two pairs of equal *adjacent* sides. |

L

Like fractions	Fractions with the same *denominator*.
Like terms	Terms of the same kind, e.g. 3*x* and 4*x*; $2a^2b$ and $5a^2b$.
Line of symmetry	The fold line or mirror line.
Linear equation	An equation with no *powers* of letters. There is always one and only one solution.
Litre	A metric unit of liquid volume equal to about 1.76 pints.
Locus (pl. loci)	The path made by a moving point.
Loss	The opposite of *profit*.
Lowest common multiple (abbrev. LCM)	The smallest number which is in the multiplication table of each of a set of numbers.

M

Magnitude	Size.
Mapping	The action of a *function*. The *domain* is mapped to the *range*.
Mean	The average found by sharing the total of all scores equally.
Median	The halfway point when the scores of a set of *data* are in *rank order*.
Mega	A million.
Metre	The unit of length after which the metric system is named, originally taken as 2.5×10^{-8} of the equator.
Micro	A millionth.
Milli	A thousandth.
Million	A thousand thousand.
Mixed number	An integer and a fraction, as $1\frac{1}{2}$.
Mode	The most frequent score(s) in a set of *data*.
Modulus	A circular system of counting, as on a clock face. A.m./p.m. time is modulo 12. Modulo 3 counts 0, 1, 2, 3, 0, 1, 2, 3, 0, 1, etc.
Mortgage	A loan secured on a property. If the loan is not paid back as agreed, the property can be sold by the lender.
Multiple	A number made by multiplying another number, as in multiplication tables.
Multiplying factor	The fraction used to increase or decrease in a given ratio. See also *scale factor*.
Mutually exclusive	See *exclusive*.

N

National insurance (abbrev. NI)	The state system by which working people pay into a state fund to support the social services.
Natural numbers	Numbers used for counting.
Net	The *plane* shape that can be folded to make a solid. An amount after *deductions*.
Network	A system of intersecting lines. See Figure G2.

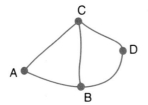

Fig. G2

Node	A junction in a *network*. See Figure G2.
Nonagon	A nine-sided *polygon*.
Notation	The symbols used in a mathematical statement.
Numerator	The top number in a *common fraction*.

O

Object	The shape that is to be *transformed* to give the *image*.
Obtuse	An angle between 90° and 180°.
Octal	Base 8, using the digits 0 to 7 only. An intermediate stage between *binary* and *hexadecimal*.
Odds	A way of stating probability. Odds of 5 to 1 against means 1 chance that the *outcome* will be favourable, 5 chances that it will not.
Operation	A way of combining elements. It may be a single action, such as $+$, $-$, $\times$, $\div$ or $\sqrt{\ }$, or a combination defined by a special sign, often $*$ or $\circ$. For example, $a*b$ could be defined as meaning double a then add on the square of b, so that $2*4 = 20$.
Ordered pair	Another name for the *coordinates* of a point.
Order of rotational symmetry	The number of times that a shape fits into a tracing of itself in one full rotation.
Outcome	In probability, the result of a *trial*.
Overtime	Extra work beyond your agreed *basic hours*.

P

Per annum	Each year.
Parabola	The curve obtained when a cone is cut by a plane parallel to its sloping edge. The general equation of a parabola is $y = ax^2 + bx + c$.

Parallelogram	A *quadrilateral* with both pairs of opposite sides parallel.
PAYE	Pay As You Earn; a method of collecting *income tax* from your pay.
Pension	An amount paid to a retired person.
Pentagon	A five-sided polygon.
Percentage	Out of every hundred.
Percentage error	An indication of the seriousness of an arithmetical error, found from the formula: error ÷ true × 100.
Percentile	One hundredth of the data when arranged in order.
Perimeter	The boundary of an area.
Perpendicular	At right angles.
Perpendicular bisector	A line which crosses the midpoint of another line at 90°.
Personal allowance	An amount a person may earn free of *income tax*.
Pictogram	A diagram showing *frequency* by pictures that stand for a certain amount, e.g. one car stands for 10 cars.
Pie chart	A diagram showing frequency by *sectors* of a circle.
Piecework	Pay based on how many pieces of work you do.
Pint	An imperial measure of liquid volume, about 0.57 litres.
Place value	The value of a *digit* according to the column it is in.
Plan	A view looking from above.
Plane	Having only two dimensions; 'flat'.
Point symmetry	A shape with point symmetry looks the same when turned upside down.
Poll tax	The popular name for the *community charge*.
Polygon	A *plane* figure bounded by straight lines. A circle can be thought of as a polygon with an *infinite* number of straight sides.
Polyhedron	A solid with flat faces; the five regular ('Platonic' from the Greek mathematician Plato) polyhedra are: tetrahedron (4 equilateral triangles), cube (6 squares), octahedron (8 equilateral triangles), dodecahedron (12 regular pentagons), icosahedron (20 equilateral triangles).
Position vector	A *vector* that starts at the origin of a graph. The numbers defining the vector are the same as the coordinates of its end.
Post	After.
Pound (abbrev. lb)	An imperial measure of weight, about 0.45 kg.
Power	The result of multiplying a number by itself a number of times, e.g. 125 is the third power of 5 (5^3 or $5 \times 5 \times 5$).
Premium	Payment made for insurance.

Prime	A number which has only two different *factors*. The lowest prime number is 2, then 3, 5, 7, 11, etc.
Principal	Money on which interest is paid.
Prism	A *three-dimensional* shape with a *constant cross-section*.
Probability fraction	A fraction from 0 (impossible) to 1 (certain) that expresses how likely it is that a certain *outcome* will occur, e.g. probability $\frac{3}{7}$ means 3 chances in 7.
Produce	To make a line longer, e.g. produce AB to C means lengthen AB beyond B to a third point, C.
Product	The result of a multiplication.
Profit	The gain made when something is sold for more than it cost; the percentage gain can be calculated from profit ÷ original cost × 100.
Proportion	Two amounts are proportional, or in the same *ratio*, when they both increase or decrease at the same rate, e.g. the number of spoons of coffee and the number of cups to be made. See *inverse proportion* and *direct proportion* and *scale factor*.
Proportional division	Dividing an amount in a given *ratio*.
Proportionate bar chart	A bar chart where all frequencies are represented by divisions along one bar.
Pythagoras' theorem	The rule that the square on the hypotenuse of a right-angled triangle is equal to the sum of the squares on the other two sides.

Q

Quadrilateral	A four-sided *polygon*.
Quadrant	A quarter of a circle.
Quadratic equation	An equation involving a squared term, e.g. $3x^2 - 3 = 4x$.
Quotient	The result of a division.

R

Range	In statistics, the difference between the highest and lowest number in the data.
Rank order	In order, usually from smallest to biggest.
Ratio	The relation of two amounts to each other, e.g. 3 parts of petrol to 1 part of oil, often written with a colon as 3 : 1. See *proportion*.
Rational	Able to be expressed as an exact fraction. See *irrational*.
Raw data	The result of a survey before any work is done on it.
Real number	A number that exists, but cannot be written as a finite or recurring decimal fraction; π is real but $\sqrt{(-1)}$ is not. (See also *rational*.)

Ream	Originally 480, but a printer's ream was 516, and now a ream is often 500!
Reciprocal	One divided by the number, e.g. $\frac{1}{2}$ is the reciprocal of 2. Calculators often have a $\frac{1}{x}$ reciprocal key.
Rectangular numbers	Numbers that are not prime.
Recurring	Repeating.
Redundancy	Losing your job because your employer no longer has work for you. If you have been employed for some while you receive a cash sum from your employer.
Reflection	A transformation when the *object* and *image* are *symmetrical* about a mirror line.
Reflex	An angle between 180° and 360°.
Region	A special area of a diagram.
Regular	Regular *polygons* have all sides and all angles equal.
Representative fraction	The scale of a map, e.g. 1 : 1000 or $\frac{1}{1000}$, meaning 1 unit on the map is 1000 units on the ground.
Resultant	In vectors, the one vector that has the same effect as all the others.
Rhombus	A *parallelogram* with four equal sides. Sometimes called a 'diamond'.
Root	Short for 'square root', the number from which a square grows, e.g. 3 is the square root of 9. The symbol is $\sqrt{}$. Similarly the cube root of 8, written $\sqrt[3]{8}$, is 2, because $2 \times 2 \times 2 = 8$.
Rotational symmetry	A shape has rotational symmetry when it fits into a tracing of itself more than once in a full turn.
Round off	To approximate, e.g. to the nearest ten or to 3 decimal places.
S	
Salary	The amount a worker is to be paid for a year's work, usually paid monthly.
Scale drawing	Mathematically *similar* in same shape but of a different size.
Scale factor	The *factor* by which a *similar* shape is made bigger or smaller.
Scalene	Having no two sides the same length.
Scientific notation	See *standard form*.
Score	Twenty. Also the total made.
Secant	A line cutting a circle. A *chord* is part of a secant.

Sector	Part of a circle bounded by two *radii* and an *arc*. See Figure G3.
Segment	Part of a circle bounded by a *chord* and an *arc*. See Figure G3.

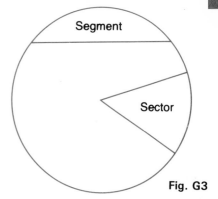

Fig. G3

Sequence	A set of numbers that are linked by a rule.
Shear	To distort a shape by pushing it sideways so that one line remains fixed, and all other points move parallel to that line.
Shift vector	A description of a move by how much *horizontally*, how much *vertically*, e.g. $\begin{pmatrix} -3 \\ 4 \end{pmatrix}$ meaning a move of 3 to the left and 4 upwards.
Significant figures	An *approximation*. All figures, except a string of zeros at the beginning, count as significant.
Similar	Exactly the same shape, but not necessarily the same size. Similar objects have their *corresponding* sides in the same ratio. Two similar solids with sides in the ratio $x:y$ have areas in the ratio $x^2:y^2$ and volumes/weights in the ratio $x^3:y^3$.
Simple interest	The interest is not added to the amount loaned. See *compound*.
Simplify	To make an expression simpler; e.g. in number by making the numbers in a fraction smaller (e.g. $\frac{1}{2}$ instead of $\frac{6}{12}$); in algebra usually by multiplying out brackets and collecting *like terms*.
Simultaneous	At the same time.
Six-figure grid reference	This fixes the position of a point on an Ordnance Survey map. In Figure G4 the grid reference of X is 234538.

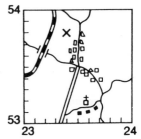

Fig. G4

Slant height	The shortest distance from the *apex* of a *pyramid* to the base, measured along a *face*.
Solution	The value(s) of the letter(s) that make(s) an equation true.
Solve	To find the numerical value of the letters in equations.

255

Sphere	The mathematical name for a ball whose *cross-section* is a circle.
Square numbers	Numbers made by multiplying an *integer* by itself.
Square root	See *root*.
Standard form	A way of writing all numbers in the same way, i.e. in the form $a \times 10^n$ where $1 \leqslant a < 10$. E.g. $1000 \to 1 \times 10^3$; $0.0045 \to 4.5 \times 10^{-3}$.
Standing order	A request to a bank to make regular payments to someone else.
Statement (bank)	A notice from a bank showing the *credits* and *debits* made on your account over a period of time.
Step graph	A graph that rises like steps. GPO letter rates can be plotted as a step graph.
Stick graph	Another name for a *bar-line graph*.
Subtend	To make an angle at a point, e.g. arc AB subtends angle AOB at the centre O.
Sum	The result of an addition.
Superannuation	Payments made through your employer towards a *pension*.
Supplementary angles	Angles which together make 180°.
Surd	An *irrational* number.
Symmetry	See *rotational symmetry* and *line of symmetry*.
Symmetrical	Having *line symmetry*.
Symbol	Using a letter or a sign to represent something else. In mathematics and science a letter usually represents a number, but sometimes it represents a measurement, like h for height.

T

Tally	Counting by using marks, like ///. Often every five marks are connected, so 5 is 卌.
Tangent	A straight line that touches but will never cross a curve. One of the trigonometric functions (see the index).
Tariff	A table of prices.
Taxable income	The amount of earnings on which *income tax* has to be paid.
Tax code	A code to show the income a person may have free of income tax. For reasons best known to the Inland Revenue, the final figure is omitted, so a code of 356 means you can earn £3560 free of tax.
Tessellation	A pattern of shapes which entirely covers a surface.
Tetrahedron	A pyramid on a triangular base. A regular tetrahedron has four equilateral triangles as its sides.
Three-figure bearings	Directions given by the amount of turn clockwise from north.

Time and a half	Overtime (more than your *basic hours*) when you are paid half as much again as your *basic wage*.
Tonne	A metric unit of weight, equal to 1000 *kilograms*.
Top-heavy fraction	Another name for an *improper fraction*.
Transformation	A change of position or shape according to a rule. In this course we have met *reflection, rotation, enlargement* and *translation*.
Translate	To slide a shape.
Transpose	To *change the subject* of a formula.
Trapezium	A *quadrilateral* with one pair of parallel sides.
Travel graph	Also called a journey graph or a time/distance graph. It represents the average speeds and directions of a journey by lines on a graph, time being *horizontal* and distance *vertical*. The steeper the line, the faster the speed.
Tree diagram	Used in probability to represent choices branching out from the starting point.
Trial	In probability the carrying out of the experiment, e.g. picking two cards from a pack.
Triangular numbers	Numbers that can be represented by an equilateral triangle of dots, starting 1, 3, 6, 10.
Trundle wheel	A wheel of standard circumference, usually a metre, that can be rolled along the ground to measure distance.

U

Unbiased	Free from prejudice. See *biased*.
Unitary method	Finding the cost or value of one item to help find the cost or value of several.

V

Variable	A letter which may stand for various numbers.
VAT	Value added tax. A tax put on goods and services by the government.
Vertex (pl. vertices)	The corner of a shape.
Vertical	Upright, or going towards the top of a page.
Vertically opposite angles	Equal angles made by two lines crossing, e.g. angles b and c in Figure G1.
Vulgar fraction	Another name for a *common fraction*.

Y

Yard	An imperial length, 0.9144 metres.

Answers

Note: Answers not printed here are given in the Teachers' Resource Book.

Chapter 1

Test yourself

1 A, (2, 2); B, (1, 0); C, (−2, 2);
   D, (0, −2)
2 (a) B (b) D (c) A (d) C
3 (4, 4); (2½, 2½); (0, 0); (−3, −3)
   (−1, −1)
4 (4, −4); (−2½, 2½); (0, 0); (−3, 3);
   (1, −1)
*5 See Figure A1:1.

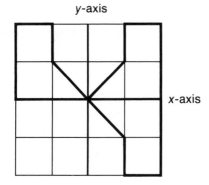

Fig. A1:1

*6 (a) $\begin{pmatrix} 2 \\ 4 \end{pmatrix}$ (b) $\begin{pmatrix} -2 \\ -4 \end{pmatrix}$ (c) $\begin{pmatrix} 4 \\ -1 \end{pmatrix}$
    (d) $\begin{pmatrix} -4 \\ 1 \end{pmatrix}$

*7 See Figure A1:2.

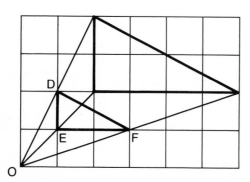

Fig. A1:2

8 (a) (2, 2), 180° (b) (2, 2), 180°
   (c) (2, 1), 270° (d) (2, 2), 270°

9 $\begin{pmatrix} -6 \\ 2 \end{pmatrix}$

10 See Figure A1:3.

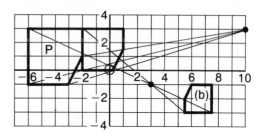

Fig. A1:3

11 S, H, E, B, K, A, T, C, D, Z, P, Y
    (You may enjoy a similar exercise
    reflecting and rotating the digits.)
12 (a) rotation of 180° about (0, 0)
    (b) reflection in $y = -x$
    (c) enlargement, scale factor −1,
         centre (0, 0)
    (d) reflection in $y = 0$ followed by
         reflection in $x = 0$; reflection in
         $x = 0$ followed by reflection in
         $y = 0$
13 See Figure A1:4.

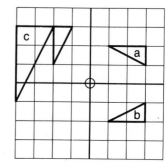

Fig. A1:4

14 (a)–(d) See Figure A1:5.

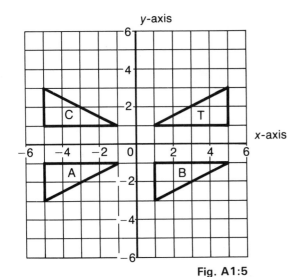

Fig. A1:5

(d) (i) translation of $\begin{pmatrix} 6 \\ 0 \end{pmatrix}$

(ii) reflection in the x-axis

Chapter 2

Test yourself

1 (a) −3 (b) 5 (c) 1 (d) 2 (e) −3
   (f) −3 (g) 2 (h) −3 (i) $\frac{1}{2}$
2 (a) $3x + 12$ (b) $2a - 10$
   (c) $12 + 8a$ (d) $4a - 10$
   (e) $-3 - a$ (f) $-h + 1$ (g) $-6x - 3$
   (h) $-2x + 8$ (i) $-9 - 12a$
3 (a) −3 (b) $\frac{1}{4}$ (c) 3 (d) 1 (e) −2
   (f) −7 (g) −6 (h) $1\frac{1}{4}$ (i) $-2\frac{1}{2}$
   (j) $5\frac{1}{3}$ (k) −3 (l) $-\frac{2}{3}$
*4 (a) $6 + 9a$ (b) $9a - 12$ (c) $-x - 1$
   (d) $-2x - 8$ (e) $-8 + 4a$
   (f) $-4a + 6$ (g) $6a - 16$
*5 (a) 4 (b) 2 (c) −7 (d) −2
   (e) −2 (f) 3 (g) $8\frac{1}{2}$ (h) −1
   (i) $-2\frac{1}{3}$ (j) −3 (k) −4 (l) 2
6 (a) 12 (b) −16 (c) 5 (d) −4
   (e) 1
7 (a) 32 (b) 10 (c) 12 (d) 3 (e) 2
   (f) $2\frac{1}{2}$
8 (a) $x = 9, y = 6$ (b) $x = 2, y = 2$
   (c) $x = 3, y = 8$
9 (a) $x = 1, y = -1$ (b) $x = 4, y = 1$
   (c) $a = 9\frac{1}{2}, b = 5\frac{1}{2}$
   (d) $s = \frac{5}{11}, t = -1\frac{9}{11}$

10 (a) $12 - a$ (b) $7a + 18$ (c) $a - 35$
   (d) $26 - 4a$ (e) $36a - 25$
   (f) $4 - 18a$
11 (a) $-6\frac{2}{3}$ (b) $\frac{1}{2}$ (c) $3\frac{2}{7}$ (d) $\frac{2}{63}$
12 (a) $a = 3, b = 6$ (b) $a = 10, b = 1$
   (c) $a = 2, b = 1\frac{1}{2}$ (d) $a = 12, b = -5$

Exercise

3 (a) 10 (b) 1 (c) 4
4 (a) −1 (b) −1 (c) 6
5 (a) 9 (b) 2
6 (a) 6 (b) 9 (c) 0
7 (a) 5 (b) $7\frac{1}{2}$ (c) 0 (d) 1.2
8 (b) Dad is twice as old as Josie.
   (c) When Josie is 10.
   (d) $1\frac{1}{2}(x + 5) = 25 + x \Rightarrow x = 35$;
       when Josie is 40 and her dad is 60.
9 74 min
10 4 units per side
11 $x = 6$; sides 4 cm, 4 cm, 11 cm, which
   is not a triangle!
   $x = 3$; sides 2 cm, 2 cm, 1 cm
   $x = 2\frac{1}{2}$; sides $\frac{1}{2}$ cm, $\frac{1}{2}$ cm, $1\frac{2}{3}$ cm, which
   is not a triangle!
12 $x = 20$ cm; $y = 10$ cm

Chapter 3

Test yourself

1 (a) (i) 0.2 (ii) 0.35 (iii) 0.125
   (b) (i) $\frac{1}{5}$ (ii) $\frac{7}{20}$ (iii) $\frac{1}{8}$
2 (a) 25% (b) 80% (c) $62\frac{1}{2}$%
   (d) $33\frac{1}{3}$% (e) 42% (f) 2%
   (g) $62\frac{1}{2}$%
3 (a) £0.80 (b) £7.50 (c) 45 g
   (d) 21 m (e) £1.30 (f) £3
4 (a) 25% (b) 20% (c) 80%
   (d) 300% (e) 125%
5 (a) 60 (b) 18 (c) $62\frac{1}{2}$ kg
   (d) 81.6 m
6 (a) 20% profit (b) 10% loss
7 80%
8 375 g nitre; 50 g sulphur;
   75 g charcoal
9 25%
10 £21
11 96%
12 13.5 litres
13 £307.80
14 7 g

15 11.25 kg

16 $11\frac{1}{9}$%

17 12%

18 (a) $86\frac{2}{3}$% (b) $46\frac{3}{7}$%

19 (a) £5300; £5830; £6063.20; £6669.52

(b) 33%

Exercise

3 £5.44

4 50p

5 Rachel, by $13\frac{1}{3}$%

6 £900

7 £60

8 £980

9 £363.75

10 £450

11 150 mm

12 $83\frac{1}{3}$ litres

13 £576

14 £2.65

15 (a) £3.20 (b) 25p

Chapter 4

Test yourself

1

	(i)	(ii)	(iii)	(iv)	(v)	(vi)
mean	4	34	18	117	0	6
mode(s)	4	34	none	109, 116	−4	8
median	4	34	15.5	116	−2	7.5

2 (a) 13 y 4 mth (b) 10 min 20 s

(c) 13 y

***3** 24 °C

***4** (a) (i) £110 (ii) £112

(b) (i) £135 (ii) £112

***5** £567

***6** 24 y 2 mth

***7** (a) 85 min (b) 14 min 10 s

***8** (a) £262 (b) £26 (c) £26

9 (a) 3 °C (b) 5 °C (c) 5 °C

10 12 y 7 mth

11 (a) 7 (b) 6.5 (c) 6.1

12 (a) 12 (b) 15 (c) 13

13 (a) 181 (b) £382

14 (a) 59.5 mm (b) 39 mm

15 69.4%

16 26 y 11 mth

17 (a) (i) $5\frac{1}{7}$, 3, $4\frac{5}{7}$, $4\frac{6}{7}$ (ii) $4\frac{3}{7}$

(b) week 1, 0.0143%

Exercise

1

0–9	//	2
10–19	$\cancel{||||}\ \cancel{||||}$	10
20–29	$\cancel{||||}\ \cancel{||||}\ \cancel{||||}\ //$	17
30–39	$\cancel{||||}\ \cancel{||||}\ \cancel{||||}\ \cancel{||||}\ \cancel{||||}\ \cancel{||||}\ //$	32
40–49	$\cancel{||||}\ \cancel{||||}\ ///$	13
50–59	$\cancel{||||}\ /$	6

30–39 is the modal class.

2

4.5	22.5
14.5	87
24.5	196
34.5	345
44.5	311.5
55	220

mean $\simeq$ 30

3 (i) 11.3 (ii) 13.75 (iii) 48.9 (iv) 11.9

(Note: It would be sensible to round all these to the nearest unit. Why?)

4 Tally: 0, 7, 21, 48, 24. Mean: 33.5

5 (a) 56

(b) (i) 11 (ii) 14 (iii) 47 (iv) 11

6 (a) 32.25 (b) 31 (c) 32.3 (d) 33

Chapter 5

Test yourself

1 (a) (i) 7:10 (ii) $1:1\frac{3}{7}$ (iii) $\frac{7}{10}:1$

(b) (i) 25:1 (ii) $1:\frac{1}{25}$ (iii) 25:1

(c) (i) 200:3 (ii) $1:\frac{3}{200}$ (iii) $66\frac{2}{3}:1$

(d) (i) 1:600 (ii) 1:600 (iii) $\frac{1}{600}:1$

2 £21.60

3 320 g

4 £150 and £210

5 640 g nettle tops   50g butter

2 medium onions $1\frac{1}{4}$ litres stock

25 cl cream

Spinach, salt, pepper, lemon juice to taste

Cook for 30 min

Serves 8

***6** (a) 10:1 (b) 5:1 (c) 3:10

(d) 1:8 (e) 1:100 000

***7** 37.5 g calamine;   12.5 g zinc oxide;

7.5 g bentonite;   1.25 g sodium citrate;

1.25 ml liquified phenol;

12.5 ml glycerin;   235 ml water

***8** (a) 2:1 (b) £8400 (c) 16:11

9 (a) See Figure A5:1.

m.p.g.	10	20	30	40	50
litres/100km	28.4	14.2	9.5	7.1	5.7

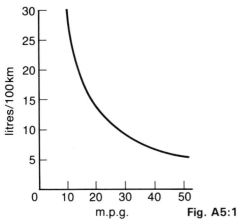

Fig. A5:1

(b) 2CV   6.8 litres/100 km
    Civic   8.4 litres/100 km
    Rover   14.2 litres/100 km
    Visa   5.5 litres/100 km

10 (a) direct, £30.60   (b) inverse, 9 days
    (c) direct, £192   (d) direct, £7.20
    (e) inverse, $1\frac{1}{8}$ hours
    (f) direct, £10 800

11 (a) 12 days   (b) 24 days
    (c) $1\frac{1}{2}$ days

12 £812.50

13 (a) See Figure A5:2.

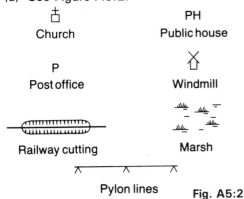

Church   PH Public house

P Post office   Windmill

Railway cutting   Marsh

Pylon lines   **Fig. A5:2**

(b) (i) 418338   (ii) 413327
    (iii) 414333   (iv) 446347
    (v) 427320
(c) 1 cm represents 100 m (or
    1 : 10 000)
(d) 400 to 500 metres

14 (a) 2 : 1   (b) 3 g
15 £4.63
16 (a) Army, $900 000;
     Air Force, $1 500 000;
     Navy, $600 000
    (b) $650 000
17 £1260
18 (a) See Figure A5:3.

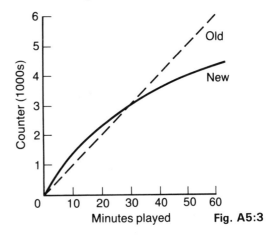

Fig. A5:3

(b) 18 min: 1800, 2100;
    48 min: 4900, 3950
(c) See Figure A5:4.

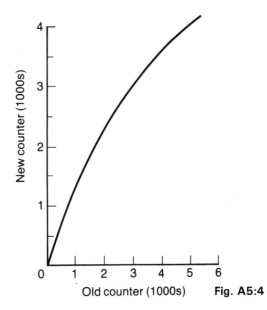

Fig. A5:4

(d) 0000 Decimals   3400 Volumes
    0800 Sequences   3950 Graphs
    2350 Percentages   4300 Circles

19 (a) 320

Age group	15 to 30	31 to 45	46 to 60	61 +
(b)	51%	33%	9%	7%
(c)	816 000	528 000	144 000	112 000

    (d) Discuss your opinions with the class.

20 Your teacher has the answers!

Chapter 7

Exercise

3 (a) $e = \dfrac{3 - g}{f}$ (b) $e = \sqrt{\dfrac{x + 4f}{2}}$

  (c) $e = \sqrt{\dfrac{a(7 - h)}{6}}$ (d) $e = \dfrac{1}{a - h}$

  (e) $e = \dfrac{2u}{c - v}$ (f) $e = \dfrac{h^2}{(t + c)^2}$

4 (a) $c = 2(g - f) - a$ (b) $c = \sqrt{h - a^2}$

  (c) $c = \left(\dfrac{t}{2\pi}\right)^2$

  (d) $c = \frac{1}{2}\left(R - \dfrac{d}{ab}\right) = \dfrac{abR - d}{2ab}$

  (e) $c = \dfrac{s}{r(a - t)}$

  (f) $c = \dfrac{3d - t}{f} - b = \dfrac{3d - t - bf}{f}$

5 (a) $r = \dfrac{3a + 2gp}{2g + 1}$

  (b) $r = \dfrac{-st}{2 + bc - a} = \dfrac{st}{a - bc - 2}$

  (c) $r = \dfrac{at}{a + t}$ (d) $r = \dfrac{bs}{2 - 3as}$

  (e) $r = \dfrac{18w^2}{s^2}$

6 (a) $t = \dfrac{s}{3 - 2a^2}$ (b) $t = \dfrac{2a + 3}{3}$

  (c) $t = \sqrt{ab}$ (d) $t = a(1 - a)$

  (e) $t = \dfrac{9a^2p}{e^2}$ (f) $t = \dfrac{1}{(g - 4s^2)^2}$

Chapter 8

Test yourself

1 (a) 6.7 cm   (b) 6.4 cm   (c) 5.7 cm
    (d) 5.2 cm   (e) 72 m   (f) 5.6 cm
    (g) 13.0 cm   (h) 11 m

Exercise 8A

4 (a) 40.3 cm; 48.5 cm
    (b) 15.9 cm; 25.4 cm
    (c) 20.5 cm; 24.6 cm

5 1.1 metres

6 (a) 5.6 n.m.   (b) 9.8 n.m.

Exercise 8B

3 (a) 56.3°   (b) 8.5°   (c) 66.0°

4 (a) $\angle P = 33.3°$; $\angle Q = 56.7°$
    (b) $\angle P = 39.8°$; $\angle Q = 50.2°$
    (c) $\angle P = 25.3°$; $\angle Q = 64.7°$
    (d) $\angle P = 70.0°$; $\angle Q = 20.0°$

Chapter 9

Test yourself

1 (a) 2.923 65   (b) 0.799 043
    (c) −0.2166

2 (a) 1.357 224   (b) 36.430 69
    (c) 60.030 77   (d) 25.124 75
    (e) 6.790 0915   (f) 4.932 72

3 (a) 0.115   (b) 0.738   (c) 54.8
    (d) 77.2   (e) 22.3   (f) 7.04
    (g) 1.32   (h) 20.3   (i) 0.153

Exercise

1 (a) 19 000   (b) 30 400   (c) 1.12

2 (a) 2.71   (b) 3.50   (c) 5.67
    (d) 2.13   (e) 2.60   (f) 6.69

3 (a) 0.641   (b) 0.138   (c) 3
    (d) 0.667   (e) 0.571

5 (a) (i) 8 h 36 min 52 s
      (ii) 11 h 59 min 21 s
     (iii) 27 h 51 min 41 s
     (iv) 24 h 45 min 35 s
      (v) 8 h 20 min 16 s
     (vi) 58 h 23 min 13 s

(b) (i) 46° 48′ (ii) 60° 15′
      (iii) 41° 52′ (iv) 163° 46′

(c) (i) 32.3° (ii) 21.1° (iii) 80.7°
      (iv) 18.9°

(d) (i) 169 yd 1 ft 6 in
      (ii) 225 yd 2 ft 10 in
      (iii) 277 yd 2 ft 4 in

Chapter 12

Test yourself

1 (a) 220 (b) 213
2 £10; £9.97
4 (a) 17.14 (b) 0.78 (c) 1.01
    (d) 10.11 (e) 19.11 (f) 206.80
5 (a) 17 (b) 0.78 (c) 1.0 (d) 10
    (e) 19 (f) 210

Exercise 12A

4

Sun	—	1.4×10^6
Mercury	5.8×10^7	4.9×10^3
Venus	1.1×10^8	1.2×10^4
Earth	1.5×10^8	1.3×10^4
Mars	2.3×10^8	6.8×10^3
Jupiter	7.8×10^8	1.4×10^5
Saturn	1.4×10^9	1.2×10^5
Uranus	2.9×10^9	5.2×10^4
Neptune	4.5×10^9	5.0×10^4
Pluto	5.9×10^9	6.0×10^3

5 4×10^0 $(10^0 = 1)$
6 (a) 2.45×10^5 (b) 2.28×10^6
    (c) 1.78×10^7 (d) 6.51×10^{10}
    (e) 3.296×10^8 (f) 8.82×10^{14}
7 (a) 950 000; 1 050 000
    (b) 995 000; 1 005 000
    (c) 999 500; 1 000 500
    (d) 999 950; 1 000 050
    (e) 999 995; 1 000 005

Exercise 12B

3 Energy 1.678×10^3 kJ
    Protein 1.22×10 g
    Fat 8.6×10^0 g
    Carbohydrate 7.2×10 g
    Vitamins: A, 1.2×10^{-3} g
              B1, 1.8×10^{-3} g
              B2, 2.3×10^{-3} g
              C, 4.2×10^{-2} g
              D, 1.7×10^{-5} g
    Niacin 2.7×10^{-2} g Iron 2×10^{-2} g
    Calcium 1.2×10^0 g

*4 (a) 7.9×10^2 (b) 8.0×10^3
    (c) 4×10^2 (d) 2.50×10
    (e) 1.04×10^2 (f) 6.1×10^4
    (g) 3.17×10^3 (h) 4.3×10^3
    (i) 4.00×10^6
*5 (a) 7.6×10^{-1} (b) 9.9×10^{-3}
6 (a) 8.2×10^{-1} (b) 1.64×10
    (c) 1.44×10 (d) 1.23×10^{-3}
    (e) 2×10^5 (f) 4×10^0
    (g) 2.5×10^5 (h) 2×10^{-1}
    (i) 3.1×10 (j) 3.3×10^{-5}
7 (a) 5.129×10^8 (b) 1.8665×10^5
    (c) 2.989×10^{12} (d) 4.7564×10^{-5}
8 (a) $\frac{1}{3}$ (b) $\frac{1}{9}$ (c) $\frac{1}{16}$ (d) $\frac{1}{8}$ (e) $\frac{1}{81}$
    (f) $\frac{1}{400}$

Chapter 13

Exercise 13A

7 (a) £127.50 (b) £662.50 (c) 8%
    (d) 7% (e) £2500 (f) £1500
    (g) 8% (h) £25 (i) £2500
    (j) £35.10 (k) $3\frac{1}{2}$% (l) £12 500
8 £7500
9 £315
10 (a) £4470 (b) £370 (c) June, £30

Exercise 13B

3 (a) £655.40 (b) £125.88
    (c) £31.06 (d) £14 909.02
4 £25, £26.25, £27.56, £28.94,
    £30.39, £31.91
5 £9500, £9025, £8573.75, £8145.06,
    £7737.81
6 (a) £701.27 (b) £1607.69
    (c) £1948.40 (d) £1518.07
    (e) £62 458.50
7 (a) £822 973 (b) £90 900
    (c) £63 000

Chapter 14

Exercise

11 (a) 4.20 cm (b) 48.2°
12 (a) 19.2° (b) 3.29 cm (c) 3.29 cm
    (d) 9.44 cm (e) 70.8° (f) 70.8°
    (g) 47.6° (h) 47.6° (i) 42.4°
    (j) 42.4°
13 (a) 69.5° (b) 20.5° (c) 69.5°
    (d) 4.20 m (e) 11.2 m (f) 1.57 m
    (g) 4.48 m

14 FH = 12 m;   EG = 13 m
   ∠FHD = ∠EDF = ∠GFH = 22°37′
   ∠FDH = ∠EFD = ∠FHG = 67°23′
   EF = 1.92 m;   FG = 11.08 m
   ED = GH = 4.62 m

15 (a) (i) $\theta + \alpha = 90°$ (ii) $\sin \theta = \dfrac{AB}{AC}$

(iii) $\cos \theta = \dfrac{AB}{AC}$

(b) (i) 30°   (ii) 40°   (iii) 16.7°
   (iv) 9.9°

Chapter 15

Exercise 15A
*4 (a) $b^2 + b - 20$ (b) $a^2 + 10a + 16$
   (c) $a^2 - 8a + 15$ (d) $a^2 - 4a - 32$
*5 (a) $r^2 - 3r - 28$ (b) $p^2 + 12p + 36$
   (c) $b^2 - 6b + 9$ (d) $m^2 - 14m + 49$
6 (a) $15 + 8x + x^2$ (b) $8 + 2x - x^2$
   (c) $15 - 2x - x^2$ (d) $14 + 5x - x^2$
   (e) $6 - 5x + x^2$ (f) $16 - 8x + x^2$
7 (a) $x^2 + ax + bx + ab$
   (b) $x^2 - ax + bx - ab$
   (c) $x^2 + ax - bx - ab$
   (d) $x^2 - ax - bx + ab$
8 (a) $x^2 + 2x$ (b) $x^2 + 6x + 8$
   (c) $x^2 + x - 6$ (d) $x^2 + 2x - 15$
   (e) $x^2 - 4x + 4$
9 (a) $x^2 + ax + 4x + 3a + 3$
   (b) $x^2 + ax + 2a - 4$
   (c) $x^2 + ax + 2x - a - 3$

Exercise 15B
*3 (a) $6x^2 + 22x + 20$
   (b) $9x^2 - 12x + 4$ (c) $6x^2 - 8x - 8$
   (d) $12a^2 - 23a + 10$
*4 (a) $4x^2 + 12x + 9$
   (b) $3x^2 - 14x + 8$
   (c) $4x^2 + 23x - 35$
   (d) $16x^2 - 40x + 25$
5 (a) $6m^2 - mn - 12n^2$
   (b) $15a^2 - 34ab - 16b^2$
   (c) $12a^2 - 13ab - 14b^2$
   (d) $9a^2 - 12ab + 4b^2$

Chapter 16

Test yourself
1 and 2 See Figure A16:1.

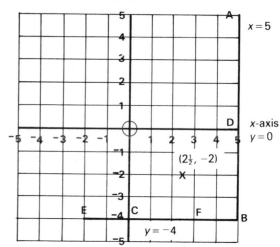

Fig. A16:1

*3 See Figure A16:2.

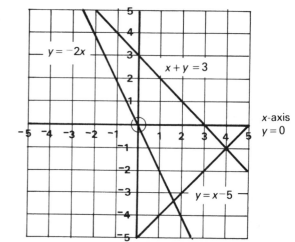

Fig. A16:2

4 $y = \frac{2}{3}x + 1$
5 (a) $y = -\frac{1}{2}x + 2$ (b) $y = \frac{2}{3}x - 2$
   (c) $y = \frac{3}{4}x - 1$ (d) $y = -x$
   (e) $y = 2x - 1$ (f) $y = \frac{5}{2}x + 2$
   (g) $y = -\frac{3}{2}x$ (h) $3x - 2$
6 (a) 3   (b) $-\frac{1}{4}$ (c) $\frac{1}{4}$ (d) 3   (e) -3
   (f) 1   (g) -2 (h) $\frac{1}{2}$

7 (a) $\frac{3}{2}$ (b) $\frac{2}{3}$ (c) 1 (d) 2 (e) 2
(f) 2

8 See question 5 above.

Exercise

8 See Figure A16:3.

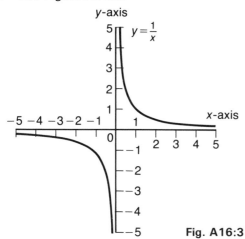

Fig. A16:3

9 (a) (i) (0, 2) (ii) (0, −5) (iii) (0, *a*)
(b) $x = 0$

10 See Figure A16:4.

(a) $y = x^2 + 1$

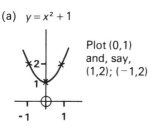

Plot (0,1)
and, say,
(1,2); (−1,2)

(b) $y = x^2 - 3$

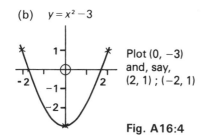

Plot (0, −3)
and, say,
(2, 1) ; (−2, 1)

Fig. A16:4

11 See Figure A16:5.

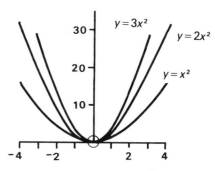

Fig. A16:5

12 See Figure A16:6.

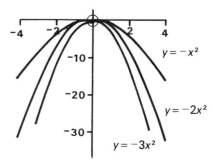

Fig. A16:6

15 See Figure A16:7.

(a)

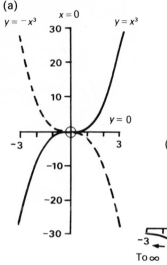

(b) $x = 0$

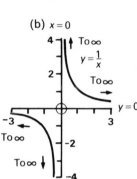

(c)

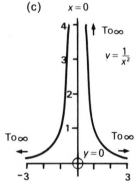

(d)

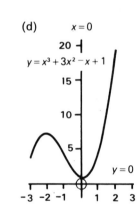

(e)

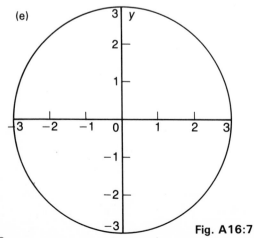

Fig. A16:7

Chapter 17

Exercise 17A

5 (a) $3x(1 - 2y)$ (b) $a(m - n)$
(c) $4ab(4c - 3)$ (d) $3ab(x - 2y)$

6 (a) $x(2x - 1)$ (b) $3a(a + 5)$
(c) $2xy(x - y)$ (d) $6mn(2m - 3n^2)$

7 (a) $a(b - c)$ (b) $b(ac - 3d)$
(c) $4y(3y - 2)$ (d) no factors

8 (a) $2mp(2n + 3)$ (b) $3mn(2n - 3m)$
(c) no factors (d) $2\pi r(r + h)$

9 (a) no factors (b) $8x(3x - 2)$
(c) $7h(3h - 2n)$ (d) $ab(a - b^2)$

10 (a) $4a(1 - 4ab)$ (b) $3ab(1 - a^2b)$
(c) $mx(ay - bd)$

11 (a) $2(2m - 6n - 3b + 4d)$
(b) $3(2a + 3b - 4c - 1)$

12 (a) $(x + y)(3 + a)$ (b) $(a + 5)(m + 3)$
(c) $(a + 1)(b + 4)$
(d) $(1 - 2c)(5b - 2d)$
(e) $(x + 2y)(c - d)$
(f) $(a + 2b)(p + d)$

13 (a) $\frac{2}{y}$ (b) $\frac{a}{3b}$ (c) $\frac{4a}{5b}$ (d) $\frac{2a}{3b}$

Exercise 17B

3 (a) $2(a + 4)(a - 4)$
(b) $2(2 + x)(2 - x)$
(c) $3(3 + b)(3 - b)$
(d) $3(5 + b)(5 - b)$

4 (a) $a(a + 3)(a - 3)$
(b) $2a(3 + b)(3 - b)$ (c) $2\pi r(r + h)$
(d) $(5x + 6y)(5x - 6y)$
(e) $(7x + 1)(5x - 1)$
(f) $(6 + 7x)(6 - 5x)$

Chapter 18

Test yourself

15 (a) {7.9, 690, 7100}
(b) {7.88, 691.40, 7108.80}

17 (a) -8 (b) -30 (c) 12 (d) -3
(e) -2 (f) 21 (g) 11 (h) -9

18 (a) 3; 30 (b) 4; 480

19 (a) £7.04 (b) £5.72 (c) £9.02

20 (a) 3.5 cg (b) 78 mm (c) 0.350 km
(d) 30 litres (e) 5000 kg (f) 4650 m
(g) 7.5 mm (h) 19 cm (i) 50 000 cm
(j) 1000 cm³ (k) 10 000 cm²
(l) 1 000 000 cm³

21 (a) FRF 1483.5; NLG 498; DM 442.5;
   Pta 28 800
   (b) £34.27
22 576 days
23 (a) about ,153156
   (b) (i) about 153185
      (ii) about 162176
      (iii) about 177154
      (iv) about 142157
   (c) Discuss with a friend.
24 All answers are approximate.
   (a) 1020 (b) 1030 (c) 1050
   (d) 1115 (e) 2 km
25 Discuss with a friend. Some
   suggestions are in the Teachers'
   Resource Book.
26 (a) 3.6×10^8 km (b) about $3\frac{1}{2}$ h
27 (a) 2 kg (b) 1.5 litres
28 £112.50
29 1.5×10^{10} litres
30 7.65 cm; 2.85 cm; 21.8025 cm²
31 (a) 400 (b) 74.4 metres

Exercise
8 (a) £643.62 (b) £617.64
   (c) £606.86
   (Full answers are in the Teachers'
   Resource Book.)
9 (a) £1498.88 (b) £205.40
   (c) £240.35 (d) £6634.05
   (e) £482.74 (f) £6137.63
10 (a) £1153.25 (b) £205.40
   (c) £115.92 (d) £6226.21
   (e) £90.95 (f) £5024.48

Chapter 19

Exercise
*2 (c) 33 days
   (d) 40 days, 24 days, 16 days

*3 (a) frequency: 6, 10, 13, 11, 8, 3, 1;
   cumulative frequency: 6, 16, 29,
   40, 48, 51, 52
   (b) See Figure A19:1.

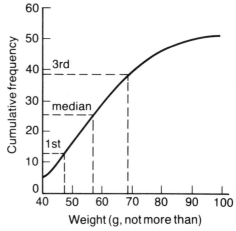

Fig. A19:1

   (c) 57 g (d) 47.5 g, 69 g, 21.5 g
4 (b) 14 scored 20 or les;
   17 scored more than 20.
   (c) 26 scored 28 or less;
   5 scored more than 28.
   (d) 2 scored 8 or less;
   29 scored more than 8.
5 (a) (i) 14 (ii) 17 (iii) 26 (iv) 5
   (b) (i) 24 (ii) 18 (iii) 14
6 (a) 14 (b) 19
7 (a) (i) 25 (ii) 12 (iii) 41 (iv) 29
   (b) (i) 35 (ii) 17 (iii) 56 (iv) 39
8 table 1, 3.78; table 2, 4.26;
   table 3, 27.4; table 4, 58.6

Chapter 20

Exercise
6 See Figure A20:1.

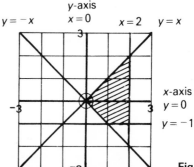

Fig. A20:1

7 See Figure A20:2.

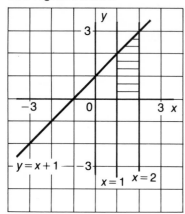

Fig. A20:2

8 (a) 1   (b) $x < 1$ (d) -1
(e) $-1 < y < 0$ (g) $x < 3\frac{1}{2}$
(h) $n < \frac{3}{4}$ and $n > 1\frac{1}{2}$

9 See Figure A20:3.

(a) 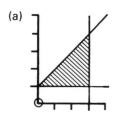   (b)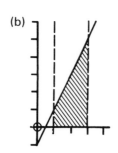

(c) 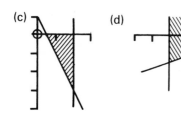   (d)

(e) 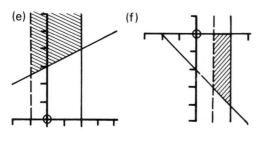   (f)

Fig. A20:3

10 $x + y \leqslant 6$, $6 \geqslant x \geqslant 1$, $y \leqslant 3$,
$y \leqslant 2x$
See Figure A20:4.

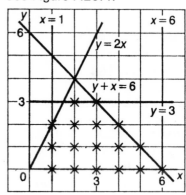

Fig. A20:4

Chapter 21

Exercise 21A

3 (a)

-3	-2	-1	0	1	2
9	4	1	0	1	4
-6	-4	-2	0	2	4
1	1	1	1	1	1
4	1	0	1	4	9

(b)

-1	0	1	2	3	4
-1	0	1	4	9	16
2	0	-2	-4	-6	-8
2	2	2	2	2	2
5	2	1	2	5	10

(c)

0	$\frac{1}{2}$	1	$1\frac{1}{2}$	2	$2\frac{1}{2}$	3
0	$\frac{1}{4}$	1	$2\frac{1}{4}$	4	$6\frac{1}{4}$	9
0	$-1\frac{1}{2}$	-3	$-4\frac{1}{2}$	-6	$-7\frac{1}{2}$	-9
1	1	1	1	1	1	1
1	$-\frac{1}{4}$	-1	$-1\frac{1}{4}$	-1	$-\frac{1}{4}$	1

(d)

−1	0	1	2
2	0	2	8
−1	0	1	2
1	1	1	1
2	1	4	11

(e)

−1	0	1	2	3
1	1	1	1	1
−2	0	2	4	6
−1	0	−1	−4	−9
−2	1	2	1	−2

*4 See Figure A21:1.

(a)

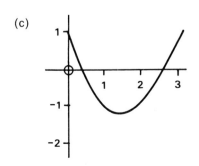

(b)

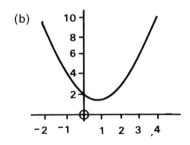

(c)

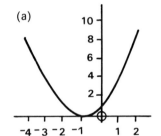

(d)

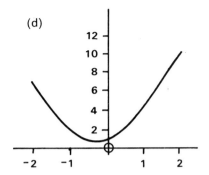

(e)

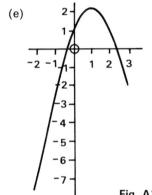

Fig. A21:1

5 (a) $x = -1$ (b) $x = 1$ (c) $x = 1\frac{1}{2}$
   (d) $x = -\frac{1}{4}$ (e) $x = 1$

6 (c) $x = 0.25$
   (d) $-10\frac{1}{8}$ when $x = 0.25$

7 (a) See Figure A21:1(a).
   (b) -2 and 0 (d) -3 and 1
   (e) about -3.4 and 1.4; $x^2 + 2x = 5$
   (f) about -3.8 and 1.8; $x^2 + 2x = 7$
   (g) It is never true for any value of x.

8 (a) See Figure A21:1(b).
   (b) (i) $x = 1$; $x^2 - 2x = -1$
      (ii) $x = 0$ and $x = 2$; $x^2 - 2x = 0$
      (iii) $x = -1$ and $x = 3$; $x^2 - 2x = 3$
      (iv) about -0.7 and 2.7;
         $x^2 - 2x = 2$
      (v) about -1.6 and 3.6;
         $x^2 - 2x = 6$

9 (a) $x^2 - 3x = -1$
   (b) $2x^2 + 3x = -1$ (c) $x^2 - x = 3$
   (d) $3x^2 - 2x = 1$ (e) $2x^2 - 3x = 0$

11 (a) $y = x^2$ (b) $y = \frac{1}{2}x^2$ (c) $y = 2x^2$
   (d) $y = \frac{1}{4}x^2$ (e) $y = \frac{1}{8}x^2$

Exercise 21B

1 $x^2 - 3x + 1 = 1$; $y = 1$; $x = 0$; $x = 3$
2 (a) $y = -1$ (b) $y = -6$ (c) $y = -4$
   (d) $y = -8$ (e) $y = 0$ (f) $y = -5$
3 (a) -4.45; 0.45 (b) -3.87; -0.13
   (c) -4.12; 0.12 (d) -3.58; -0.42
   (e) -4.55; 0.55 (f) -4; 0
4 $x^2 = -3x + 4$ or $x^2 + 3x - 4 = 0$;
   $x = -4$; $x = 1$
5 (a) $x^2 - 2x - 1 = 0$
   (b) $x^2 + 2x - 1 = 0$
   (c) $x^2 - 3x + 2 = 0$
   (d) $x^2 + 2x + 4 = 0$
   (e) $2x^2 - x - 6 = 0$
   (f) $3x^2 - x + 3 = 0$
6 (a) -0.4; 2.4 (b) -2.4; 0.4 (c) 1; 2
   (d) no solution (e) -1.5; 2
   (f) no solution

Chapter 22

Exercise 22A

4 40 cm

5 $\theta = \dfrac{360 \times A}{C}$; $120°$

6 (a) (i) $D = \dfrac{360 \times A}{\theta \times \pi}$ (ii) $\theta = \dfrac{360 \times A}{\pi \times D}$

   (b) 9 cm (c) $90°$
7 (a) $57.3°$ (b) 24 cm

Exercise 22B

*2 54.4 cm; 172 cm²
4 10 cm
5 (b) 11.25^2 (c) 6.25^c
6 126.6 cm²

Chapter 23

Exercise 23A

3 (a) AB = $1\frac{1}{2}$ cm, BZ = $2\frac{1}{4}$ cm
   (b) HI = $9\frac{1}{3}$ cm, EG = $6\frac{3}{4}$ cm
   (c) LN = $6\frac{3}{4}$ cm, LM = $4\frac{1}{2}$ cm
4 Alternate angles are only equal if
   between parallel lines.
5 ED = 15 cm, BC = 3.6 cm
6 ST = $3\frac{3}{4}$ cm, TV = 6 cm
8 (a) AY = $3\frac{1}{2}$ cm, XY = 4 cm

Exercise 23B

3 (a) not congruent (angle not included)
   (b) $\dfrac{\text{UVW}}{\text{XWV}}$; right angle, hypotenuse, side
   (c) not congruent (no side given)
   (d) $\dfrac{\text{DEF}}{\text{HFG}}$; 2 sides, included angle
   (e) not congruent (side not
       corresponding)
   (f) $\dfrac{\text{MNP}}{\text{ONP}}$; 2 sides, included angle
4 (c) (i) $\angle ABE = \angle FBC = 90° + \angle CBE$
5 (b) $BD = DC$; $\angle BAD = \angle CAD$

Chapter 24

9 (a) 1 (b) 1 (c) 1 (d) 4 (e) 3
10 (a) $9a^2$ (b) $-a^3$ (c) $27a^3c^3$
    (d) -64 (e) $-a^3b^3$ (f) $81a^8$
    (g) $4a^4b^2$ (h) $\dfrac{1}{b^6}$ (i) $\dfrac{8a^3}{27b^3}$ (j) $\dfrac{a^4}{b^6}$
11 (a) 3 (b) 5 (c) 3 (d) 5 (e) 2
12 (a) 9 (b) 8 (c) 8 (d) 27 (e) 32
    (f) 125 (g) 32
13 (a) $\frac{1}{4}$ (b) $\frac{1}{3}$ (c) $\frac{1}{8}$ (d) 1 (e) $\frac{1}{4}$
14 (a) $\frac{1}{2}$ (b) $\frac{1}{2}$ (c) 6 (d) $\frac{1}{6}$ (e) 5
15 (a) $\frac{1}{9}$ (b) 8 (c) $\frac{1}{8}$ (d) $\frac{1}{27}$ (e) 32
16 (a) $\frac{1}{8}$ (b) $\frac{1}{64}$ (c) $\frac{1}{25}$ (d) $\frac{1}{1\,000\,000}$
    (e) 16
17 (a) $\dfrac{1}{9a^2}$ (b) $\dfrac{3}{a^2}$ (c) $\dfrac{1}{2a}$ (d) $4a^2$
    (e) $\dfrac{1}{16a^4}$ (f) 8 (g) $6a$ (h) 4 (i) $\frac{1}{3}$
    (j) $6a$ (k) 3 (l) $1\frac{1}{4}$ (m) $2\frac{1}{2}$ (n) 1
    (o) 4 (p) 0.2 (q) 1 (r) 0.09
    (s) 1 (t) $\dfrac{1}{a^2}$

Chapter 25

Exercise 25A

24 (a) 24 cm square, 8 cm deep;
        18 cm square, 6 cm deep
    (b) 160 g marzipan, 64 g icing;
        90 g marzipan, 36 g icing
25 6.7 m side and 7.6 m long
26 (a) 1 : 50 000 (b) 1 : 15 000
    (c) 1 : 20 000
27 (a) 1 km (b) 1 km by 2.4 km

28 (a) 64 cm² (b) 144 cm² (c) 48 cm²
29 96 cm²
30 (a) 48 cm² (b) 108 cm² (c) 3 cm²
31 4 cm
32 (a) 30 m (b) 500 m (c) 1.8 km
   (d) 7 km (e) 175 m (f) 2.3 km
33 (a) 40 km by 40 km
   (b) 1 km and 10 km
   (c) (i) 1600 km² (ii) 1 km²
       (iii) 100 km²
34 (a) 0.25 km² (b) 1.84 km²

Chapter 26

Exercise 26A
7 12 cm
8 11 cm
9 £19.63
10 (a) 66 cm (b) 10½ cm
11 (a) 1.57 cm² (b) 15.7 cm²
   (c) 2.04 cm² (d) 19.31 cm²
12 (a) 504 cm² (b) 459 cm²

Exercise 26B
4 (a) 72 cm³ (b) 2.16 cm³
   (c) 0.707 cm³ (d) 0.53̇ cm³
5 55 m³
6 2640 cm²; 10 400 cm³
7 1430 cm²; 3470 cm³
8 100
9 80 m
10 99 h
11 (a) 10 053 096 mm³
   (b) 14.137 167 mm³ (c) 711 100
12 64
13 1188
14 2.49 m³
15 2770

Chapter 27

Exercise 27B
6 50.9 cm³
7 340 cm³
8 $\frac{1}{8}$
9 7.5 × 10⁵ litres
10 (c) (i) 8.94 cm (ii) 9.79 cm (iii) 26.6°
      (iv) 24.1°
11 (b) 12.1 cm (c) 19.3°
12 6.93 cm

13 yes (longest diagonal = 3.74 cm)
14 (b) 10.8 cm (c) 19.7 cm
   (d) 20.1 cm (e) 21.8°; 11.5°
15 (c) ∠BCF
16 (a) 36.9° (b) 15.6°
17 5.77 cm
18 43 cm³

Chapter 28

Test yourself
1 See Figure A28:1.

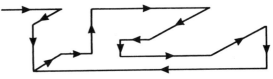

Fig. A28:1

*2 (a) $\begin{pmatrix} 2 \\ -2 \end{pmatrix}$ (b) $\begin{pmatrix} 1 \\ 0 \end{pmatrix}$ (c) $\begin{pmatrix} 3 \\ 0 \end{pmatrix}$

(d) $\begin{pmatrix} -2 \\ -1 \end{pmatrix}$ (e) $\begin{pmatrix} 3 \\ -2 \end{pmatrix}$ (f) $\begin{pmatrix} 5 \\ 2 \end{pmatrix}$

(g) $\begin{pmatrix} 3 \\ 2 \end{pmatrix}$ (h) $\begin{pmatrix} -1 \\ -1 \end{pmatrix}$ (i) $\begin{pmatrix} 1 \\ 3 \end{pmatrix}$ (j) $\begin{pmatrix} 2 \\ 0 \end{pmatrix}$

*3 See Figure A28:2

(a) (b) (c)

(d) (e) (f)

(g) (h)

(i) (j)

Fig. A28:2

*4 (a) 2 (b) 2 (c) √5 ≃ 2.24
   (d) √13 ≃ 3.61 (e) √5 ≃ 2.24
   (f) √5 ≃ 2.24

5 (b) 5.83
6 (a) $-b$ (b) $-a$ (c) b (d) $-b$
(e) a (f) $-a$ (g) $a + b$
7 $\overrightarrow{SQ} = -a + b; \overrightarrow{QS} = -b + a$
8 (a) $-x$ (b) $-y$ (c) $2z$ (d) $-z$
(e) $-z$ (f) $x + z$ or $y - z$
(g) $-z - x$ or $z - y$
9 (a) $-b$ (b) a (c) $\frac{1}{2}b$ (d) $-a + \frac{1}{2}b$
(e) $\frac{1}{2}b + a$
10 (a) $2c$ (b) $-d$ (c) d (d) $2d$
(e) $c + d$ (f) $c + 2d$ (g) $-c + 2d$
(h) $-c + d$
11 (a) $\overrightarrow{AC}$ (b) $\overrightarrow{BF}$
12 See Figure A28:3.

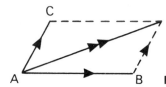

Fig. A28:3

13 See Figure A28:4.

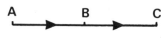

Fig. A28:4

14 (a) $3x$ (b) $2x$
15 (a) If $c = d$ then they would have to be
parallel. (This is very important.
Remember it!)
(b) As $c \neq d$ then this can only be true
if $h + k = 0$ and $h - k + 1 = 0$,
$\therefore h = -\frac{1}{2}$ and $k = \frac{1}{2}$.
16 $\overrightarrow{BC} = -\overrightarrow{AB} + \overrightarrow{AC}; \quad \overrightarrow{BM} = \frac{1}{2}(-\overrightarrow{AB} + \overrightarrow{AC});$
$\overrightarrow{AM} = \overrightarrow{AB} + \frac{1}{2}(-\overrightarrow{AB} + \overrightarrow{AC}) =$
$\frac{1}{2}\overrightarrow{AB} + \frac{1}{2}\overrightarrow{AC} = \frac{1}{2}(\overrightarrow{AB} + \overrightarrow{AC})$
17 (a) Parallel, with XY:BC = h:1 (or XY
is h times as long as BC)
(b) Hint:
Show that $\overrightarrow{XY} = h(-\overrightarrow{AB} + \overrightarrow{AC})$.

Exercise
4 222° (about SW)
5 104 m/s; 343°
6 18 knots; 024°
7 279.6°; 1140
8 25° wire, 1990 N; 35° wire, 1460 N

Chapter 29

Exercise
9 See Figure A29:1.
10 There is some evidence of negative
correlation.

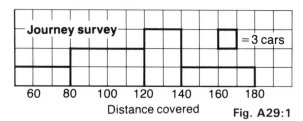

Distance covered   Fig. A29:1

11 (c) 9.8 feet per year (d) 1993
12 (a) developed: about 1.2 bn/y in 1900;
about 1.6 bn/y in 1990
developing: about 2.9 bn/y in 1900;
about 8.2 bn/y in 1990
(bn/y = billions per year)

Chapter 30

Exercise 30A
5 (a) 4.33 cm (b) 9.46 cm
(c) 15.1 cm
6 (a) a circle (b) 10 cm − 8 cm = 2 cm
(c) 10 cm + 8 cm = 18 cm
7 4 cm + 3 cm = 7 cm;
4 cm − 3 cm = 1 cm

Exercise 30B
4 15°
5 45°; 60°; 75°

Exercise 30C
3 (a) (i) 90° (∠ in semicircle)
(ii) 50° (∠ sum of triangle)
(iii) 50° (Alt. ∠ s, CB // AD)
(vi) 50° (∠ s of isos. △)
(v) 80° (∠ sum of △)
(b) ∠ CAD = 40° + 50° = 90°
∴ CADO is a semicircle.
(c) Reasons as (a): (i) 90° (ii) 55°
(iii) 55° (iv) 55° (v) 70°
4 5.7 cm

Chapter 32

Exercise 32A

4. (a) d ($\angle$s in same segment)
   (b) g ($\angle$s in same segment)
   (c) f ($\angle$s in same segment)
   (d) h ($\angle$s in same segment)
   (e) k (vert. opp. $\angle$s)
   (f) l (vert. opp. $\angle$s)
5. (a) 90° ($\angle$ in semicircle)
   (b) 30° ($\angle$ sum of $\triangle$)
   (c) 30° ($\angle$s in same segment)
6. (a) equal $\angle$s in isos. $\triangle$
   (b) $\angle$s in same segment
   (c) both $= d$
   (d) a and c are equal alternate $\angle$s
7. (a) a diameter   (b) $\angle$BAC: $\angle$BDC
8. $\angle$ACD = 50° ($\angle$s in same segment);
   $\angle$DAC = 50° ($\angle$ sum of $\triangle$)
9. (a) 90° (b) 90° (c) 90° (d) 90°
   (e) both $+ c = 90°$
   (f) $\angle$s in same segment
   (g) both $= a$
10. $\angle$ABX $= \angle$AXB $= \angle$DXC and
    $\angle$ABD $= \angle$ACD

Exercise 32B

6. ABCE; ABDE; BCDE; BDFE; CDFE
7. Square or rectangle.
8. (a) $g = 80°$; $e = 100°$
   (b) $g = 60°$; $e = 120°$
   (c) $g = 105°$; $e = 75°$
9. $\angle$ABC = 70°; $\angle$ADC = 110°;
   $\therefore$ opposite $\angle$s total 180°
10. $\angle$AOX $= 2\angle$AYX;
    $\angle$AYX $= \angle$CBX (both $+ \angle$ABX = 180°)

11. (a) $a = 80°$ (exterior $\angle$ equals
       opposite interior $\angle$)
       $b = 100°$ (opposite $\angle$s of cyclic
       quad.)
    (b) $\angle$A $+ \angle$B = 180° (interior $\angle$s)
    (c) $f = x$; $b = 180 - x$;
       $\therefore \angle$A $+ \angle$B $= x + 180 - x = 180°$
12. Opposite $\angle$s total 180° (60° + 120°;
    80° + 100°)
13. $\angle$C = 90°; $\angle$CBA = 60°;
    $\angle$CBD = 30°; $\angle$CAD = 30°
14. $\angle$PQR $= \angle$PST;
    $\angle$PQR $= \angle$PRQ $= \angle$PSQ

Chapter 33

Exercise

11. (a) $(3x - 4)(2x - 1)$
    (b) $(3x + 4)(2x + 1)$
    (c) $(3x - 4)(2x + 1)$
    (d) $(3x + 4)(2x - 1)$
12. (a) $(x - 3)(x + 2)$ (b) $(x - 3)(x - 2)$
    (c) not possible (d) not possible
    (e) not possible (f) $(3x + 2)(x - 1)$
    (g) $(3x + 2)(x + 3)$ (h) not possible
    (i) not possible (j) not possible
    (k) $(4x + 1)(x + 1)$
    (l) $(2x + 3)(3x + 2)$
    (m) $(3x + 4)(x + 3)$
    (n) $(6x + 1)(x - 4)$
    (o) $(4x + 1)(2x + 3)$
    (p) $(4x + 5)(2x - 3)$
13. (a) $3(x + 2)(x + 2)$
    (b) $2(x + 3)(x + 4)$
    (c) $3(x - 1)(x - 4)$
    (d) $3(3x - 1)(x + 1)$
    (e) $2(2x - 1)(x - 2)$
    (f) $4(3x - 8)(x + 2)$
14. (a) $(3a - b)(3a - b)$
    (b) $(7 - x)(5 - x)$
    (c) $(7 + x)(5 - x)$
    (d) $(3x - y)(x + 2y)$
    (e) $(4x - 3)(2x - 3)$
    (f) $(5x - 3y)(5x - 3y)$
    (g) $(x + \frac{1}{2})(x + \frac{1}{2})$ (h) $(x - \frac{1}{2})(x + 1\frac{1}{2})$
    (i) $(6 + x)(4 - x)$

Chapter 34

Exercise

*5. (a) 7.92 cm (b) 24.0° (c) 9.31 cm
    (d) 2.21 m (e) 44.4° (f) 18.5 mm
*6. (a) AC = 8.87 cm; $\angle$C = 26.8°
    (b) HI = 4.92 cm; $\angle$I = 66.0°
    (c) KL = 5.86 cm; $\angle$K = 57.8°
    (d) MN = 3.45 m; $\angle$D = 57.4°
    (e) QR = 4.90 cm; $\angle$R = 45.6°
    (f) XV = 19.4 mm; $\angle$X = 72°

7 (a) ∠A = 70.8°; ∠B = 19.2°;
  AB = 9.16 cm
 (b) ∠F = 51.8°; FH = 11.7 m;
  GH = 14.9 m
 (c) ∠K = 35.2°; ∠J = 54.8°;
  KL = 21.4 cm
 (d) ∠D = 29.0°; DF = 32.4 cm;
  DE = 37.0 cm
 (e) Angles: 90°, 60°, 30°;
  QR = 5.3 km; PT = QP = 3.06 km;
  RS = PR = PS = 6.12 km
 (f) ∠Z = 54.8°; ∠X = 70.4°;
  XY = XZ = 15.3 m
 (g) ∠Q = ∠R = 68.3°; ∠P = 43.5°.
  PQ = 17.08 cm

8 (a) (i) 6.17 cm (ii) 85° (iii) 11.3 cm
 (b) (i) 30.4° (ii) 85.6° (iii) 9.26 cm
 (c) (i) 20.5 cm (ii) 65° (iii) 19.3 cm

9 (a) ∠A = 71.2°; ∠C = 68.6°;
  AB = 18.2 m
 (b) ∠D = 70.5°; DF = 8.74 cm;
  DE = 10.8 cm
 (c) ∠H = 27.9°; ∠I = 73.4°;
  GH = 8.84 cm

10 (a) $\frac{4}{5}$ (b) $\frac{5}{12}$
12 (a) 80° (b) 63.2° (c) 27.8°
12 (a) 104.1° (b) 12.0 cm (c) 7.45 cm

Chapter 35

Exercise 35A

11 (a) 5, −5 (b) −4, 8 (c) −9, 10
 (d) −11, 2 (e) 1, 6 (f) 0, $\frac{3}{7}$
12 (a) 2 m by 10 m (b) 11 cm side
 (c) −13 or 3 (d) $-\frac{1}{5}$ or $\frac{9}{2}$
13 (a) $x^2 - 6x + 8 = 0$ (b) $x^2 - 4 = 0$
 (c) $x^2 - 2x - 15 = 0$
 (d) $x^2 + 6x + 8 = 0$
 (e) $x^2 + 4x = 0$ (f) $6x^2 + x - 2 = 0$
14 (a) (3, 0); (−1, 0); (0, −3)
 (b) (4, 0); (−1, 0); (0, −4)
 (c) (3, 0); (−3, 0); (0, −9)
 (d) (−2, 0) (tangential); (0, 4)
 (e) (1½, 0); (1, 0); (0, 3)
 (f) (−3, 0) (tangential); (0, 9)

15 See Figure A35:1.

(a) 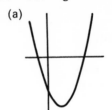 (b)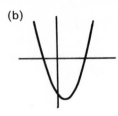

(c) 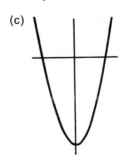 (d)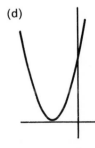

(f)

(e)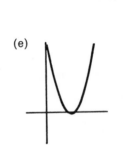

Fig. A35:1

16 (a) 12 cm (b) 7 (c) 20

Exercise 35B

1 (a) −4.24, 0.24 (b) −1.45, 3.45
 (c) −4.30, −0.70
2 (a) −1.42, 8.42 (b) −6.55, −1.35
 (c) −2.30, 1.30
3 (a) −1.37, 0.37 (b) 0.29, 1.71
 (c) −2.14, 0.47
*4 (a) −0.79, 3.79 (b) −1.71, −0.29
 (c) −0.77, 0.43
5 (a) $2x^2 - 4x - 1 = 0$
 (b) $3x^3 - 4x + 1 = 0$
 (c) $2x^2 - x - 2 = 0$
 (d) $2x^2 + 4x - 3 = 0$
 (e) $x^2 - 3x + 3 = 0$
 (f) $x^2 - 4x + 4 = 0$
6 (a) −4.12, 0.12 (b) −5.85, 0.85
 (c) −0.54, 1.87

7 (a) $3x^2 + 9x + 7 = 0$
   (b) $8x^2 - 3x + 2 = 0$
   (c) $3x^2 - 2x + 5 = 0$
   (d) $3x^2 - 2x - 1 = 0$
   (e) $9x^2 - 6x + 1 = 0$
   (f) $4x^2 - 5x - 2 = 0$
8 (c) A; 5(a), 5(b), 5(c), 5(d), 7(d), 7(f)
   B: 5(e), 7(a), 7(b), 7(c)
   C: 5(f), 7(e)

Chapter 36

Test yourself
1 (a) (10 10) (b) (14 16)
   (c) (22 14) (d) (11 7)
2 (a) $\begin{pmatrix} 5 & 4 \\ 10 & 12 \end{pmatrix}$ (b) $\begin{pmatrix} 15 & 10 \\ 1 & 2 \end{pmatrix}$

   (c) $\begin{pmatrix} 8 & 6 \\ 9 & 13 \end{pmatrix}$ (d) $\begin{pmatrix} 14 & 8 \\ 6 & 7 \end{pmatrix}$

   (e) $\begin{pmatrix} 19 & 23 \\ 8 & 4 \end{pmatrix}$ (f) $\begin{pmatrix} 16 & 20 \\ 8 & 4 \end{pmatrix}$

   (g) $\begin{pmatrix} 7 & 12 \\ 16 & 8 \end{pmatrix}$ (h) $\begin{pmatrix} 8 & 11 \\ 16 & 7 \end{pmatrix}$

3 (a) 14 (b) (4 7) (c) $\begin{pmatrix} 2 \\ 3 \end{pmatrix}$

   (d) $\begin{pmatrix} 0 & -3 & 1 \\ 0 & 0 & 0 \end{pmatrix}$ (e) $\begin{pmatrix} 1 & -1 & 0 \\ -1 & 1 & 2 \end{pmatrix}$

4 (a) $\begin{pmatrix} -1 & 1 & -1 \\ 2 & 0 & 1 \end{pmatrix}$
   (b) There must be the same number of columns in the first matrix as rows in the second.

Exercise
1 See Figure A36:1.

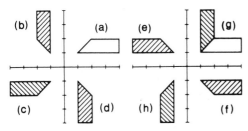

Fig. A36:1

Identity (this has no effect):
(a) $\begin{pmatrix} 1 & 0 \\ 0 & 1 \end{pmatrix}$

Rotations (+ve rotation is anticlockwise):
(b) $\begin{pmatrix} 0 & -1 \\ 1 & 0 \end{pmatrix}$; 90° rotation about (0, 0)

(c) $\begin{pmatrix} -1 & 0 \\ 0 & -1 \end{pmatrix}$; 180° rotation about (0, 0)

(d) $\begin{pmatrix} 0 & 1 \\ -1 & 0 \end{pmatrix}$; 270° rotation about (0, 0)

Reflections:
(e) $\begin{pmatrix} -1 & 0 \\ 0 & 1 \end{pmatrix}$; reflects in y-axis

(f) $\begin{pmatrix} 1 & 0 \\ 0 & -1 \end{pmatrix}$; reflects in x-axis

(g) $\begin{pmatrix} 0 & 1 \\ 1 & 0 \end{pmatrix}$; reflects in $y = x$

(h) $\begin{pmatrix} 0 & -1 \\ -1 & 0 \end{pmatrix}$; reflects in $y = -x$

2 See Figure A36:2.

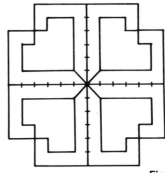

Fig. A36:2

4 (a) Shear, invariant line $x = 0$;
       (1, 0) → (1, -1)
   (b) Shear, invariant line $x = 0$;
       (1, 0) → (1, -2)
   (c) Shear, invariant line $y = 0$;
       (0, 1) → (3, 1)
   (d) Shear, invariant line $y = 0$;
       (0, 1) → (-1, 1)
   (e) Shear, invariant line $y = 0$;
       (0, 1) → (2, 1)

(f) Shear, invariant line $y = 0$; $(0, 1) \rightarrow (-2, 1)$

(g) Enlargement, scale factor -2; centre $(0, 0)$

(h) One-way stretch from $x = 0$, stretch factor 2

(i) One-way stretch from $y = 0$, stretch factor 2

5 See Figure A36:3.

(b)

(c) (i)

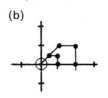

(c) (ii)

(c) (iii)

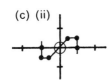
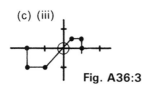

Fig. A36:3

6 See Figure A36:4.

(a)

(b)

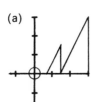
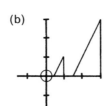

(c)

(d)

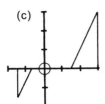
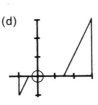

Fig. A36:4

7 Q5(b) Enlargement, scale factor 2, centre $(0, 0)$

   Q5(c) (i) Enlargement, scale factor 3, centre $(0, 0)$

     (ii) Enlargement, scale factor -1, centre $(0, 0)$

     (iii) Enlargement, scale factor -2, centre $(0, 0)$

   Q6(a) Enlargement, scale factor $\frac{1}{2}$, centre $(0, 0)$

Q6(b) Enlargement, scale factor $\frac{1}{3}$, centre $(0, 0)$

Q6(c) Enlargement, scale factor $-\frac{1}{2}$, centre $(0, 0)$

Q6(d) Enlargement, scale factor $-\frac{1}{3}$, centre $(0, 0)$

8 See Figure A36:5.

(a)

(b)

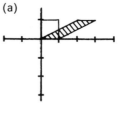
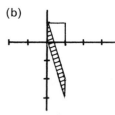

(c)

(d)

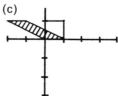
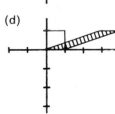

(e)

(f)

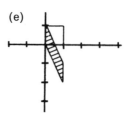
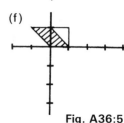

Fig. A36:5

(b) Shearing, invariant line $x = 0$, such that $(1, 0) \rightarrow (1, -3)$

(c) Shearing, invariant line $y = 0$, such that $(0, 1) \rightarrow (-2, 1)$

9 (a) One-way stretch from $x = 0$, stretch factor 2

(b) One-way stretch from $x = 0$, stretch factor 3

(c) One-way stretch from $y = 0$, stretch factor 2

(d) One-way stretch from $y = 0$, stretch factor 3

(e) Two-way stretch from $x = 0$, stretch factor 2 and from $y = 0$, stretch factor 3

(f) Two-way stretch from $x = 0$, stretch factor 3 and from $y = 0$, stretch factor 2

Index

This index gives the chapter numbers where the topics are treated.